PRENTICE HALL
ASSESSMENT
SYSTEM

Program Assessment

Chapter Tests
With Exam*View*® Test Bank CD-ROM

PRENTICE HALL

WORLD HISTORY

CONNECTIONS TO TODAY

PEARSON
Prentice
Hall

Upper Saddle River, New Jersey
Glenview, Illinois
Needham, Massachusetts

SOFTWARE SUPPORT HOTLINE 1-800-848-9500

ISBN 0-13-062893-X

4 5 6 7 8 9 10   07 06 05 04 03

TABLE OF CONTENTS

QUESTION BANKS

About the *Prentice Hall Dial-A-Test®* Service

If you do not have access to a computer or would like the convenience of designing your own tests without typing a word, you may want to take advantage of our free Dial-A-Test® Service. Available to all users of *World History: Connections to Today*, Dial-A-Test® is simple to use.

Here's How It Works

1. **Choose the questions you want** from the ready-made Chapter Test Questions.

2. **Enter the numbers of the questions** in the order you want on a Dial-A-Test® Order Form (see page 6 for a master that you may photocopy). Be sure to include the chapter number on the form. For example, in the case of test question 17, taken from Chapter 1 Test Form A, mark the order form with the designation 1A, 17.

3. **Use a separate Dial-A-Test® order form** for each original test you request.

4. **If you would like another version** of your original test with the questions scrambled or put in another sequence, simply check the line labeled *Alternate Version I* on the order form. For a third version, check the line labeled *Alternate Version II*. Please note that Prentice Hall reserves the right to limit the number of tests and versions you can request at any one time, especially during the busier times of the year when midterms and finals are given.

5. **Choose the method** by which you would like to order your original test and/or multiple versions of your original test. To order by telephone, call toll free 1-800-468-8378 between 9:00 a.m. and 4:30 p.m. Eastern Standard Time and read the test question numbers to our Dial-A-Test® operator. Give the customer service representative the following reference number: 0-13-062893-X. To order by mail, send your completed Dial-A-Test® order form to the address listed below. You may also FAX your order to 1-614-771-7365.

6. **You may order** up to 100 questions per test by telephone on our toll-free 800 number or up to 200 questions per test by mail.

7. **Please allow a minimum of two weeks** for shipping, especially if you are ordering by mail. Although we process your order within 48 hours of your call or the receipt of your form by mail, mailing may take up to two weeks. Thus we ask you to plan accordingly and expect to receive your original test, any alternate test versions that you requested, and complete answer keys within a reasonable amount of time.

8. **Tests are available all year.** You can order tests before the school year begins, during vacation, or as you need them.

9. **For additional order forms** or to ask questions regarding this service, please write to the following address:

Dial-A-Test®
Prentice Hall School Division
P. O. Box 2500
Lebanon, IN 46052

DIAL-A-TEST®
PRENTICE HALL SCHOOL DIVISION
CUSTOMIZED TESTING SERVICE
TOLL-FREE NUMBER 800-468-8378 (H O-T-T-E-S-T)

You may **call** the PH Dial-A-Test® toll-free number during our business hours (9:00 A.M.-4:30 P.M. EST). Now you may also FAX your order to 1-614-771-7365 anytime.

DIAL-A-TEST®
PRENTICE HALL SCHOOL DIVISION
PO BOX 2500
LEBANON, IN 46052-3009

FOR PH USE	DATE REC.	DATE SENT
__ PHONE __ MAIL __ FAX	_____	_____

EXACT TEXT TITLE/VOL.   _World History: Connections to Today_

© DATE __2003__ **CODE** ____0-13-062893-X____

CUSTOMER INFORMATION
NAME _____
SCHOOL _____
ADDRESS _____
CITY _____ STATE ____ ZIP _____
PHONE _____ EXT. _____

DATE BY WHICH TEST IS NEEDED _____

TEST USAGE (CHECK ONE)

__ SAMPLE   __ QUIZ   __ CHAPTER TEST

__ UNIT TEST __ SEMESTER TEST __ FINAL EXAM

VERSIONS (SEE page viii, point 4.)
__ 1. Original
__ 2. Alternate Version I
__ 3. Alternate Version II

TEST IDENTIFICATION (This information will appear at the top of your test.)

_____

_____   EXAMPLE: Mr. Hernandez

_____   History 101, Period 5

_____   Chapter Test

1 ____	26 ____	51 ____	76 ____	101 ____	126 ____	151 ____	176 ____
2 ____	27 ____	52 ____	77 ____	102 ____	127 ____	152 ____	177 ____
3 ____	28 ____	53 ____	78 ____	103 ____	128 ____	153 ____	178 ____
4 ____	29 ____	54 ____	79 ____	104 ____	129 ____	154 ____	179 ____
5 ____	30 ____	55 ____	80 ____	105 ____	130 ____	155 ____	180 ____
6 ____	31 ____	56 ____	81 ____	106 ____	131 ____	156 ____	181 ____
7 ____	32 ____	57 ____	82 ____	107 ____	132 ____	157 ____	182 ____
8 ____	33 ____	58 ____	83 ____	108 ____	133 ____	158 ____	183 ____
9 ____	34 ____	59 ____	84 ____	109 ____	134 ____	159 ____	184 ____
10 ____	35 ____	60 ____	85 ____	110 ____	135 ____	160 ____	185 ____
11 ____	36 ____	61 ____	86 ____	111 ____	136 ____	161 ____	186 ____
12 ____	37 ____	62 ____	87 ____	112 ____	137 ____	162 ____	187 ____
13 ____	38 ____	63 ____	88 ____	113 ____	138 ____	163 ____	188 ____
14 ____	39 ____	64 ____	89 ____	114 ____	139 ____	164 ____	189 ____
15 ____	40 ____	65 ____	90 ____	115 ____	140 ____	165 ____	190 ____
16 ____	41 ____	66 ____	91 ____	116 ____	141 ____	166 ____	191 ____
17 ____	42 ____	67 ____	92 ____	117 ____	142 ____	167 ____	192 ____
18 ____	43 ____	68 ____	93 ____	118 ____	143 ____	168 ____	193 ____
19 ____	44 ____	69 ____	94 ____	119 ____	144 ____	169 ____	194 ____
20 ____	45 ____	70 ____	95 ____	120 ____	145 ____	170 ____	195 ____
21 ____	46 ____	71 ____	96 ____	121 ____	146 ____	171 ____	196 ____
22 ____	47 ____	72 ____	97 ____	122 ____	147 ____	172 ____	197 ____
23 ____	48 ____	73 ____	98 ____	123 ____	148 ____	173 ____	198 ____
24 ____	49 ____	74 ____	99 ____	124 ____	149 ____	174 ____	199 ____
25 ____	50 ____	75 ____	100 ____	125 ____	150 ____	175 ____	200 ____

To the Teacher

This test bank contains multiple-choice, matching, completion, and short-answer questions covering all chapters of the textbook. The questions are grouped by type (short answer, multiple choice, etc.) within each chapter. These questions and the test-generator software have been prepared to assist you in developing tests for your students.

Each test question is designated with one of three levels of difficulty (DIF): easy, average, or difficult. Use this information when you select questions to help you tailor your test to the exact needs and abilities of your students.

In addition, the page reference (REF) of the relevant student edition content is given to help students review content for questions they miss.

The text objective (OBJ) covered by the question is listed with a code number. You can see which objective goes with each code by referring to the Objectives Correlation table that follows this letter.

The questions are also matched to topics (TOP), which can be used to create a test that covers only the content you are interested in.

Components

- Question Bank
- **Exam***View*® Testmaker User's Guide
- **Exam***View*® Hybrid CD-ROM

The test generator consists of a Computer Test Bank booklet, a CD-ROM, and a software user's guide. This Computer Test Bank contains a printed listing of all the questions that accompany the test-generator software. Use this guide to preview the available questions and to make your choices for inclusion on tests; or, if you prefer, you may view and select questions on-screen, using the included computer program. The test-generator software lets you retrieve the questions you want and then print tests. It also lets you edit and add questions as needed. The user's guide contains instructions for the setup and use of the software. There is a more detailed user's guide available on the CD-ROM in a PDF document called "Manual." There is also a Quick Start Card in your Prentice Hall Assessment System that will help you in creating and editing your own tests and test questions.

In the Windows version, if you have already installed the test-generator program for other textbooks, you may have to select the folder named the same as the title of the textbook to locate the question-bank files.

Prentice Hall
World History: Connections to Today
Chapter Objectives

(ChapterSection-Objective)

| C1 | S1 | - | 1 |

C1S1-1	Explain how geography and history are linked.
C1S1-2	Identify the methods that anthropologists and archaeologists use to find out about early people.
C1S1-3	Describe the ways historians try to reconstruct the past.
C1S2-1	Identify the advances that people made during the Old Stone Age.
C1S2-2	Describe the ways we can learn about the religious beliefs of early people.
C1S2-3	Explain why the Neolithic agricultural revolution was a turning point in history.
C1S3-1	Explain how the first cities emerged.
C1S3-2	Identify the basic features of civilizations.
C1S3-3	Describe the ways that cultures can spread and change.
C2S1-1	Explain how geography influenced ancient Egypt.
C2S1-2	Identify and compare the main features and achievements of Egypt's kingdoms.
C2S1-3	Describe how trade and warfare affected Egypt and Nubia.
C2S2-1	Summarize how religious beliefs shaped the lives of Egyptians.
C2S2-2	Describe how Egyptian society was organized.
C2S2-3	Identify the advances that Egyptians made in learning and the arts.
C2S3-1	Explain how geographic features influenced Fertile Crescent civilizations.
C2S3-2	Describe the main features of Sumerian civilization.
C2S3-3	Identify Sumerian advances in learning.
C2S4-1	Describe how early empires arose in Mesopotamia.
C2S4-2	Explain how ideas and technology spread.
C2S4-3	Identify Phoenician contributions.
C2S5-1	Summarize the main events in the early history of the Israelites.
C2S5-2	Explain how the Jews viewed their relationship with God.
C2S5-3	Describe the moral and ethical ideas that the prophets taught.

C3S1-1	Describe how geography has influenced ancient India.
C3S1-2	Explain how archaeology has provided clues about the Indus Valley civilization.
C3S1-3	Identify the theories that scholars had about the decline of the Indus Valley civilization.

C3S2-1	Identify the main characteristics of Aryan civilization in India.
C3S2-2	Describe how expansion led to changes in Aryan civilization.
C3S2-3	Summarize what ancient Indian epics reveal about Aryan life.

C3S3-1	Explain how geography influenced early Chinese civilization.
C3S3-2	Describe how Chinese culture took shape under the Shang and the Zhou.
C3S3-3	Identify the key cultural achievements in early China.

C4S1-1	Explain how Hinduism is a complex religion.
C4S1-2	Describe the major teachings of the Buddha.
C4S1-3	Outline how Buddhism became a major world religion.

C4S2-1	Explain how the Maurya rulers created a strong central government.
C4S2-2	Describe some major achievements of the Deccan kingdoms.
C4S2-3	Identify features of the Gupta period that led to an Indian golden age.

C4S3-1	Explain effects of the caste system.
C4S3-2	Identify the values that influenced Indian family life.
C4S3-3	Describe how the traditional Indian village functioned economically and politically.

C4S4-1	Summarize the major teachings of Confucius.
C4S4-2	Compare the views on government of Legalism and Daoism.
C4S4-3	Explain why many Chinese people accepted Buddhist ideas.

C4S5-1	Describe how Shi Huangdi united China.
C4S5-2	Summarize how Han rulers strengthened the economy and government of China.
C4S5-3	Identify features of the Han period that led to a Chinese golden age.

C5S1-1	Identify the civilizations that influenced the Minoans.
C5S1-2	Explain how the Mycenaean civilization affected the later Greeks.
C5S1-3	Describe what the epics of Homer reveal.

C5S2-1	Describe the influence of geography.
C5S2-2	Describe the kinds of governments the Greek city-states developed.
C5S2-3	Compare Athens and Sparta.
C5S2-4	Identify the unifying forces.
C5S3-1	Describe the impact the Persian Wars had on Greece.
C5S3-2	Explain how Athens enjoyed a golden age under Pericles.
C5S3-3	Identify the causes and effects of the Peloponnesian War.
C5S4-1	Outline the political and ethical ideas that Greek philosophers developed.
C5S4-2	Describe architects' and artists' goals.
C5S4-3	Identify the themes that Greek writers and historians explored.
C5S5-1	Explain how Alexander built an empire.
C5S5-2	Summarize the results of Alexander's conquests.
C5S5-3	Describe how individuals contributed to Hellenistic civilization.
C6S1-1	Identify ways that geography shaped the early development of Rome.
C6S1-2	Describe the major characteristics of government and society in the Roman republic.
C6S1-3	Explain how Rome succeeded in expanding in Italy.
C6S2-1	Describe how Rome won an empire.
C6S2-2	Explain why the republic declined.
C6S2-3	Outline how Roman emperors promoted peace and stability in the empire.
C6S3-1	Analyze how Greco-Roman civilization was formed.
C6S3-2	Outline Roman contributions to literature, the arts, and technology.
C6S3-3	Identify principles of Roman law.
C6S4-1	Describe Rome's policy toward different religions in the early empire.
C6S4-2	Summarize the major teachings of Jesus and how they spread.
C6S4-3	Explain how the early Christian Church developed.
C6S5-1	Outline how Roman emperors tried to end the crisis in the empire.
C6S5-2	Explain how the Hun invasions contributed to the decline of Rome.
C6S5-3	Describe how economic and social problems led to the fall of Rome.

C9S3-1	Identify the advanced civilizations of 1050.
C9S3-2	Analyze Crusades' causes and effects.
C9S3-3	Summarize the Christian Reconquista of Spain.

C9S4-1	Describe how medieval universities advanced learning.
C9S4-2	Explain how "new" learning affected medieval thought.
C9S4-3	Identify the styles of literature, architecture, and art that developed.

C9S5-1	Explain how the Black Death caused social and economic decline.
C9S5-2	Identify problems of the Church.
C9S5-3	Analyze the causes, turning points, and effects of the Hundred Years' War.

C10S1-1	Summarize how Justinian extended Byzantine power.
C10S1-2	Outline the key elements of Byzantine Christianity.
C10S1-3	Explain why the Byzantine empire collapsed.
C10S1-4	Describe the Byzantine heritage.

C10S2-1	Identify how geography helped shape early Russia and the growth of Kiev.
C10S2-2	Describe how the Mongol conquest affected Russia.
C10S2-3	Explain why Moscow emerged as the chief power in Russia.

C10S3-1	Identify how geography influenced developments in Eastern Europe.
C10S3-2	Explain why Eastern Europe became a cultural crossroads with a diverse mix of people.
C10S3-3	Describe the threats that the early kingdoms of Eastern Europe faced.

C11S1-1	Explain how Muhammad became the prophet of Islam.
C11S1-2	Summarize the teachings of Islam.
C11S1-3	Describe how Islam helped shape the lives of believers.

C11S2-1	Summarize how Muslims conquered many lands.
C11S2-2	Describe the movements that emerged within Islam.
C11S2-3	Explain why the empire of the caliphs declined.

C11S3-1	Describe how the Muslim society and economy were organized.
C11S3-2	Explain what traditions influenced Muslim arts and literature.
C11S3-3	Identify the advances Muslims made in centers of learning.

C11S4-1	Describe the impact of the Delhi sultanate on India.
C11S4-2	Outline how Muslim and Hindu traditions clashed and blended.
C11S4-3	Explain how Akbar strengthened Mughal rule.

C13S5-1	Explain how feudalism developed in Japan.
C13S5-2	Summarize the changes that took place under the Tokugawa shoguns.
C13S5-3	Describe the cultural and artistic traditions that emerged in feudal Japan.

C14S1-1	Explain why the Italian city-states were a favorable setting for a cultural rebirth.
C14S1-2	Define the Renaissance.
C14S1-3	Identify the themes and techniques Renaissance artists and writers explored.

C14S2-1	Cite the artists who brought the Renaissance to northern Europe.
C14S2-2	Paraphrase the themes that humanist thinkers and other writers explored.
C14S2-3	Relate the impact that the printing revolution had on Europe.

C14S3-1	State how abuses in the Church sparked widespread criticism.
C14S3-2	Relate how Martin Luther challenged Catholic authority.
C14S3-3	Identify the role John Calvin played in the Reformation.

C14S4-1	Outline what ideas radical reformers supported.
C14S4-2	Explain why England formed a new church.
C14S4-3	Describe how the Catholic Church reformed itself.
C14S4-4	Enumerate why some groups faced persecution.

C14S5-1	Assess how astronomers changed the way people viewed the universe.
C14S5-2	Describe the new scientific method.
C14S5-3	Summarize the advances made by Newton and other scientists.

C15S1-1	Explain why Europeans crossed the seas.
C15S1-2	Identify how Portugal's eastward explorations led to the development of a trading empire.
C15S1-3	Trace how Columbus's voyages affected the search for a passage to the Indies.

C15S2-1	Determine the key geographic features of Southeast Asia.
C15S2-2	Summarize the impact Indian civilization had on new kingdoms and empires.
C15S2-3	Identify the factors that contributed to the growth of Vietnamese culture.

C17S3-1	Outline how the Tudors and Stuarts differed in their relations with Parliament.
C17S3-2	Analyze how the English Civil War led to the rise of the Commonwealth.
C17S3-3	Identify the causes and results of the Glorious Revolution.
C17S4-1	Identify the causes and results of the Thirty Years' War.
C17S4-2	Relate how Austria and Prussia emerged as great powers.
C17S4-3	Describe how European diplomats tried to maintain the balance of power.
C17S5-1	Describe how Peter the Great tried to make Russia into a modern state.
C17S5-2	Identify the steps Peter the Great took to expand Russia's borders.
C17S5-3	Explain how Catherine the Great strengthened Russia.
C18S1-1	Describe how scientific progress promoted trust in human reason.
C18S1-2	Explain how the social contract and separation of powers affected views on government.
C18S1-3	Outline how new ideas affected society and the economy.
C18S2-1	Point out the roles censorship and salons played in the spread of new ideas.
C18S2-2	Identify how *philosophes* influenced Enlightenment despots.
C18S2-3	Summarize how the Enlightenment affected arts and literature.
C18S2-4	Explain why the lives of the majority were unaffected by the Enlightenment.
C18S3-1	Identify the influences that spurred Britain's rise to global power.
C18S3-2	Relate how the growth of constitutional government reflected conditions in politics and society.
C18S3-3	Explain how George III reasserted royal power.
C18S4-1	Identify the chief characteristics of the 13 colonies.
C18S4-2	Describe how growing discontent led to the American Revolution.
C18S4-3	Summarize how the new Constitution reflected the ideas of the Enlightenment.
C19S1-1	Describe the social structure of the old regime.
C19S1-2	Outline why France faced economic troubles in 1789.
C19S1-3	Explain why Louis XVI called the Estates General.
C19S1-4	Summarize why a Paris crowd stormed the Bastille.

C19S2-1	Describe how popular revolts contributed to the French Revolution.
C19S2-2	Enumerate the moderate reforms enacted by the National Assembly.
C19S2-3	Explain how foreign reaction to the revolution helped lead to war.
C19S3-1	Explain why radicals abolished the monarchy.
C19S3-2	Describe how the excesses of the Convention led to the Directory.
C19S3-3	Specify what impact the revolution had on women and daily life.
C19S4-1	Explain how Napoleon rose to power.
C19S4-2	Specify how revolutionary reforms changed under Napoleon.
C19S4-3	Describe how Napoleon built an empire in Europe.
C19S5-1	Identify the challenges that threatened Napoleon's empire.
C19S5-2	Describe the events that led to Napoleon's defeat.
C19S5-3	Enumerate the goals of the Congress of Vienna.
C20S1-1	Specify the reasons that the Industrial Revolution was a turning point in world history.
C20S1-2	State the ways that an agricultural revolution contributed to population growth.
C20S2-1	Cite the reasons that Britain was the starting point for the Industrial Revolution.
C20S2-2	Describe the changes that transformed the textile industry.
C20S2-3	Outline the new technologies that were part of the revolution in transportation.
C20S3-1	Describe life in the new industrial city.
C20S3-2	Explain how the factory system changed the way people worked.
C20S3-3	Enumerate the benefits and problems industrialization brought to the working class and the new middle class.
C20S4-1	Explain laissez-faire economics.
C20S4-2	Compare how the views of utilitarians differed from those of socialists.
C20S4-3	Summarize the ideas of "scientific socialism" introduced by Karl Marx.
C21S1-1	Identify the goals of conservatives.
C21S1-2	Describe how liberalism and nationalism challenged the old order.
C21S1-3	Outline why Europe was plagued by revolts after 1815.

C23S5-1	Analyze how conditions in Russia affected progress.
C23S5-2	Explain why czars followed a cycle of absolutism, reform, and reaction.
C23S5-3	Describe how the problems of industrialization contributed to the growing crisis and outbreak of revolution in Russia.

C24S1-1	Summarize why reformers sought to change Parliament in the 1800s.
C24S1-2	Describe the values Queen Victoria represented.
C24S1-3	Identify how the Liberal and Conservative parties helped bring a new era to British politics.

C24S2-1	Identify the social and economic reforms that benefited British workers and others.
C24S2-2	Explain how British women worked to win the vote.
C24S2-3	Specify the goals of Irish nationalists.

C24S3-1	Outline the domestic and foreign policies of Napoleon III.
C24S3-2	Describe the impact of the Dreyfus affair and other challenges on the Third Republic.
C24S3-3	Specify the steps the French government took toward reform in the early 1900s.

C24S4-1	Explain how the United States extended its territory.
C24S4-2	Outline the ways American democracy grew before and after the Civil War.
C24S4-3	Summarize the impact that economic growth and social reform had on the United States.

C25S1-1	Outline causes of the "new imperialism."
C25S1-2	Explain why western imperialism was so successful.
C25S1-3	Describe how governments ruled their empires.

C25S2-1	Identify forces shaping Africa in the early 1800s.
C25S2-2	Describe how European contact with Africa increased.
C25S2-3	Summarize how Leopold II started a scramble for colonies.
C25S2-4	Explain how Africans resisted imperialism.

C25S3-1	Identify the stresses in the Muslim world.
C25S3-2	Define problems faced by the Ottoman empire.
C25S3-3	Outline how Egypt sought to modernize.
C25S3-4	Explain the European powers' interest in Iran.

C25S4-1	Summarize the causes and effects of the Sepoy Rebellion.
C25S4-2	Assess how British rule affected India.
C25S4-3	Explain how Indians viewed western culture.
C25S4-4	Trace the origins of Indian nationalism.

C25S5-1	Enumerate the trade rights that westerners sought in China.
C25S5-2	Summarize the internal problems that Chinese reformers tried to solve.
C25S5-3	Describe how the Qing monarchy came to an end.
C26S1-1	Outline how discontent in Japanese society and the opening of Japan led to the Meiji restoration.
C26S1-2	Summarize the main reforms under the Meiji.
C26S1-3	State how Japanese military strength promoted imperialism.
C26S2-1	Discuss the impact of European colonization on Southeast Asia.
C26S2-2	Explain how Siam remained independent.
C26S2-3	Outline the ways imperialism spread to the Philippines and other Pacific islands.
C26S3-1	Summarize how Canada achieved self-rule.
C26S3-2	Give examples that show how European settlement changed the course of Australian history.
C26S3-3	Identify how New Zealand emerged as an independent nation.
C26S4-1	Describe the political and economic problems that faced new Latin American nations.
C26S4-2	Relate how Mexico struggled for stability.
C26S4-3	Analyze United States influence in Latin America.
C26S5-1	Explain how imperialism led to new economic patterns.
C26S5-2	Describe the cultural impact of imperialism.
C26S5-3	Summarize how new political tensions developed as a result of imperialism.
C27S1-1	Summarize efforts toward peace in the early 1900s.
C27S1-2	Describe how nationalism and international rivalries pushed Europe toward war.
C27S1-3	Outline the causes and effects of the European alliance system.
C27S2-1	Describe how ethnic tensions in the Balkans sparked a political assassination.
C27S2-2	Relate how the conflict between Austria-Hungary and Serbia widened.
C27S2-3	Explain how historians view the outbreak of World War I.
C27S3-1	Identify why a stalemate developed on the Western Front.
C27S3-2	Assess how technology made World War I different from other wars.
C27S3-3	Explain how the war became a global conflict.

C27S4-1	Explain how World War I became a total war.
C27S4-2	Specify the effect that the continuing conflict had on morale.
C27S4-3	Summarize causes and results of the American entry into the war.

C27S5-1	Identify the costs of the war.
C27S5-2	Enumerate the issues faced by the delegates to the Paris Peace Conference.
C27S5-3	Explain the dissatisfaction with the Treaty of Versailles and other peace settlements.

C28S1-1	Explain why the revolution occurred in Russia in March 1917.
C28S1-2	Outline why Lenin and the Bolsheviks launched the November revolution.
C28S1-3	Analyze why the Communists defeated their opponents in the Russian civil war.

C28S2-1	Describe how the Communist state developed under Lenin.
C28S2-2	Summarize the effects of Stalin's five-year plans.
C28S2-3	Explain why Stalin launched the Great Purge.
C28S2-4	Assess how Soviet foreign policy affected relationships with the western powers.

C28S3-1	Explain how Stalin created a totalitarian state.
C28S3-2	Summarize how communism changed Soviet society.
C28S3-3	Relate how state control affected the arts in the Soviet Union.

C29S1-1	Analyze causes of the Mexican Revolution.
C29S1-2	Cite reforms introduced in Mexico.
C29S1-3	Explain how nationalism affected Mexico.
C29S1-4	Describe the Good Neighbor Policy.

C29S2-1	Outline the ways Africans resisted colonial rule.
C29S2-2	Describe signs of nationalism that developed in Africa.
C29S2-3	Illustrate how Turkey and Iran modernized.
C29S2-4	Explain how European mandates contributed to the growth of Arab nationalism.

C29S3-1	Trace factors that sparked India's independence movement after World War I.
C29S3-2	Assess how Mohandas Gandhi influenced the independence movement.
C29S3-3	Interpret what the Salt March symbolized.

C29S4-1	Point out key challenges to the Chinese Republic.
C29S4-2	Identify leaders of the "new" China.
C29S4-3	Determine how invasion by Japan affected China.

C29S5-1	Trace how liberal changes affected Japan in the 1920s.
C29S5-2	Describe how the nationalists reacted to Japan's problems during the Great Depression.
C29S5-3	Summarize militarists' use of power.
C30S1-1	Discuss issues that Europe faced after World War I.
C30S1-2	Outline how the Great Depression began and spread.
C30S1-3	Summarize the ways Britain, France, and the United States tried to meet the challenges of the 1920s and 1930s.
C30S2-1	Analyze how new views revolutionized modern science and thought.
C30S2-2	Identify the artistic and literary trends that emerged in the 1920s.
C30S2-3	Summarize changes in western society after World War I.
C30S3-1	Explain how conditions in Italy favored the rise of Mussolini.
C30S3-2	Describe how Mussolini reshaped Italy.
C30S3-3	Restate the values and goals of fascist ideology.
C30S4-1	Identify the problems the Weimar Republic faced.
C30S4-2	Trace how Hitler came to power.
C30S4-3	Enumerate the political, social, economic, and cultural policies Hitler pursued.
C30S4-4	Discuss how Hitler took action against German Jews.
C31S1-1	Articulate how dictators and the Spanish Civil War challenged peace.
C31S1-2	Trace how continuing German aggression led toward war.
C31S1-3	Outline the factors that encouraged the coming of war.
C31S2-1	Describe the early gains that allowed the Axis powers to control much of Europe.
C31S2-2	Identify the Battle of Britain and Operation Barbarossa.
C31S2-3	Summarize how Japan responded to growing American involvement.
C31S3-1	Describe how Germany and Japan treated people in occupied lands.
C31S3-2	Outline how the Allies turned the tide of the war.
C31S3-3	Explain how the Red Army and the Allied invasion of France undid German plans.
C31S4-1	Relate how the Pacific war was fought.
C31S4-2	Reconstruct how the Allies defeated Nazi Germany.
C31S4-3	Analyze the debates that surrounded the defeat of Japan.

C31S5-1	Describe the issues that arose in the aftermath of war.
C31S5-2	Explain why the Allies organized the United Nations.
C31S5-3	Summarize how the breakup of the wartime alliance led to new conflicts.

C32S1-1	Explain how the end of colonialism and the Cold War shaped the world.
C32S1-2	Summarize the ways new nations tried to form stable governments.
C32S1-3	Analyze the role world organizations played.
C32S1-4	Discuss the enduring issues that the world faces today.

C32S2-1	Explain the ways that the global North and South are economically interdependent.
C32S2-2	Outline the obstacles that developing nations face.
C32S2-3	Relate how economic development and environmental issues are linked.

C32S3-1	Trace how new ways of life are replacing old ways.
C32S3-2	Give examples of how modernization has affected the lives of women.
C32S3-3	Compare and contrast the benefits and limits of modern science and technology.
C32S3-4	Identify the forces that have shaped a new global culture.

C33S1-1	List issues that troubled Europe after the Cold War.
C33S1-2	Describe how recent economic and political trends affected the West.
C33S1-3	Explain how Europe has moved toward greater unity.
C33S1-4	Summarize changes in social trends.

C33S2-1	Explain how Britain's policies changed after World War II.
C33S2-2	Relate how French power was revived.
C33S2-3	Describe how Germany reunified.
C33S2-4	Enumerate problems of other democratic nations.

C33S3-1	Specify actions the United States took as a global superpower.
C33S3-2	Outline developments that have shaped the economy.
C33S3-3	Identify recent issues Canada has faced.

C33S4-1	Summarize the ideas that guided Soviet political, economic, and foreign policy.
C33S4-2	Explain why the Soviet Union collapsed.
C33S4-3	Describe Russia's current problems.

C33S5-1	Describe how Eastern European nations opposed Soviet domination.
C33S5-2	Identify effects of the fall of communism.
C33S5-3	Enumerate the causes and effects of the Yugoslavian civil war.

C34S1-1	Identify the factors that made Japan's recovery an economic miracle.
C34S1-2	Summarize how Japan interacted economically and politically with other nations.
C34S1-3	Analyze how patterns of life are changing in Japan.

C34S2-1	Describe effects of communist policies in China.
C34S2-2	Enumerate challenges that China faced during the Cold War.
C34S2-3	Explain how calls for reform spurred renewed repression in China.
C34S2-4	State the challenges that China faces today.

C34S3-1	Relate how China has influenced Taiwan and Hong Kong.
C34S3-2	Discuss how Singapore modernized.
C34S3-3	Explain why Korea has remained divided for more than 50 years.

C34S4-1	Analyze how war affected Vietnam and Cambodia.
C34S4-2	Describe challenges faced by the Philippines and the developing nations of Southeast Asia.
C34S4-3	Summarize factors that make the Pacific Rim a vital region.

C35S1-1	Explain why India was partitioned.
C35S1-2	Discuss how India has dealt with political, economic, and social change.
C35S1-3	Identify problems Pakistan and Bangladesh faced.
C25S1-4	Show how South Asia is linked to world affairs.

C35S2-1	Point out how diversity and nationalism shaped the Middle East.
C35S2-2	Identify what political and economic patterns that emerged.
C35S2-3	Explain why an Islamic revival grew.
C35S2-4	Describe how women's lives vary in the Middle East.

C35S3-1	Outline issues that Turkey faced.
C35S3-2	Analyze why Egypt was a leader in the Arab world.
C35S3-3	Summarize causes and results of the revolution in Iran.

C35S4-1	Describe how the Cold War increased tensions in the Middle East.
C35S4-2	Analyze why Arab-Israeli conflict was difficult to resolve.
C35S4-3	Restate why conflicts arose in Lebanon and the Persian Gulf.

C36S1-1	Explain how the colonial legacy contributed to a growing spirit of nationalism.
C36S1-2	Trace routes to freedom that Ghana, Kenya, and Algeria followed.
C36S1-3	Summarize how the Cold War affected Africa.
C36S2-1	Discuss barriers to unity and stability in Africa.
C36S2-2	Outline economic choices that African nations faced.
C36S2-3	Identify critical issues that affect Africa today.
C36S2-4	Give examples of how modernization affected patterns of life in Africa.
C36S3-1	Enumerate the pressures for change in Nigeria.
C36S3-2	Describe the effects dictatorship had on the Congo.
C36S3-3	Discuss the outcome of Tanzania's socialism experiment.
C36S4-1	Identify challenges that Zimbabwe faced.
C36S4-2	Explain how the long struggle to end apartheid led to a new South Africa.
C36S4-3	Discuss how the Cold War affected southern African nations.
C37S1-1	Explain why Latin America is culturally diverse.
C37S1-2	Summarize conditions that contributed to unrest in Latin American countries.
C37S1-3	Analyze forces that shaped political, economic, and social patterns in Latin America.
C37S2-1	Describe how communist rule affected Cuba.
C37S2-2	Identify policies the United States followed in Latin America.
C37S2-3	Point out global issues that link Latin America to other regions of the world.
C27S3-1	Compare conditions that have changed and those that have remained the same in Mexico.
C37S3-2	Determine why Central American countries suffer civil wars.
C37S3-3	Restate causes of Haiti's political and economic struggles.
C37S4-1	Identify challenges Argentina has faced on the road to democracy.
C37S4-2	Describe how Brazil's government changed in the late 1900s.
C37S4-3	Determine what has limited Brazil's "economic miracle."

CHAPTER 1—TOWARD CIVILIZATION (PREHISTORY–3000 B.C.)

Matching

Match each term with the correct statement below.

a. archaeology   e. geography
b. artifact   f. glacier
c. city-state   g. nomad
d. cultural diffusion   h. Old Stone Age

____ 1. The study of people, their environments, and the resources available to them

____ 2. The study of the ways of life of early peoples through the examination of their physical remains

____ 3. Object made by people

____ 4. The earliest period of human history

____ 5. Person who moves from place to place in search of food

____ 6. A huge sheet of ice

____ 7. A political unit consisting of a city and its surrounding land

____ 8. The spread of ideas, customs, and technology from one people to another

Match each term with the correct statement below.

a. archaeology   e. nomad
b. artisans   f. Old Stone Age
c. cultural diffusion   g. polytheistic
d. New Stone Age   h. technology

____ 9. ____ is the study of the ways of life of early people through the examination of their artifacts.

____ 10. The skills and tools people use to meet their basic needs are known as ____.

____ 11. The ____ is the earliest period of human history.

____ 12. A ____ moves from place to place following animals and ripening fruit.

____ 13. The ____ began when people gave up the nomadic life and settled down to farm.

____ 14. Ancient people are called ____ because they believed in many gods.

____ 15. ____, or skilled craftworkers, made pottery or finely carved or woven goods.

____ 16. The spread of ideas, customs, and technologies is called ____.

Multiple Choice
Identify the letter of the choice that best completes the statement or answers the question.

_____ 17. Why is geography important to history?
    a.   It helps us predict the future.
    b.   It shows us the connections between people, places, and events.
    c.   It tells us when events took place.
    d.   It uncovers artifacts left by early people.

_____ 18. How do archaeologists find out about early peoples?
    a.   They read historical novels.   c.   They study old photographs.
    b.   They dig to find artifacts.   d.   They go to museums.

_____ 19. Which of the following is the job of a historian?
    a.   to study written evidence about the past
    b.   to track down criminals
    c.   to analyze rocks
    d.   to study geology

_____ 20. Which of the following was characteristic of the Old Stone Age?
    a.   farming   c.   toolmaking
    b.   written language   d.   organized government

_____ 21. Which of the following beliefs was probably held by Stone Age people?
    a.   The world is round.   c.   People are evil by nature.
    b.   There is only one god.   d.   There is life after death.

_____ 22. What was the Neolithic revolution?
    a.   the change from hunting and food-gathering to farming
    b.   a war for independence
    c.   a rejection of Paleolithic values by Neolithic people
    d.   the movement of people to North America

_____ 23. Which was a key feature of early civilizations?
    a.   cities
    b.   social equality
    c.   steel making
    d.   a system of exchanging goods for money

_____ 24. Which of the following caused ancient civilizations to change?
    a.   lack of traditions
    b.   contact with other people through trade, warfare, and migration
    c.   poor leaders
    d.   nomadic herders

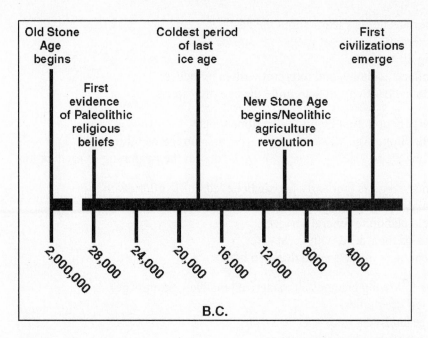

Figure 1-1

_____ 25. According to Figure 1-1, approximately when did the first civilization emerge?
    a.   4000 B.C.
    b.   10,000 B.C.
    c.   3000 B.C.
    d.   2,000,000 B.C.

_____ 26. About how many years were there between the Neolithic revolution and the beginning of civilization, according to Figure 1-1?
    a.   10,000
    b.   6,000
    c.   4,000
    d.   11,000

_____ 27. According to Figure 1-1, approximately what year did the Neolithic agricultural revolution take place?
    a.   8000 B.C.
    b.   9000 B.C.
    c.   11,000 B.C.
    d.   12,000 B.C.

_____ 28. Between which of the following events did the longest period of time elapse, according to Figure 1-1?
    a.   beginning of the Old Stone Age and the Neolithic revolution
    b.   the Neolithic revolution and the emergence of civilization
    c.   the coldest period of the last ice age and the emergence of civilization
    d.   the first evidence of Paleolithic religious beliefs and the emergence of civilization

_____ 29. A new discovery about Stone Age life would most likely be made by which of the following?
    a.   a geographer
    b.   a physicist
    c.   a geologist
    d.   an archaeologist

_____ 30. How do historians help us learn about the past?
   a.   They determine the age of rocks.
   b.   They dig up artifacts.
   c.   They collect, evaluate, and interpret written evidence.
   d.   They use radioactivity to determine the age of artifacts.

_____ 31. When did early people first begin to use stone tools?
   a.   in the Old Stone Age
   b.   in the New Stone Age
   c.   in the Neolithic age
   d.   at the beginning of civilization

_____ 32. What evidence suggests that early people believed in life after death?
   a.   They painted angels on cave walls.
   b.   They held elaborate funeral services.
   c.   They buried their dead with great care.
   d.   They kept track of their good deeds in books.

_____ 33. Which of the following changes characterized the New Stone Age?
   a.   People left their cities.
   b.   People began living in caves.
   c.   People established farming villages.
   d.   People migrated to North America.

_____ 34. Which of the following marked the beginning of civilization?
   a.   the development of cities
   b.   the building of temples
   c.   the discovery of fire
   d.   the creation of farming villages

_____ 35. Where did the first cities emerge?
   a.   along trade routes
   b.   in river valleys
   c.   along the Mediterranean coast
   d.   in the Americas

_____ 36. Which of the following aided cultural diffusion among ancient peoples?
   a.   trade
   b.   new technology
   c.   poor leaders
   d.   farming

Short Answer

37. Describe how a historian would use evidence to reconstruct an event that happened 2,000 years ago.

38. List three advances made by people during the Old Stone Age.

39. Compare the religious beliefs of Stone Age people and people in early civilizations.

40. Explain how the agricultural revolution made civilization possible.

41. List five features of early civilization and briefly describe each one.

42. Explain the role of rivers in the development of the first civilizations.

43. Define the term *cultural diffusion* and describe three ways it can take place.

    Read the following excerpt written by historian Leften Stavrianos. Then answer the questions that follow on a separate sheet of paper.

    "[T]ribal societies, whether of Neolithic times or today, have a built-in brake on productivity. Output is geared to the limited traditional needs of the family, so there is no incentive to produce a surplus. This in turn means that labor is episodic [irregular]. . . . The daily grind—the eight-hour day, five-day week—is conspicuously [obviously] absent. The typical tribesman worked fewer hours per year than modern man and furthermore he worked at his pleasure. The basic reason was that he labored and produced in his capacity as a social person—as a husband or father or brother or village member. Work was not a necessary evil tolerated for the sake of making a living; rather it was concomitant [part] of kin [family] and community relations."

44. What assumptions does the author make about Neolithic attitudes toward work?

45. Compare the author's views of work in Neolithic times and in the modern age.

46. Whose relationship toward work does the author think is healthier—Neolithic peoples or modern peoples? Explain.

Essay
On a separate sheet of paper, write an answer to the following questions.

47. **Identifying Main Ideas** What role did geography play in the development of early civilizations?

48. **Drawing Conclusions** Compare the peoples of the Old Stone Age with the peoples of the New Stone Age in terms of how they obtained their food.

49. **Identifying Main Ideas** Describe the role of rivers in the development of civilization.

50. **Synthesizing Information** How did farming technology transform the lives of Neolithic people?

51. **Synthesizing Information** Explain how the geographic theme of human-environment interaction helps us understand the rise of the first cities.

52. **Asking Questions** Imagine you went back in time to 3000 B.C. List five questions you could ask people you met to determine if they were from a city or a Neolithic village.

CHAPTER 1—TOWARD CIVILIZATION (PREHISTORY–3000 B.C.)
Answer Section

MATCHING

1. ANS: E   DIF: E   REF: 6,7   OBJ: C1S1-1
   TOP: Geography, Natural resources
2. ANS: A   DIF: E   REF: 8,9   OBJ: C1S1-2
   TOP: Social systems, Archaeology
3. ANS: B   DIF: E   REF: 8,13   OBJ: C1S1-2
   TOP: Art and literature, Artifacts
4. ANS: H   DIF: E   REF: 4,11   OBJ: C1S1-2
   TOP: Continuity and change, Old Stone Age
5. ANS: G   DIF: E   REF: 11   OBJ: C1S2-1
   TOP: Social systems, Nomads
6. ANS: F   DIF: E   REF: 12   OBJ: C1S2-1
   TOP: Geography, Nomads
7. ANS: C   DIF: E   REF: 18   OBJ: C1S3-1
   TOP: Political systems, City-states
8. ANS: D   DIF: E   REF: 19   OBJ: C1S3-3
   TOP: Continuity and change, Cultural diffusion

9. ANS: A   DIF: E   REF: 8   OBJ: C1S1-2
   TOP: Social systems, Archaeology
10. ANS: H   DIF: E   REF: 14   OBJ: C1S1-2
    TOP: Technology, Early tools
11. ANS: F   DIF: E   REF: 11   OBJ: C1S2-1
    TOP: Continuity and change, Old Stone Age
12. ANS: E   DIF: E   REF: 11   OBJ: C1S2-1
    TOP: Social systems, Hunter/Gatherers
13. ANS: D   DIF: E   REF: 12   OBJ: C1S2-3
    TOP: Continuity and change, Neolithic revolution
14. ANS: G   DIF: E   REF: 16   OBJ: C1S3-2
    TOP: Religion, Polytheism
15. ANS: B   DIF: E   REF: 16   OBJ: C1S3-2
    TOP: Art and literature, Artisans
16. ANS: C   DIF: E   REF: 19   OBJ: C1S3-3
    TOP: Continuity and change, Cultural diffusion

MULTIPLE CHOICE

17. ANS: B   DIF: A   REF: 6,7   OBJ: C1S1-1
    TOP: Geography, Historical methods
18. ANS: B   DIF: E   REF: 8,9,13   OBJ: C1S1-2
    TOP: Social systems, Archaeology

19. ANS: A   DIF: E   REF: 10,21   OBJ: C1S1-3
    TOP: Geography, Historical methods
20. ANS: C   DIF: A   REF: 11   OBJ: C1S2-1
    TOP: Social systems, Old Stone Age
21. ANS: D   DIF: A   REF: 12   OBJ: C1S2-2
    TOP: Religion, Old Stone Age
22. ANS: A   DIF: E   REF: 12,14   OBJ: C1S2-3
    TOP: Continuity and change, Agriculture
23. ANS: A   DIF: E   REF: 15   OBJ: C1S3-1
    TOP: Political systems, City-states
24. ANS: B   DIF: D   REF: 19   OBJ: C1S3-3
    TOP: Continuity and change, Cultural diffusion
25. ANS: C   DIF: E   REF: 5,15   OBJ: C1S3-1
    TOP: Continuity and change, First civilizations
26. ANS: B   DIF: A   REF: 5   OBJ: C1S2-3
    TOP: Continuity and change, First civilizations
27. ANS: B   DIF: E   REF: 12   OBJ: C1S2-3
    TOP: Technology, Agriculture
28. ANS: A   DIF: D   REF: 4,5   OBJ: C1S2-1
    TOP: Continuity and change, Historical perspective
29. ANS: D   DIF: E   REF: 8,13   OBJ: C1S1-2
    TOP: Social systems, Archaeology
30. ANS: C   DIF: E   REF: 10   OBJ: C1S1-3
    TOP: Social systems, Historical methods
31. ANS: A   DIF: D   REF: 15,16   OBJ: C1S2-1
    TOP: Technology, Early tools
32. ANS: C   DIF: A   REF: 12   OBJ: C1S2-2
    TOP: Religion, Burial practices
33. ANS: C   DIF: A   REF: 12   OBJ: C1S2-3
    TOP: Continuity and change, Agriculture
34. ANS: A   DIF: A   REF: 16   OBJ: C1S3-1
    TOP: Political systems, City-states
35. ANS: B   DIF: E   REF: 16   OBJ: C1S3-1
    TOP: Political systems, City-states
36. ANS: A   DIF: A   REF: 19   OBJ: C1S3-3
    TOP: Continuity and change, Cultural diffusion

SHORT ANSWER

37. ANS:
    First they would collect all the written evidence available concerning the event they were studying; then they would evaluate it for its reliability; finally they would interpret it.

    DIF: A   REF: 10   OBJ: C1S1-3
    TOP: Social systems, Historical methods

38. ANS:
Answers will vary, but should include three of the following: the use of tools, the development of spoken language, fire building, the invention of clothing, or the expression of spiritual beliefs through art and burial customs.

DIF: E   REF: 11,12   OBJ: C1S2-1
TOP: Continuity and change, Advancement

39. ANS:
Stone Age people and people in early civilizations were both polytheistic and believed that gods and goddesses controlled nature and human activities. People during both times believed in an afterlife. The religious practices of ancient people were more complex than their Stone Age ancestors, however, and required the attention of priests, who had special training and knowledge of the divine.

DIF: D   REF: 12,16   OBJ: C1S2-2
TOP: Religion, Polytheism

40. ANS:
By producing their own food and crop surpluses, people could stay in one place and populations could grow.

DIF: A   REF: 16   OBJ: C1S2-3
TOP: Continuity and change, Agriculture

41. ANS:
Answers should include five of the following: cities, well-organized central governments, complex religions, job specialization, social classes, arts and architecture, public works, or writing.

DIF: A   REF: 15,16   OBJ: C1S3-2
TOP: Social systems, First civilizations

42. ANS:
Rivers provided water for irrigation and spread rich silt across the valleys, which enabled farmers to produce the surplus of crops necessary to feed growing populations. Also, people had to work together to control the rivers' waters, which encouraged the development of well-organized governments.

DIF: A   REF: 15   OBJ: C1S3-1
TOP: Technology, First civilizations

43. ANS:
Cultural diffusion is the spread of ideas, customs, and technologies from one people to another. It occurred through migration, trade, and warfare.

DIF: D   REF: 19   OBJ: C1S3-3
TOP: Continuity and change, Cultural diffusion

44. ANS:
The author assumes Neolithic people enjoyed work and that they found it satisfying.

DIF: D   REF: 12-14   OBJ: C1S2-3
TOP: Social systems, Labor theory

45. ANS:
The author views work in Neolithic times as good and life enhancing because it connected people to the social organism; whereas he sees work in the modern age as unfulfilling and empty of any meaning beyond survival.

DIF: D   REF: 14   OBJ: C1S2-3
TOP: Continuity and change, Labor theory

46. ANS:
Neolithic peoples

DIF: D   REF: 14   OBJ: C1S2-3
TOP: Continuity and change, Labor theory

ESSAY

47. ANS:
The first cities rose in river valleys—locations where the physical conditions favored farming and farmers could produce a surplus of food. The cooperation necessary to control the rivers' waters, that is, to stop flooding and build irrigation canals, required leadership and cooperation, which contributed to the establishment of well-organized governments.

DIF: A   REF: 16,19   OBJ: C1S3-1
TOP: Geography, First civilizations

48. ANS:
The peoples of the Old Stone Age led a nomadic existence following herds of game animals and gathering wild fruits and nuts. The women gathered food and the men hunted. New Stone Age peoples lived in settled communities and farmed and herded domesticated animals for a living.

DIF: D   REF: 11,12,14   OBJ: C1S2-3
TOP: Continuity and change, Subsistence

49. ANS:
Rivers provided water for irrigation and spread rich silt across the valleys, which enabled farmers to produce the surplus of crops necessary to feed growing populations. Also, people had to work together to control the rivers' waters, which encouraged the development of well-organized governments.

DIF: A   REF: 16   OBJ: C1S3-1
TOP: Geography, River societies

50. ANS:
Farming technology enabled people to settle down into permanent villages and produce their own food, instead of relying wholly on their environment. This change was the inspiration for New Stone Age people to develop a new set of skills and tools. The Neolithic revolution made life more complex and, in some ways, easier.

DIF: D   REF: 14,19   OBJ: C1S2-3
TOP: Technology, Agriculture

51. ANS:
Answers will vary, but should follow the idea that people who built the first cities used the environment—the water and fertile land of river valleys—to grow crops that would sustain an expanding population. In turn, the environment, particularly the need to control the rivers' waters, led ancient peoples to make advances in social and political organization and religion.

DIF: D   REF: 15,19   OBJ: C1S1-1
TOP: Geography, First civilizations

52. ANS:
Questions will vary but should point out differences in ways of life, including technology, social structure, religion, and political organization, between people living in Neolithic villages and people living in early cities.

DIF: A   REF: 12-16   OBJ: C1S3-2
TOP: Continuity and change, Historical methods

CHAPTER 2—FIRST CIVILIZATIONS: AFRICA AND ASIA (3200 B.C.–500 B.C.)

Matching

Match each person with the correct statement below.
a. Darius
b. Hammurabi
c. a Hebrew
d. a pharaoh
e. a Phoenician
f. Queen Hatshepsut
g. a satrap
h. Zoroaster

_____ 1. "Let your hands build a great tomb to me, the one who rules this great land."

_____ 2. "I wear this false beard as a sign of my authority."

_____ 3. "I, king of Babylon, will destroy the wicked and the evil and cause justice to prevail in the land."

_____ 4. "I have united the Persian empire—the largest empire the world has yet known."

_____ 5. "The great Darius has made me governor."

_____ 6. "When Ahura Mazda triumphs over Ahriman, then you will be judged for your good and your evil."

_____ 7. "We have sailed many seas and traded with many peoples."

_____ 8. "There is only one God and He has said 'You shall have no other gods beside Me.'"

Match each term with the correct definition below.
a. delta
b. monotheistic
c. mummification
d. satrap
e. ziggurat

_____ 9. Triangular area of marshland formed by deposits of silt at the mouth of some rivers

_____ 10. The preservation of the dead

_____ 11. A pyramid-shaped temple built by the Sumerians

_____ 12. Governor of a province of the Persian empire

_____ 13. Teaching a belief in one God

Match each person with the correct description below.
a. Darius
b. Hammurabi
c. Hatshepsut
d. Nebuchadnezzar
e. Ramses II

_____ 14. Egyptian queen who encouraged trade with lands along the eastern Mediterranean

_____ 15. Pharaoh who spread Egyptian rule northward to Syria and conquered Nubia

_____ 16. Ruler who published a code of laws to help unite Babylonia

_____ 17. King who encouraged Babylonian learning

_____ 18. Ruler who united the Persian empire

Multiple Choice
Identify the letter of the choice that best completes the statement or answers the question.

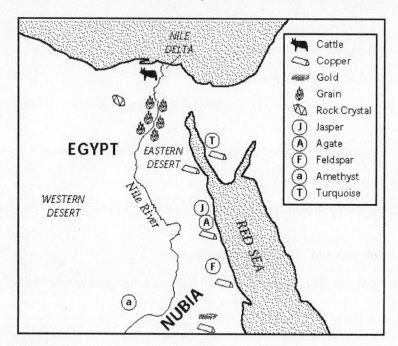

Figure 2-1

_____ 19. According to Figure 2-1, where were cattle raised?
    a. on oases
    b. in the Eastern Desert
    c. in the Nile Delta
    d. along the Red Sea

_____ 20. According to Figure 2-1, which of the following resources was the most widely distributed?
    a. gold
    b. amethyst
    c. copper
    d. feldspar

_____ 21. What information in Figure 2-1 supports the claim that Egypt was the "breadbasket of the world"?
    a. Grain was grown along the Nile.
    b. There are resources spread throughout the land.
    c. Cattle were raised in the delta region.
    d. The Nile flows the entire length of Egypt.

_____ 22. According to Figure 2-1, what valuable resource was mined in Nubia?
    a. turquoise
    b. rock crystal
    c. gold
    d. agate

_____ 23. How did ancient Egyptians view their pharaohs?
    a. as gods
    b. as cruel rulers
    c. as father figures
    d. as equals

_____ 24. The Pyramid Age is another name for
    a. the New Kingdom.
    b. the Old Kingdom.
    c. ancient Egyptian civilization.
    d. the Middle Kingdom.

_____ 25. The Egyptians believed in which of the following?
    a. life after death
    b. that God would lead them to the promised land
    c. one god
    d. Ahriman and Ahura Mazda

_____ 26. The need to keep records led to the development of which of the following in Egypt?
    a. cuneiform
    b. pharaohs
    c. pyramids
    d. hieroglyphics

_____ 27. Sumer was made up of
    a. provinces.
    b. independent city-states.
    c. satrapies.
    d. two kingdoms.

_____ 28. *The Epic of Gilgamesh* is
    a. the story of the Hebrew's flight from Egypt.
    b. an Egyptian folktale.
    c. a tale about King Assurbanipal.
    d. a poem recounting the adventures of a Sumerian hero.

_____ 29. The Code of Hammurabi was a major achievement for which of the following reasons?
    a. It was the first major collection of laws.
    b. It treated men and women as equals.
    c. It ended capital punishment.
    d. It rejected the principle of an "eye for an eye and a tooth for a tooth."

_____ 30. According to the Torah, who united the Hebrew tribes into a single nation?
    a. Solomon
    b. David
    c. Moses
    d. Deborah

_____ 31. Why does Egyptian art often feature people from Nubia?
    a. The Nubians defeated the Assyrians.
    b. Religious beliefs forbid the portrayal of Egyptians.
    c. The Egyptians adopted their religion from the Nubians.
    d. After centuries of trade and warfare between Egypt and Nubia, the Nubians were a part of Egyptian culture.

_____ 32. Which of the following geographic features had the greatest influence on ancient Egypt?
    a. the Mediterranean Sea
    b. the Nile River
    c. the Nubian Desert
    d. the Red Sea

_____ 33. Most Egyptians were members of which of the following groups?
      a.   farmers   c.   merchants
      b.   slaves   d.   nobles

_____ 34. The movement of people across the Fertile Crescent resulted in the
      a.   belief in one god.
      b.   exchange of ideas.
      c.   building of pyramids.
      d.   creation of colonies along the Mediterranean.

_____ 35. How did the Sumerians differ from the Egyptians in the way they viewed their rulers?
      a.   They saw their rulers as the gods' chief servants.
      b.   They allowed their rulers to govern for only ten years.
      c.   They worshiped their rulers as gods.
      d.   They obeyed their rulers without question.

_____ 36. Middle Eastern civilization was spread throughout the Mediterranean by the
      a.   Hittites.   c.   Persians.
      b.   Phoenicians.   d.   Hebrews.

Short Answer

37. List three ways Egyptian civilization depended on the Nile River for its survival.

38. Identify the three main periods of early Egyptian history and describe one significant achievement in each.

39. Describe two pieces of historical evidence that support the idea that the Egyptians believed in life after death.

40. Explain why the Fertile Crescent became a "crossroads of civilization."

41. Describe five significant achievements of peoples of the ancient Middle East and tell why each one was important.

42. What were the two most important ways ideas and new technology spread throughout the ancient Middle East?

43. Describe three basic teachings of Judaism.

Read the following excerpt from the Instructions of the Vizier Ptah-hotep, *a book of advice for young people written by Ptah-hotep. Then answer the following questions.*

"If you are a leader, commanding the conduct of many, seek out every good aim, so that your policy may be without error. A great thing is truth, enduring and surviving; it has not been upset since the time of Osiris. He who departs from its laws is punished. . . .
If you want your conduct to be good, free from every evil, then beware of greed. It is an evil and incurable sickness. . . . A man thrives if his conduct is right. He who follows the right course wins wealth thereby. But the greedy man has no tomb."

44. Based on these comments, what kind of a man is Ptah-hotep?

45. Assume you are an Egyptian teenager during Ptah-hotep's time. Would you take this advice seriously? Explain.

46. What does Ptah-hotep mean by the phrase "the greedy man has no tomb"?

Essay
On a separate sheet of paper, write an answer to the following questions.

47. **Comparing** Compare the geography of Mesopotamia and Egypt. How were they similar and how were they different?

48. **Linking Past and Present** Explain how the laws and ideas of the ancient Hebrews still influence our life today.

49. **Recognizing Cause and Effect** List three advances in technology and learning made by peoples of the ancient Middle East and tell why each one was important.

50. **Identifying Main Ideas** Explain how Hebrew religious beliefs differed from the beliefs of other peoples in the ancient Middle East.

51. **Making Inferences** Based on the religious beliefs of the Sumerians and the Hebrews, compare how these two peoples viewed the world.

52. **Recognizing Causes and Effects** How does geography help explain why several civilizations developed in Mesopotamia, while only one grew up in Egypt?

CHAPTER 2—FIRST CIVILIZATIONS: AFRICA AND ASIA (3200 B.C.–500 B.C.)
Answer Section

MATCHING

1. ANS: D   DIF: A   REF: 25-26   OBJ: C2S1-2
    TOP: Religion, Burial practices
2. ANS: F   DIF: A   REF: 27   OBJ: C2S1-2
    TOP: Impact of individual, Hatshepsut
3. ANS: B   DIF: A   REF: 38-40   OBJ: C2S4-1
    TOP: Impact of individual, Hammurabi
4. ANS: A   DIF: A   REF: 42   OBJ: C2S4-1
    TOP: Impact of individual, Darius
5. ANS: G   DIF: A   REF: 42   OBJ: C2S4-3
    TOP: Political systems, Persian empire
6. ANS: H   DIF: A   REF: 43   OBJ: C2S4-3
    TOP: Religion, Zoroaster
7. ANS: E   DIF: A   REF: 43-44   OBJ: C2S4-4
    TOP: Economics, Phoenicians
8. ANS: C   DIF: A   REF: 46   OBJ: C2S5-2
    TOP: Religion, Judaism

9. ANS: A   DIF: E   REF: 25   OBJ: C2S1-1
    TOP: Geography, River valleys
10. ANS: C   DIF: E   REF: 29   OBJ: C2S2-1
    TOP: Religion, Burial practices
11. ANS: E   DIF: E   REF: 36   OBJ: C2S3-2
    TOP: Religion, Sumerians
12. ANS: D   DIF: E   REF: 42   OBJ: C2S4-3
    TOP: Political systems, Persian empire
13. ANS: B   DIF: E   REF: 46   OBJ: C2S5-2
    TOP: Religion, Monotheism

14. ANS: C   DIF: E   REF: 27   OBJ: C2S1-2
    TOP: Impact of individual, Hatshepsut
15. ANS: E   DIF: E   REF: 27,31,33   OBJ: C2S1-3
    TOP: Impact of individual, Ramses II
16. ANS: B   DIF: E   REF: 38-41   OBJ: C2S4-1
    TOP: Impact of individual, Hammurabi
17. ANS: D   DIF: E   REF: 42   OBJ: C2S4-2
    TOP: Impact of individual, Nebuchadnezzar
18. ANS: A   DIF: E   REF: 42-43   OBJ: C2S4-3
    TOP: Impact of individual, Darius

MULTIPLE CHOICE

19. ANS: C   DIF: E   REF: 24   OBJ: C2S1-1
    TOP: Economics, Nile Valley
20. ANS: C   DIF: A   REF: 24   OBJ: C2S1-1
    TOP: Geography, Natural resources
21. ANS: A   DIF: A   REF: 24,31   OBJ: C2S1-1
    TOP: Economics, Nile Valley
22. ANS: C   DIF: E   REF: 27   OBJ: C2S1-1
    TOP: Economics, Nubia
23. ANS: A   DIF: A   REF: 28   OBJ: C2S2-2
    TOP: Political systems, Pharoahs
24. ANS: B   DIF: E   REF: 26   OBJ: C2S1-2
    TOP: Social systems, Old kingdom Egypt
25. ANS: A   DIF: A   REF: 28-29   OBJ: C2S2-1
    TOP: Religion, Ancient egypt
26. ANS: D   DIF: A   REF: 31,32   OBJ: C2S2-3
    TOP: Technology, Hieroglyphics
27. ANS: B   DIF: A   REF: 35   OBJ: C2S3-2
    TOP: Political systems, City-states
28. ANS: D   DIF: D   REF: 34,36   OBJ: C2S3-2
    TOP: Art and literature, Epic poems
29. ANS: A   DIF: A   REF: 38-42   OBJ: C2S4-1
    TOP: Political systems, Laws and codes of justice
30. ANS: B   DIF: D   REF: 45   OBJ: C2S5-1
    TOP: Religion, Judaism
31. ANS: D   DIF: A   REF: 27,33   OBJ: C2S1-3
    TOP: Art and literature, Cultural diffusion
32. ANS: B   DIF: E   REF: 24   OBJ: C2S1-1
    TOP: Geography, Nile Valley
33. ANS: A   DIF: A   REF: 31   OBJ: C2S2-2
    TOP: Social systems, Ancient egypt
34. ANS: B   DIF: A   REF: 34   OBJ: C2S3-1
    TOP: Continuity and change, Migration
35. ANS: A   DIF: D   REF: 28,35   OBJ: C2S3-2
    TOP: Political systems, Sumer
36. ANS: B   DIF: D   REF: 43-44   OBJ: C2S4-4
    TOP: Continuity and change, Cultural diffusion

SHORT ANSWER

37. ANS:
Egypt depended on the Nile to irrigate its fields, to cover its farmland with silt and make it fertile, and for transportation.

> DIF: A   REF: 24-25   OBJ: C2S1-1
> TOP: Economics, Nile Valley

38. ANS:
Old Kingdom—built the pyramids; Middle Kingdom—created new farmland, expanded trade ties with other Middle Eastern peoples; New Kingdom—expanded Egyptian empire to reach the Euphrates River.

> DIF: D   REF: 25-27   OBJ: C2S1-2
> TOP: Continuity and change, Ancient egypt

39. ANS:
Evidence includes the art of mummification and other burial practices; writings on monuments and wall paintings in tombs; pyramid building.

> DIF: A   REF: 29-31   OBJ: C2S2-1
> TOP: Religion, Ancient egypt

40. ANS:
Is was a fertile region. Because there were few natural barriers to prevent migrating or invading people, many different groups came to the area.

> DIF: E   REF: 34   OBJ: C2S3-1
> TOP: Geography, Cultural diffusion

41. ANS:
Answers may include but are not limited to the following: wheeled vehicles—helped transportation and trade; iron working—could make stronger weapons and more sophisticated farming tools; hieroglyphics and cuneiform—made record keeping possible; alphabet—made writing quicker and easier; astronomy—led to the development of a calendar and made it possible to predict sky phenomena such as eclipses and the positions of the planets; coins—made trade easier.

> DIF: D   REF: 38-43   OBJ: C2S4-2
> TOP: Technology, Fertile crescent

42. ANS:
Answers may include warfare, trade, and migration.

> DIF: A   REF: 41, 44   OBJ: C2S4-3
> TOP: Technology, Fertile crescent

43. ANS:
    Answers might include three of the following teachings of Judaism: There is only one god; the Ten Commandments are the laws of God; no one is above God's laws; God made a covenant with them promising to protect them if they obeyed his laws; justice should be tempered with mercy.

    DIF: A   REF: 46-47   OBJ: C2S5-3   TOP: Religion, Judaism

44. ANS:
    a man of high moral and ethical standards

    DIF: D   REF: 25-26   OBJ: C2S1-2
    TOP: Impact of individual, Ptah-hotep

45. ANS:
    Answers may vary, but most students will probably say they would because of the tone of the comments, which are made especially serious and intimidating by his reference to Osiris, the Egyptian god who judges a person's life to see if his or her soul merits eternal life, and his statement that "the greedy man has no tomb."

    DIF: D   REF: 26-27   OBJ: C2S1-2
    TOP: Impact of individual, Ptah-hotep

46. ANS:
    He means that the greedy man has no hope for eternal life.

    DIF: D   REF: 26-27   OBJ: C2S1-2
    TOP: Religion, Ancient egypt

ESSAY

47. ANS:
    They are similar in that they both have rivers that provide water and fertile soil left behind after the rivers flood. They are different in that Egypt is protected by deserts on two sides, the Mediterranean Sea to the north, and the cataracts in the Nile to the south. Mesopotamia is unprotected by natural barriers.

    DIF: A   REF: 24-25, 34-35 OBJ: C2S3-1
    TOP: Geography, River valleys

48. ANS:
    Answers will vary, but should point out that Hebrew laws like the Ten Commandments still guide our moral conduct in society. Hebrew beliefs also influence our ideas about social justice, especially ideas about mercy and compassion for the less fortunate.

    DIF: D   REF: 47   OBJ: C2S5-3
    TOP: Continuity and change, Judaism

49. ANS:
Answers should list three advances and explain why they were significant. These may include the following: wheeled vehicles—helped transportation and trade; iron working—could make stronger weapons and more sophisticated farming tools; hieroglyphics and cuneiform—made record keeping possible; alphabet—made writing quicker and easier; astronomy—led to the development of a calendar and made it possible to predict sky phenomena such as eclipses and the positions of the planets; coins—made trade easier.

DIF: A REF: 38-44 OBJ: C2S4-2
TOP: Technology, Fertile crescent

50. ANS:
The Hebrews were monotheistic while most other peoples were polytheistic. They believed that God handed down a moral law that bound the actions of all people, including rulers.

DIF: A REF: 28,36,46 OBJ: C2S5-2 TOP: Religion, Judaism

51. ANS:
The Sumerians seemed to feel their world was unpredictable and that they were at the mercy of capricious gods. Based upon their belief that people descended into a grim underworld upon death, they do no appear to have been optimistic. The Hebrews, on the other hand, believed that their God was just and merciful provided that his laws were followed. In this way, the Hebrews felt their fate was ultimately in their control. Their world, unlike the Sumerians', would be good if they followed God's laws.

DIF: D REF: 36,46-47 OBJ: C2S5-2
TOP: Religion, Ancient beliefs

52. ANS:
The location of Egypt isolated it from migrating peoples and protected it from invaders. The land of Mespotamia is relatively open and unprotected. As a result, Mesopotamia attracted different peoples with different cultures and technological achievements.

DIF: A REF: 24-25, 34-36 OBJ: C2S3-1
TOP: Geography, Ancient world

CHAPTER 3—EARLY CIVILIZATIONS IN INDIA AND CHINA (2500 B.C.–256 B.C.)

Matching

Match each term with the correct statement below.

a. caste
b. clan
c. feudalism
d. ideograph

e. loess
f. monsoon
g. rajah
h. subcontinent

_____ 1. Large land mass that juts out from a continent

_____ 2. A seasonal wind

_____ 3. Social group into which people are born and from which they cannot change

_____ 4. Aryan tribal chief

_____ 5. Fine, windblown yellow soil

_____ 6. A group of families who claim a common ancestor

_____ 7. Sign that expresses a thought or idea

_____ 8. System of government in which local lords governed their own lands but owed military service and other kinds of support to the ruler

Match each term with the correct statement below.

a. brahman
b. calligraphy
c. dynastic cycle
d. feudalism

e. ideograph
f. mystic
g. rajah
h. subcontinent

_____ 9. A _____ is a large landmass that juts out from a continent.

_____ 10. A single spiritual power that resides in all things is called _____.

_____ 11. A _____ devotes his or her life to seeking spiritual truth.

_____ 12. A _____ was the chief of an Aryan tribe.

_____ 13. The term for a sign that expresses a thought or an idea is _____.

_____ 14. _____ is an artistic form of handwriting done with ink and a brush.

_____ 15. _____ is a term describing the rise and fall of dynasties.

_____ 16. A system of government in which local lords governed their own lands but owed militia service and other kinds of support to the ruler is called _____.

Multiple Choice
Identify the letter of the choice that best completes the statement or answers the question.

_____ 17. Which of the following two water bodies influenced early Indian civilization?
a. Yellow and Yangzi rivers
b. Indus and Ganges rivers
c. Arabian and Mediterranean seas
d. Tigris and Euphrates rivers

_____ 18. What evidence suggests that the Indus Valley cities had a well-organized government?
a. well-planned cities
b. writings on stone seals
c. records left by kings
d. statues of goddesses

_____ 19. Which of the following is a true statement about the Indus Valley civilization?
a. It lasted for thousands of years.
b. It spread to other parts of Asia.
c. It thrived until modern times.
d. It disappeared without a trace and was only rediscovered in 1922.

_____ 20. The Aryans divided people into classes by
a. age.
b. race.
c. occupation.
d. sex.

_____ 21. During the Vedic age, the Aryans changed
a. from nomads to farmers.
b. from warriors to merchants.
c. from servants to rulers.
d. from farmers to nomads.

_____ 22. Which of the following is contained in the *Mahabharata*?
a. a blend of Indian history, mythology, and religion
b. Aryan laws
c. the story of Rama and Sita
d. the *Ramayana*

_____ 23. The Chinese system of writing was difficult to learn because it used
a. a complex alphabet.
b. hundreds of letters.
c. thousands of characters.
d. numbers instead of letters.

_____ 24. The Mandate of Heaven is the idea behind which of the following?
a. the feudal system
b. the dynastic cycle
c. ancestor worship
d. the Shang social order

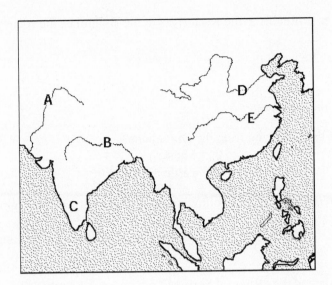

Figure 3-1

_____ 25. Which letter in Figure 3-1 shows the site of Shang civilization?
    a. A   c. C
    b. B   d. D

_____ 26. Which letter in Figure 3-1 shows the Indus Valley civilization?
    a. A   c. C
    b. B   d. E

_____ 27. Which two letters in Figure 3-1 show the sites of early Indian civilizations?
    a. A and D   c. C and D
    b. A and B   d. A and C

_____ 28. Which letter in Figure 3-1 shows the site of the civilization that developed along the Huang He?
    a. A   c. C
    b. B   d. D

_____ 29. The fact that the city of Mohenjo-Daro was carefully planned is evidence of which of the following?
    a. Its inhabitants worshiped the goddess of order.
    b. It had a well-organized government.
    c. It was ruled by the Sumerians.
    d. It produced a surplus of food.

_____ 30. Which of the following most likely contributed to the decline of civilization in the Indus Valley?
    a. an ecological or natural disaster
    b. conquest by the Sumerians
    c. conquest by the Persians
    d. a disease that killed its population

_____ 31. In Aryan society, as the power shifted from the Kshatriyas to the Brahmins, the society became more
   a. warlike.
   b. democratic.
   c. focused on trade.
   d. focused on spiritual and moral issues.

_____ 32. The Aryans learned which of the following from the Dravidians?
   a. the art of war
   b. farming
   c. Sanskrit
   d. cattle breeding

_____ 33. According to the *Bhagavad-Gita*, which of the following is an important Aryan religious belief?
   a. devotion to one's duty
   b. belief in one god
   c. belief in the forces of yin and yang
   d. ancestor worship

_____ 34. Why was the Huang He nicknamed the "River of Sorrows"?
   a. The Chinese believed its waters were actually the tears of a god.
   b. The emperor drowned in it.
   c. It often flooded and destroyed crops.
   d. It often dried up.

_____ 35. Which of the following was true under feudalism?
   a. Peasants owned the lands they farmed.
   b. Local lords exercised great power.
   c. The king exercised absolute power.
   d. The king had no real power.

_____ 36. Which of the following was first achieved by the Chinese?
   a. ironworking
   b. the horse-drawn chariot
   c. a writing system based on the alphabet
   d. silkmaking

Short Answer

37. Identify five important geographic features in India and tell how each one influenced the development of early Indian civilization.

38. Explain why an air of mystery surrounds the Indus Valley civilization.

39. Describe the four groups into which Aryan society was divided.

40. List two Aryan ideals regarding human behavior found in the *Mahabharata* and/or the *Ramayana*.

41. Describe the relationship between China's geography and its belief that it was the sole source of civilization.

42. Identify the following: yin and yang; Mandate of Heaven; dynastic cycle; feudalism.

43. List one Chinese achievement in the arts and one in technology.

Read the following excerpt in which archaeologist Jacquetta Hawkes gives some details about people of the Indus Valley civilization. Then answer the questions that follow on a separate sheet of paper.

> "The skeletal evidence, the best of which comes from a cemetery used by the ordinary citizens of Harappa, suggests that two distinct types prevailed. The majority had fairly long heads, low foreheads and strongly marked brow ridges; they were tallish for the period—5 feet 8–9 inches. . . . .
> In their dress and hair styles the Indus people seem to show definite similarities with the Sumerians. The men wore trimmed beards but shaved their upper lips; their hair was rolled into a bun at the back and held by a fillet [a thin band]. A light robe left the right shoulder bare. As far as can be judged from crude 'mother goddess' figurines [tiny statues], the women (like those of the villages) went in for quantities of necklaces and huge headdresses; for the rest they wore miniskirts and ornamental belts round the hips."

44. Why does the archaeologist think the women wore necklaces and miniskirts?

45. What can be assumed about the peoples' religious beliefs from the fact that "mother goddess" figurines have been excavated from the Indus Valley?

46. What can be assumed about the prosperity of early Indus Valley civilization based on its physical remains and why?

Essay
On a separate sheet of paper, write an answer to the following questions.

47. **Recognizing Causes and Effects** Describe the effect geography had on the development of early civilization in China.

48. **Linking Past and Present** Compare the class structure in India during the Vedic age with that in the United States today.

49. **Making Inferences** What does the Indian name for river, *lok-mata*, "mother of the people," tell us about the role of rivers in Indian civilization?

50. **Applying Information** Imagine you are living during the time of the Shang dynasty. Explain the flooding of the Huang He in terms of the dynastic cycle.

51. **Drawing Conclusions** By about 500 B.C., the people of India developed a written language, Sanskrit. How did this development promote unity in India?

52. **Applying Information** Imagine that you are a Chinese peasant and the Huang He has flooded and destroyed your harvest. Explain this occurrence in terms of the forces of yin and yang.

CHAPTER 3—EARLY CIVILIZATIONS IN INDIA AND CHINA (2500 B.C.–256 B.C.)
Answer Section

MATCHING

1. ANS: H   DIF: E   REF: 52   OBJ: C3S1-1
    TOP: Geography, India
2. ANS: F   DIF: E   REF: 53   OBJ: C3S1-1
    TOP: Geography, Weather patterns
3. ANS: A   DIF: E   REF: 57   OBJ: C3S2-1
    TOP: Social systems, Caste systems
4. ANS: G   DIF: E   REF: 57   OBJ: C3S2-2
    TOP: Political systems, Aryan society
5. ANS: E   DIF: E   REF: 60-61   OBJ: C3S3-1
    TOP: Geography, Soil erosion
6. ANS: B   DIF: E   REF: 62   OBJ: C3S3-2
    TOP: Social systems, Clans
7. ANS: D   DIF: E   REF: 63   OBJ: C3S3-2
    TOP: Technology, Ideographs
8. ANS: C   DIF: E   REF: 64   OBJ: C3S3-2
    TOP: Political systems, Feudalism

9. ANS: H   DIF: E   REF: 52   OBJ: C3S1-1
    TOP: Geography, India
10. ANS: A   DIF: E   REF: 57   OBJ: C3S2-1
    TOP: Religion, Indus Valley civilization
11. ANS: F   DIF: E   REF: 57   OBJ: C3S3-2
    TOP: Religion, Mysticism
12. ANS: G   DIF: E   REF: 57   OBJ: C3S2-2
    TOP: Political systems, Aryan society
13. ANS: E   DIF: E   REF: 63   OBJ: C3S3-2
    TOP: Technology, Ideographs
14. ANS: B   DIF: E   REF: 63   OBJ: C3S3-2
    TOP: Art and literature, Caligraphy
15. ANS: C   DIF: E   REF: 64   OBJ: C3S3-2
    TOP: Continuity and conflict, Dynastic cycles
16. ANS: D   DIF: E   REF: 64   OBJ: C3S3-2
    TOP: Political systems, Feudalism

MULTIPLE CHOICE

17. ANS: B   DIF: E   REF: 52   OBJ: C3S1-1
    TOP: Geography, Early Indian civilization

18. ANS: A DIF: A REF: 53 OBJ: C3S1-2
    TOP: Social systems, Indus Valley civilization
19. ANS: D DIF: A REF: 52,54 OBJ: C2S1-2
    TOP: Continuity and change, Indus Valley civilization
20. ANS: C DIF: A REF: 55 OBJ: C3S2-1
    TOP: Social systems, Aryan society
21. ANS: A DIF: A REF: 55 OBJ: C3S2-2
    TOP: Continuity and change, Aryan society
22. ANS: A DIF: A REF: 56 OBJ: C3S2-3
    TOP: Art and literature, Mahabharata
23. ANS: C DIF: A REF: 63 OBJ: C3S3-2
    TOP: Technology, Ideographs
24. ANS: B DIF: D REF: 63-64 OBJ: C3S3-2
    TOP: Social systems, Shang dynasty
25. ANS: D DIF: A REF: 51,60 OBJ: C3S3-1
    TOP: Geography, Early Chinese dynasties
26. ANS: A DIF: A REF: 51,53 OBJ: C3S1-1
    TOP: Geography, Early Indian civilization
27. ANS: B DIF: A REF: 51,53 OBJ: C3S1-1
    TOP: Geography, Early Indian civilization
28. ANS: D DIF: A REF: 51,60 OBJ: C3S3-1
    TOP: Geography, Early Chinese dynasties
29. ANS: B DIF: A REF: 54 OBJ: C3S1-2
    TOP: Political systems, Mohenjo-Daro
30. ANS: A DIF: A REF: 55 OBJ: C3S1-3
    TOP: Continuity and change, Indus Valley civilization
31. ANS: D DIF: D REF: 56-57 OBJ: C3S2-1
    TOP: Continuity and change, Aryan society
32. ANS: B DIF: D REF: 57 OBJ: C3S2-2
    TOP: Technology, Aryan society
33. ANS: A DIF: D REF: 58 OBJ: C3S2-3
    TOP: Religion, Hinduism
34. ANS: C DIF: E REF: 60 OBJ: C3S3-1
    TOP: Geography, Early Chinese dynasties
35. ANS: B DIF: D REF: 64 OBJ: C3S3-2
    TOP: Political systems, Feudalism
36. ANS: D DIF: A REF: 65 OBJ: C3S3-3
    TOP: Technology, Fabric

SHORT ANSWER

37. ANS:
Answers should include five of the following: Himalayas—limited contact with other peoples; Hindu Kush—passes through these mountains served as gateways for invading and migrating peoples; northern plain—fertile land supported first cities; Ganges, Indus, and Brahma-putra rivers—made agriculture possible.

DIF: A   REF: 52   OBJ: C3S1-1
TOP: Geography, Early Indian civilization

38. ANS:
Archaeologists are just beginning to learn about Indus Valley civilization and still have no clues as to its origin or why it disappeared.

DIF: E   REF: 52-54   OBJ: C3S1-2
TOP: Continuity and change, Indus Valley civilization

39. ANS:
The four groups were Brahmins (priests); Kshatriyas (warriors); Vaisyas (herders, farmers, artisans, and merchants); and Sudras (laborers).

DIF: D   REF: 55   OBJ: C3S2-1
TOP: Social systems, Caste systems

40. ANS:
Answers should include the following: One should concentrate on duty; one should be loyal and obedient to one's husband.

DIF: E   REF: 58,67   OBJ: C3S2-3
TOP: Social systems, Aryan society

41. ANS:
Long distances and physical barriers, including mountains, deserts, jungles, and an ocean, separated China from the rest of the world. As a result, the Chinese knew nothing about other early civilizations and thought they were the only civilized people.

DIF: A   REF: 59   OBJ: C3S3-1
TOP: Geography, Early Chinese dynasties

42. ANS:
yin and yang—two forces representing darkness (yin) and light (yang), which needed to be in harmony for everything to be right in the universe; Mandate of Heaven—divine right to rule; dynastic cycle—describes the rise and fall of Chinese dynasties; feudalism—system of government in which local lords governed their own lands, but owed military allegiance and other kinds of support to the ruler.

DIF: E   REF: 63-64   OBJ: C3S3-2
TOP: Social systems, Early Chinese dynasties

43. ANS:
    Answers should include one of the following from each category: arts—calligraphy, bronze sculpture, bookmaking, literature (*Book of Songs*); technology—silk and bronze making, systems for water control (irrigation, dams, and dikes).

    DIF: E   REF: 63-65   OBJ: C3S3-3
    TOP: Arts and literature, Early Chinese dynasties

44. ANS:
    Because that is how the "mother goddess" figurines were dressed.

    DIF: D   REF: 54   OBJ: C3S1-2
    TOP: Arts and literature, Indus Valley civilization

45. ANS:
    A female deity played a significant role in their religious beliefs.

    DIF: D   REF: 54   OBJ: C3S1-2
    TOP: Arts and literature, Indus Valley civilization

46. ANS:
    It was probably a prosperous civilization. Its inhabitants were well dressed and carefully groomed.

    DIF: D   REF: 54   OBJ: C2S1-2
    TOP: Economics, Indus Valley civilization

ESSAY

47. ANS:
    The fertile plains of the Huang He River allowed early Chinese farmers to grow a surplus of crops and feed the large population necessary to support the development of civilization. Long distances and physical barriers, including the Himalaya Mountains and the Gobi Desert, cut Chinese civilization off from the rest of the world and as a result, it developed in relative isolation.

    DIF: E   REF: 59-60   OBJ: C3S3-1
    TOP: Geography, Early Chinese dynasties

48. ANS:
    Answers will vary, but should draw parallels between occupation and class in both cultures and point out that in Vedic times class was determined by birth and could not be changed; but in the United States there is class mobility.

    DIF: D   REF: 55,57   OBJ: C3S2-1
    TOP: Continuity and change, Class systems

49. ANS:
    It tells us that they were the source of nourishment for Indian civilization.

    DIF: E   REF: 52   OBJ: C3S1-1
    TOP: Geography, Early Indian civilization

50. ANS:
The river flooded because the current dynasty has neglected its duties and, as a result, is losing its divine permission from Heaven to rule.

DIF: A   REF: 60-61   OBJ: C3S3-2
TOP: Religion, Shang dynasties

51. ANS:
A single written language could work to increase communication among people who spoke different languages. Trade and the spread of ideas would be facilitated by better communication.

DIF: D   REF: 57   OBJ: C3S2-2
TOP: Technology, Written language

52. ANS:
The forces of yin and yang must not be in harmony. Someone is responsible for this imbalance. Perhaps the king has not been ruling well or has forgotten to make the proper sacrifices to Heaven.

DIF: A   REF: 63-64   OBJ: C3S3-2
TOP: Religion, Yin and yang

CHAPTER 4—EMPIRES OF INDIA AND CHINA (600 B.C.–A.D. 550)

Matching

Match each term with the correct statement below.
a. filial piety
b. monopoly
c. patriarchal
d. reincarnation
e. stupa

_____ 1. Rebirth of the soul in another bodily form

_____ 2. Large dome-shaped shrine that housed sacred remains

_____ 3. Headed by the father or oldest male

_____ 4. Respect for parents

_____ 5. Complete control of a product or business by one person or group

Match each person with the correct statement below.
a. Asoka
b. Brahma
c. Confucius
d. Siddhartha Gautama
e. Shi Huangdi

_____ 6. Hindu god known as the Creator

_____ 7. Founder of Buddhism

_____ 8. Maurya emperor who converted to Buddhism

_____ 9. Philosopher whose ideas helped shape Chinese civilization for 2,500 years

_____ 10. Emperor who united China

Match each person with the correct statement below.
a. Asoka
b. Chandragupta Maurya
c. Confucius
d. Siddhartha Gautama
e. Hanfeizi
f. Liu Bang
g. Shi Huangdi
h. Shiva

_____ 11. Hindu god known as the Destroyer

_____ 12. The "Enlightened One" who founded Buddhism

_____ 13. Ruler who established the first great Indian empire

_____ 14. Maurya emperor who paved the way for the spread of Buddhism throughout Asia

_____ 15. Chinese philosopher who believed that people were naturally good

_____ 16. Chinese philosopher who taught that "the nature of man is evil"

_____ 17. Emperor who united China and built the Great Wall

____ 18. Emperor who founded the Han dynasty

Multiple Choice
Identify the letter of the choice that best completes the statement or answers the question.

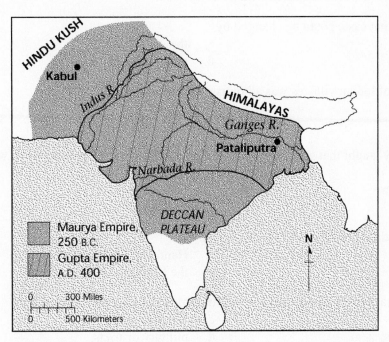

Figure 4-1

____ 19. Which of the following statements is accurate according to Figure 4-1?
   a. The Maurya and Gupta empires were about the same size.
   b. The Maurya empire included more territory than the Gupta empire.
   c. Both empires extended to the Hindu Kush.
   d. Both empires included the Deccan plateau.

____ 20. According to Figure 4-1, which part of India remained outside the control of both the Maurya and Gupta empires?
   a. the Ganges River Valley   c. the southernmost part
   b. the Indus River Valley   d. the central plateau

____ 21. According to Figure 4-1, the Maurya and Gupta empires both included the
   a. southernmost part of India.   c. Ganges River Valley.
   b. same amount of territory.   d. Hindu Kush.

____ 22. According to Figure 4-1, the Deccan plateau was part of
   a. only the Maurya empire.
   b. only the Gupta empire.
   c. both the Maurya and the Gupta empires.
   d. neither the Maurya nor the Gupta empires.

_____ 23. India enjoyed a golden age during the Gupta dynasty because
    a. the government followed the laws of Legalism.
    b. the government promoted peace and prosperity.
    c. the dynasty had specially trained women warriors.
    d. a strong central government ruled with a strong hand.

_____ 24. Hindus believed that caste could be changed by
    a. the emperor.
    b. marriage.
    c. the law of karma.
    d. moving.

_____ 25. The government of Indian villages was administered by
    a. the emperor.
    b. Brahmins.
    c. soldiers.
    d. a village council.

_____ 26. Which philosophy taught that government should pass strict laws and enforce them with harsh punishments?
    a. Confucianism
    b. Legalism
    c. Daoism
    d. Buddhism

_____ 27. Han rulers based their policies on the teachings of
    a. Confucius.
    b. Laozi.
    c. Hanfeizi.
    d. the Buddha.

_____ 28. The trade route that linked China with the west became known as the
    a. Great Wall.
    b. civil service system.
    c. Silk Road.
    d. military districts.

_____ 29. Both Hindus and Buddhists believe in
    a. nonviolence.
    b. many gods.
    c. the caste system.
    d. formal rituals.

_____ 30. The golden age of India took place during the rule of the
    a. Mauryas.
    b. Romans.
    c. Guptas.
    d. Dravidians.

_____ 31. In Hindu society, the purpose of caste rules was to
    a. punish criminals.
    b. keep foreigners out of India.
    c. aid the poor.
    d. ensure spiritual purity.

_____ 32. In an Indian household, the head of the family was the
    a. mother.
    b. father.
    c. oldest daughter.
    d. youngest son.

_____ 33. Indian villages were ruled by
    a. a priest.
    b. a soldier.
    c. a village council.
    d. the emperor.

_____ 34. Confucius taught the Chinese people that their most important duty was
    a. loyalty to the state.
    b. care of the poor.
    c. achieving salvation.
    d. respect for parents.

_____ 35. Han emperors based their rule on the teachings of
   a. the Buddha.   c. Hanfeizi.
   b. Confucius.   d. Laozi.

_____ 36. China became the most technologically advanced civilization in the world under the rule of the
   a. Gupta dynasty.   c. Qin dynasty.
   b. Zhou dynasty.   d. Han dynasty.

Short Answer

37. List three ways that Buddhism differed from Hinduism.

38. Describe three ways that Chandragupta Maurya maintained order in India.

39. Describe advances in mathematics and medicine that took place in Gupta India.

40. Identify the characteristics of family life in India.

41. List the major differences between Legalism and Daoism.

42. Describe three ways that Shi Huangdi promoted unity in China.

43. Describe advances in technology and medicine that took place in Han China.

Read the following excerpt from the Panchatantra, a collection of Indian fables. Then answer the questions that follow on a separate sheet of paper.

"In a certain pond lived two fishes whose names were Hundred-Wit and Thousand-Wit. And a frog named Single-Wit made friends with them. . . .

One day at sunset they were engaged in conversation, when fishermen with nets came there, who said to one another on seeing the pond: 'Look! This pond appears to contain plenty of fish, and the water seems shallow. We will return at dawn.' With this they went home.

The three friends felt this speech to be dreadful as the fall of a thunderbolt, and they took counsel together. The frog spoke first: 'Hundred-Wit and Thousand-Wit, my dear friends, what should we do now: flee or stick it out?'

At this Thousand-Wit laughed and said: 'My good friend, do not be frightened merely because you have heard words. An actual invasion is not to be anticipated. Yet should it take place, I will save you and myself by virtue of my wit. For I know plenty of tricks in the water.' And Hundred-Wit added: 'Yes, Thousand-Wit is quite right. . . .'

'Well,' said the frog, 'I have only a single wit, and that tells me to flee. My wife and I are going to some other body of water this very night.'

So spoke the frog and under cover of night he went to another body of water. At dawn the next day came the fish-catchers, who seemed the servants of Death, and enclosed the pond with nets. And all the fishes, turtles, frogs, crabs, and other water-creatures were caught in the nets and captured. Even Hundred-Wit and Thousand-Wit fell into a net and were killed, though they struggled to save their lives by fancy turns.

And that is why I say that intelligence is not the sole determinant of fate."

44. Which character in the story made the wisest choice? Why?

45. Why did the storyteller say, "intelligence is not the sole determinant of fate"?

46. What human qualities does Single-Wit represent?

Essay
On a separate sheet of paper, write an answer to the following questions.

47. **Making Comparisons** In what ways were Chandragupta Maurya and Shi Huangdi alike?

48. **Drawing Conclusions** Explain why Confucianism never became a religion as Hinduism or Buddhism did.

49. **Understanding Causes and Effects** How did Hinduism, Buddhism, and Confucianism help create orderly societies?

50. **Making Comparisons** How were Gupta India and Han China alike?

51. **Analyzing Information** Explain how the caste system ensured a stable social order in India.

52. **Drawing Conclusions** Explain how the teachings of Confucius promoted social harmony in China.

CHAPTER 4—EMPIRES OF INDIA AND CHINA (600 B.C.–A.D. 550)
Answer Section

MATCHING

1. ANS: D   DIF: E   REF: 77   OBJ: C4S1-3
   TOP: Religion, Hinduism

2. ANS: E   DIF: E   REF: 83   OBJ: C4S2-3
   TOP: Religion, Burial practices

3. ANS: C   DIF: E   REF: 87   OBJ: C4S3-2
   TOP: Social systems, Patriarchy

4. ANS: A   DIF: E   REF: 87,90   OBJ: C4S4-1
   TOP: Social systems, Filial piety

5. ANS: B   DIF: E   REF: 96   OBJ: C4S5-2
   TOP: Economics, Monopolies

6. ANS: B   DIF: E   REF: 77   OBJ: C4S1-1
   TOP: Religion, Hinduism

7. ANS: D   DIF: E   REF: 78   OBJ: C4S1-2
   TOP: Impact of individual, Siddhartha Gautama

8. ANS: A   DIF: E   REF: 81-82   OBJ: C4S2-1
   TOP: Religion, Buddhism

9. ANS: C   DIF: E   REF: 89-90   OBJ: C4S4-1
   TOP: Impact of individual, Confucius

10. ANS: E   DIF: E   REF: 93   OBJ: C4S5-1
   TOP: Impact of individual, Shi Huangdi

11. ANS: H   DIF: E   REF: 77   OBJ: C4S1-1
   TOP: Religion, Hinduism

12. ANS: D   DIF: E   REF: 78   OBJ: C4S1-2
   TOP: Impact of individual, Siddhartha Gautama

13. ANS: B   DIF: E   REF: 81   OBJ: C4S1-2
   TOP: Impact of individual, Chandragupta Maurya

14. ANS: A   DIF: E   REF: 81-82   OBJ: C4S2-1
   TOP: Impact of individual, Asoka

15. ANS: C   DIF: E   REF: 89   OBJ: C4S4-2
   TOP: Impact of individual, Confucius

16. ANS: E   DIF: E   REF: 90-91   OBJ: C4S4-2
   TOP: Impact of individual, Hanfeizi

17. ANS: G   DIF: E   REF: 93-94   OBJ: C4S5-1
   TOP: Impact of individual, Shi Huangdi

18. ANS: F   DIF: E   REF: 95   OBJ: C4S5-2
   TOP: Impact of individual, Liu Bang

MULTIPLE CHOICE

19. ANS: B   DIF: D   REF: 75   OBJ: C4S2-1
    TOP: Geography, Ancient empires
20. ANS: C   DIF: E   REF: 75   OBJ: C4S2-1
    TOP: Geography, Ancient empires
21. ANS: C   DIF: E   REF: 75   OBJ: C4S2-3
    TOP: Geography, Ancient empires
22. ANS: A   DIF: E   REF: 75   OBJ: C4S2-1
    TOP: Geography, Ancient empires
23. ANS: B   DIF: A   REF: 82-83   OBJ: C4S2-3
    TOP: Political systems, Gupta dynasty
24. ANS: C   DIF: A   REF: 77   OBJ: C4S3-1
    TOP: Social systems, Hinduism
25. ANS: D   DIF: A   REF: 83,88   OBJ: C4S3-3
    TOP: Political systems, Early Indian civilization
26. ANS: B   DIF: A   REF: 90-91   OBJ: C4S4-2
    TOP: Political systems, Legalism
27. ANS: A   DIF: A   REF: 90   OBJ: C4S5-2
    TOP: Political systems, Confucianism
28. ANS: C   DIF: E   REF: 95   OBJ: C4S5-3
    TOP: Economics, Silk road
29. ANS: A   DIF: A   REF: 78-79   OBJ: C4S1-2
    TOP: Religion, Hinduism
30. ANS: C   DIF: E   REF: 82   OBJ: C4S2-3
    TOP: Social systems, Gupta dynasty
31. ANS: D   DIF: D   REF: 77,86   OBJ: C4S3-2
    TOP: Social systems, Caste system
32. ANS: B   DIF: E   REF: 87   OBJ: C4S3-2
    TOP: Social systems, Early Indian civilization
33. ANS: C   DIF: A   REF: 88   OBJ: C4S3-3
    TOP: Political systems, Early Indian civilization
34. ANS: D   DIF: A   REF: 89   OBJ: C4S4-1
    TOP: Social systems, Confucianism
35. ANS: B   DIF: A   REF: 95   OBJ: C4S5-2
    TOP: Political systems, Confucianism
36. ANS: D   DIF: A   REF: 95   OBJ: C4S5-3
    TOP: Technology, Han dynasty

SHORT ANSWER

37. ANS:
Buddhism rejected the formal rituals and many gods of Hinduism. Buddhists sought enlightenment through meditation. The caste system was not part of Buddhism.

DIF: D   REF: 77-79   OBJ: C4S1-2   TOP: Religion, Hinduism

38. ANS:
Chandragupta's officials supervised the building of roads and harbors to benefit trade; other officials collected taxes and state-owned factories and shipyards; people had to go to royal courts to seek justice; and he had a brutal secret police.

DIF: D   REF: 81   OBJ: C4S2-3
TOP: Impact of individual, Chandragupta Maurya

39. ANS:
Advances in mathematics included the development of a system for writing numerals, the concept of zero, and the decimal system. Advances in medicine included the use of herbs for medicine, surgery to set bones or repair injuries, and vaccinations against smallpox.

DIF: A   REF: 83   OBJ: C4S2-3
TOP: Technology, Gupta dynasty

40. ANS:
The joint family in India was patriarchal. Family members shared property. Individuals put family interests above their own. Family bonds extended across generations.

DIF: A   REF: 87-88   OBJ: C4S3-2
TOP: Social systems, Early Indian civilization

41. ANS:
Legalism emphasized strong rulers, strict laws, and harsh punishments to achieve order. Daoism rejected government and sought harmony with nature through the virtue of yielding.

DIF: A   REF: 90-92   OBJ: C4S4-2
TOP: Political systems, Early Chinese dynasties

42. ANS:
Shi Huangdi standardized weights and measures, created a uniform currency, and promoted cultural unity through a uniform writing system. He also ended dissent through harsh rule and built the Great Wall to keep out invaders.

DIF: D   REF: 93-94   OBJ: C4S5-1
TOP: Impact of individual, Shi Huangdi

43. ANS:
Advances in technology included the following inventions: paper, rudder, bronze and iron stirrups, fishing reels, wheelbarrows, suspension bridges, and chain pumps. Advances in medicine included diagnosis of diseases, herbal remedies, and acupuncture.

DIF: A   REF: 95-96   OBJ: C4S5-3
TOP: Technology, Han dynasty

44. ANS:
Single-Wit made the wisest choice because he saved his life by leaving the pond.

DIF: D   REF: 77   OBJ: C4S1-1
TOP: Art and literature, Panchatantra

45. ANS:
Hundred-Wit and Thousand-Wit were intelligent, but they used poor judgment.

DIF: D   REF: 77   OBJ: C4S1-1
TOP: Art and literature, Panchatantra

46. ANS:
Single-Wit represents good judgment and decisive action.

DIF: D   REF: 77   OBJ: C4S1-1
TOP: Art and literature, Panchatantra

ESSAY

47. ANS:
Both established an empire, created a centralized government, imposed harsh rule, and carried out internal improvements.

DIF: D   REF: 81, 93-94   OBJ: C4S5-1
TOP: Political systems, Ancient empires

48. ANS:
Confucianism was concerned with worldly goals, such as good government and social order. It did not address religious matters as Hinduism and Buddhism did.

DIF: A   REF: 77-79, 89   OBJ: C4S1-1
TOP: Religion, Fundamental beliefs

49. ANS:
Hinduism, Buddhism, and Confucianism all placed value on harmony, duty, and nonviolence.

DIF: D   REF: 77-79, 89   OBJ: C4S4-1
TOP: Social systems, Ancient empires

50. ANS:
Gupta India and Han China both produced a golden age of learning in which the arts and technology flourished.

DIF: D   REF: 82-84, 95-96   OBJ: C4S2-3
TOP: Political systems, Ancient empires

51. ANS:
The caste system gave people a sense of identity. Indian people fulfilled their duties in order to achieve a higher state in the next life. People of different castes depended on one another to meet their needs. The caste system allowed diverse peoples to live in harmony.

DIF: A   REF: 77,86-87   OBJ: C4S3-1
TOP: Social systems, Caste systems

52. ANS:
    Confucius taught that everyone has duties and responsibilities according to his or her place in society. He stressed correct behavior based on key relationships. Confucian values promoted harmony through honesty, hard work, and concern for others.

    DIF: A   REF: 89   OBJ: C4S4-1
    TOP: Social systems, Confucianism

CHAPTER 5—ANCIENT GREECE (1750 B.C.–133 B.C.)

Matching

Match each term with the correct statement below.
a. aristocracy   d. rhetoric
b. democracy   e. strait
c. monarchy

_____ 1. Narrow water passage

_____ 2. Government in which a king or queen exercises central power

_____ 3. Rule by a landholding elite

_____ 4. Government by the people

_____ 5. Art of skillful speaking

Match each person with the correct statement below.
a. Hippocrates   d. Socrates
b. Homer   e. Solon
c. Pericles

_____ 6. Blind poet credited with creating the *Iliad* and the *Odyssey*

_____ 7. Leader of Athens who introduced social, political, and economic reforms

_____ 8. Statesman who established direct democracy in Athens

_____ 9. Philosopher who examined beliefs and ideas through critical questioning

_____ 10. Physician whose oath set ethical standards for doctors

Match each person with the correct statement below.
a. Archimedes   e. Homer
b. Aristotle   f. Solon
c. Cleisthenes   g. Pythagoras
d. Herodotus   h. Sophocles

_____ 11. Poet who is credited with creating the *Iliad* and the *Odyssey*

_____ 12. Wise Athenian who outlawed slavery and opened high office to more citizens

_____ 13. Athenian reformer who made the assembly a genuine legislature

_____ 14. Historian who wrote about the Persian Wars

_____ 15. Philosopher who taught that good conduct meant following a moderate course between extremes

_____ 16. Playwright who wrote *Antigone*

_____ 17. Mathematician who derived a formula to calculate the relationship between sides of a right triangle

_____ 18. Scientist who applied principles of physics to make practical inventions

Multiple Choice
Identify the letter of the choice that best completes the statement or answers the question.

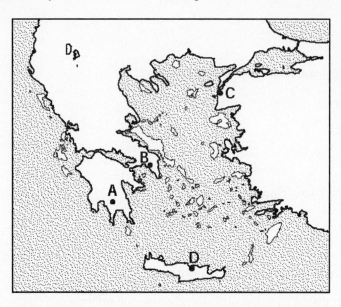

Figure 5-1

_____ 19. Which civilization began in the location marked by the letter D in Figure 5-1?
    a. Persian   c. Minoan
    b. Egyptian   d. Mycenaean

_____ 20. Which letter in Figure 5-1 marks the location of Sparta?
    a. A   c. C
    b. B   d. D

_____ 21. Which letter in Figure 5-1 marks the center of Minoan civilization?
    a. A   c. C
    b. B   d. D

_____ 22. Which of the following conflicts centered around the location marked by the letter C in Figure 5-1?
    a. Trojan War   c. Peloponnesian War
    b. Macedonian conquest   d. Persian Wars

_____ 23. The geography of Greece helped create
    a. a large Greek empire.   c. unity among Greeks.
    b. many small city-states.   d. isolation from the outside world.

____ 24. Following the Persian Wars, Greece was dominated by
    a. Persia.
    b. Delos.
    c. Sparta.
    d. Athens.

____ 25. The Peloponnesian War resulted from conflict between
    a. Athens and Sparta.
    b. Greece and Persia.
    c. Athens and Macedonia.
    d. Greece and Egypt.

____ 26. Greek theater evolved out of
    a. athletic contests.
    b. foreign influences.
    c. the works of Aristotle.
    d. religious festivals.

____ 27. Alexander's most lasting achievement was
    a. the conquest of India.
    b. the spread of Greek culture.
    c. a lasting empire.
    d. an alliance with Persia.

____ 28. The center of the Hellenistic world was
    a. Athens.
    b. Babylon.
    c. Alexandria.
    d. Mount Olympus.

____ 29. Which of the following geographic characteristics of Greece provided a link to the outside world?
    a. mountains
    b. seas
    c. valleys
    d. grasslands

____ 30. A form of government controlled by a small, powerful elite from the business class is called a(n)
    a. monarchy.
    b. aristocracy.
    c. oligarchy.
    d. democracy.

____ 31. From childhood, Spartan boys were trained to be
    a. philosophers.
    b. politicians.
    c. soldiers.
    d. artists.

____ 32. Athens enjoyed a golden age under the leadership of
    a. Pericles.
    b. Alexander.
    c. Darius.
    d. Themistocles.

____ 33. Conflict between Athens and Sparta resulted in the
    a. Persian Wars.
    b. Trojan War.
    c. Peloponnesian War.
    d. Macedonian conquest.

____ 34. According to Aristotle, the best government was
    a. a democracy.
    b. an aristocracy.
    c. one that was ruled by the military.
    d. one that was ruled by a strong and virtuous leader.

_____ 35. Which of the following descriptions applies to the works of Greek artists and architects?
    a. imitated European styles
    b. reflected concern with form and order
    c. glorified political leaders
    d. emphasized complicated and irregular designs

_____ 36. Who established an empire that extended from Greece to Egypt and India?
    a. Alexander   c. Philip II
    b. Pericles   d. Herodotus

Short Answer

37. Describe three aspects of Mycenaean civilization that influenced later Greek culture.

38. Describe three kinds of government Greeks developed between 750 B.C. and 500 B.C.

39. Identify three differences between Sparta and Athens.

40. Contrast the results of the Persian Wars and the Peloponnesian War with regard to Athens.

41. List three similarities between the ideas of Plato and Aristotle.

42. Describe three popular themes of Greek dramas.

43. Explain how Alexander's conquests led to the development of a new culture.

Read the following excerpt from the Odyssey. *Then answer the questions that follow.*

"I fear that once again the whirlwind will snatch me and carry me out on the sea where the fish swim, groaning heavily, or else the divinity from the deep will let loose against me a sea monster of whom Amphitrite [wife of Poseidon] keeps so many; for I know how bitterly the renowned Earthshaker [Poseidon] hates me.

Now as he was pondering this in his heart and spirit, meanwhile a great wave carried him against the rough rock face, and there his skin would have been taken off, his bones crushed together, had not the gray-eyed goddess Athene sent him an inkling [suggestion], and he frantically caught hold with both hands on the rock face and clung to it, groaning, until the great wave went over. This one he so escaped, but the backwash of the same wave caught him where he clung and threw him far out in the open water. . . . Now the great sea covered him over, and Odysseus would have perished, wretched, beyond his destiny, had not the gray-eyed goddess Athene given him forethought. He got clear of the surf, where it sucks against the land, and swam on along, looking always toward the shore in the hope of finding beaches that slanted against the waves or harbors for shelter from the sea, but when he came, swimming along, to the mouth of a sweet-running river, this at last seemed to him the best place, being bare of rocks, and there was even shelter from the wind there."

44. Based on this excerpt, what struggle did Odysseus face on his journey home after fighting the Trojan War?

45. How did Odysseus escape death in the sea?

46. What does this excerpt reveal about the Greeks' relationship to their gods?

Essay
On a separate sheet of paper, write an answer to the following questions.

47. **Analyzing Information** How do the works of Greek artists and architects reflect the philosophy of Plato?

48. **Making Comparisons** How did the philosophy of Zeno differ from that of Socrates?

49. **Making Inferences** What united the Greeks in spite of divisions caused by geography and economic rivalry?

50. **Drawing Conclusions** How did geography make Alexandria the center of the Hellenistic world?

51. **Analyzing Information** How did Pericles turn Athens into the cultural center of Greece?

52. **Drawing Conclusions** How did Hellenistic thinkers make important advances in the sciences and mathematics?

CHAPTER 5—ANCIENT GREECE (1750 B.C.–133 B.C.)
Answer Section

MATCHING

1. ANS: E   DIF: E   REF: 103   OBJ: C5S2-1
TOP: Geography, Water passage

2. ANS: C   DIF: E   REF: 105   OBJ: C5S2-2
TOP: Political systems, Monarchy

3. ANS: A   DIF: E   REF: 106   OBJ: C5S2-2
TOP: Political systems, Aristocracy

4. ANS: B   DIF: E   REF: 107   OBJ: C5S2-2
TOP: Political systems, Democracy

5. ANS: D   DIF: E   REF: 114   OBJ: C5S4-1
TOP: Art and literature, Rhetoric

6. ANS: B   DIF: E   REF: 103-104   OBJ: C5S1-3
TOP: Art and literature, Homer

7. ANS: E   DIF: E   REF: 107-108   OBJ: C5S2-3
TOP: Impact of the individual, Solon

8. ANS: C   DIF: E   REF: 112   OBJ: C5S3-2
TOP: Political systems, Pericles

9. ANS: D   DIF: E   REF: 115   OBJ: C5S4-1
TOP: Impact of the individual, Socrates

10. ANS: A   DIF: E   REF: 123   OBJ: C5S5-3
TOP: Impact of the individual, Hippocrates

11. ANS: E   DIF: E   REF: 103-104   OBJ: C5S1-3
TOP: Art and literature, Homer

12. ANS: F   DIF: E   REF: 107-108   OBJ: C5S2-3
TOP: Impact of the individual, Solon

13. ANS: C   DIF: E   REF: 108   OBJ: C5S2-3
TOP: Impact of the individual, Cleisthenes

14. ANS: D   DIF: E   REF: 110, 119   OBJ: C5S4-1
TOP: Impact of the individual, Herodotus

15. ANS: B   DIF: E   REF: 116   OBJ: C5S4-1
TOP: Impact of the individual, Aristotle

16. ANS: H   DIF: E   REF: 116, 118   OBJ: C5S4-3
TOP: Art and literature, Antigone

17. ANS: G   DIF: E   REF: 122-123   OBJ: C5S5-3
TOP: Impact of the individual, Pythagoras

18. ANS: A   DIF: E   REF: 123   OBJ: C5S5-3
TOP: Impact of the individual, Archimedes

MULTIPLE CHOICE

19. ANS: C   DIF: A   REF: 101   OBJ: C5S1-1
    TOP: Geography, Minoan civilization
20. ANS: A   DIF: E   REF: 101,106   OBJ: C5S2-3
    TOP: Geography, Sparta
21. ANS: D   DIF: D   REF: 101   OBJ: C5S1-2
    TOP: Geography, Minoan civilization
22. ANS: A   DIF: D   REF: 101,111   OBJ: C5S1-2
    TOP: Geography, Trojan War
23. ANS: B   DIF: D   REF: 105   OBJ: C5S2-1
    TOP: Geography, City-states
24. ANS: D   DIF: A   REF: 110-111   OBJ: C5S3-1
    TOP: Continuity and change, Persian Wars
25. ANS: A   DIF: A   REF: 114   OBJ: C5S3-3
    TOP: Political systems, Peloponnesian Wars
26. ANS: D   DIF: A   REF: 117   OBJ: C5S4-3
    TOP: Art and literature, Greek drama
27. ANS: B   DIF: D   REF: 121-122   OBJ: C5S5-1
    TOP: Impact of the individual, Alexander the Great
28. ANS: C   DIF: E   REF: 122   OBJ: C5S5-2
    TOP: Social systems, Hellenistic civilization
29. ANS: B   DIF: E   REF: 105   OBJ: C5S2-1
    TOP: Geography, Seas
30. ANS: C   DIF: A   REF: 106   OBJ: C5S2-2
    TOP: Political systems, Oligarchy
31. ANS: C   DIF: E   REF: 107   OBJ: C5S3-2
    TOP: Social systems, Sparta
32. ANS: A   DIF: E   REF: 112   OBJ: C5S3-2
    TOP: Impact of the individual, Pericles
33. ANS: C   DIF: A   REF: 114   OBJ: C5S3-3
    TOP: Continuity and change, Peloponnesian Wars
34. ANS: D   DIF: A   REF: 116   OBJ: C5S4-1
    TOP: Political systems, Aristotle
35. ANS: B   DIF: D   REF: 116   OBJ: C5S4-2
    TOP: Art and literature, Style and form
36. ANS: A   DIF: E   REF: 120-121   OBJ: C5S5-1
    TOP: Impact of the individual, Alexander the Great

SHORT ANSWER

37. ANS:
    Mycenaeans were sea traders. They passed on Minoan, Egyptian, and Mesopotamian influences. They lived in separate city-states ruled by warrior-kings.

    DIF: A   REF: 103-104   OBJ: C5S1-2
    TOP: Continuity and change, Mycenaean civilization

38. ANS:
    The first form of Greek government was a monarchy. Later, nobles won power for themselves and established an aristocracy. As trade expanded, middle-class merchants developed an oligarchy.

    DIF: D   REF: 106   OBJ: C5S2-2
    TOP: Political systems, Early governments

39. ANS:
    Sparta was a military state that isolated itself from other Greeks and had little use for new ideas or art. Athens was a limited democracy that encouraged trade and learning.

    DIF: A   REF: 106-108   OBJ: C5S2-3
    TOP: Social systems, Sparta, Athens

40. ANS:
    As a result of the Persian Wars, Athens became the most powerful city-state in Greece. The Peloponnesian War ended Athenian greatness.

    DIF: D   REF: 110-111, 114   OBJ: C5S3-1
    TOP: Continuity and change, Persian and Peloponnesian Wars

41. ANS:
    Both Plato and Aristotle rejected democracy. They favored rule by a wise and virtuous leader. They emphasized the importance of reason.

    DIF: D   REF: 115-116   OBJ: C5S4-1
    TOP: Political systems, Greek philosophers

42. ANS:
    Three popular themes of Greek dramas were popular myths, stories of human suffering, and the relationship between people and the gods.

    DIF: A   REF: 117-118   OBJ: C5S4-3
    TOP: Art and literature, Greek drama

43. ANS:
    Alexander's empire linked a vast area. He founded new cities that attracted settlers from Greece, whose culture blended with that of local people. Alexander also encouraged a blending of eastern and western cultures by marrying a Persian woman.

    DIF: D   REF: 122   OBJ: C5S5-1
    TOP: Impact of the individual, Alexander the Great

44. ANS:
     He was fighting large waves along a rocky coast, trying to get ashore for safety.

     DIF: D   REF: 103-104   OBJ: C5S1-3
     TOP: Art and literature, Odyssey

45. ANS:
     The goddess Athene helped him survive the waves and find a place to come ashore.

     DIF: D   REF: 103-104   OBJ: C5S1-3
     TOP: Art and literature, Odyssey

46. ANS:
     Odysseus believed that the gods determined his fate.

     DIF: D   REF: 103-104   OBJ: C5S1-3   TOP: Religion, Odyssey

ESSAY

47. ANS:
     Plato argued that every object has an ideal form. Greek art and architecture reflect a concern with form and order.

     DIF: D   REF: 116-117   OBJ: C5S4-2
     TOP: Art and literature, Plato

48. ANS:
     Zeno encouraged people to accept whatever life brought. Socrates encouraged people to question and critically examine their lives.

     DIF: D   REF: 115-116, 122   OBJ: C5S5-3
     TOP: Social systems, Greek philosophers

49. ANS:
     Greeks spoke the same language, honored the same heroes, and prayed to the same gods. In the Persian Wars, they united against a common enemy and won. They considered themselves superior to non-Greeks.

     DIF: D   REF: 105, 109   OBJ: C5S3-1
     TOP: Social systems, Greek culture

50. ANS:
     Alexandria was located on the sea lanes between Europe and Asia. It was accessible to people and goods from three continents.

     DIF: D   REF: 121-122   OBJ: C5S5-2
     TOP: Geography, Alexandria

51. ANS:
     Pericles hired the best architects, sculptors, thinkers, writers, and artists. He supported building programs and public festivals to encourage the arts.

     DIF: D   REF: 112   OBJ: C5S3-2
     TOP: Impact of the individual, Pericles

52. ANS:
    Hellenistic thinkers built on earlier Greek, Babylonian, and Egyptian knowledge that was made available to them through the blending of cultures in Alexander's empire.

    DIF: D   REF: 122-123   OBJ: C5S5-3
    TOP: Technology and science, Hellenistic civilization

CHAPTER 6—ANCIENT ROME AND THE RISE OF CHRISTIANITY (509 B.C.–A.D. 476)

Matching

Match each person with the correct statement below.

a.   Augustus
b.   Julius Caesar
c.   Hannibal
d.   Jesus
e.   Odoacer
f.   Paul
g.   Ptolemy
h.   Virgil

_____ 1.   Leader of Carthaginian army who crossed the Alps to invade Italy

_____ 2.   General who brought Gaul under Roman control

_____ 3.   First ruler of the Roman Empire

_____ 4.   Author of the Roman epic poem, the *Aeneid*

_____ 5.   Astronomer who theorized that the Earth was the center of the universe

_____ 6.   Central figure in Christianity

_____ 7.   Jewish convert who spread Christianity from Mesopotamia to Rome

_____ 8.   German leader who ousted the emperor in Rome

Match each term with the correct statement below.

a.   martyr
b.   mercenary
c.   messiah
d.   patrician
e.   plebeian

_____ 9.   Member of Roman landholding upper class

_____ 10.   Roman farmer, merchant, artisan, or trader

_____ 11.   Anointed king sent by God

_____ 12.   Person who suffers or dies for his or her beliefs

_____ 13.   Foreign soldier who serves for pay

Match each term with the correct statement below.

a.   aqueduct
b.   heresy
c.   legion
d.   republic
e.   bishop

_____ 14.   Government in which officials are chosen by the people

_____ 15.   Basic unit of the Roman army

_____ 16.   Bridge-like stone structure that brought water from hills to cities

_____ 17. Church official responsible for all Christians in an area

_____ 18. A belief that is contrary to official church teachings

Multiple Choice

Identify the letter of the choice that best completes the statement or answers the question.

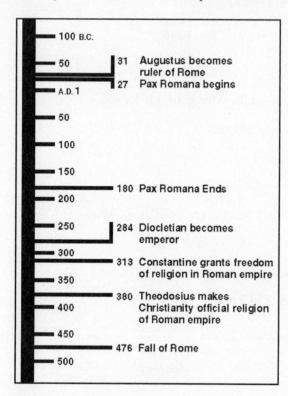

Figure 6-1

_____ 19. According to Figure 6-1, the Pax Romana began shortly after the beginning of the rule of
     a.   Augustus.
     b.   Diocletian.
     c.   Constantine.
     d.   Theodosius.

_____ 20. According to Figure 6-1, about how long after the end of the Pax Romana did Rome fall?
     a.   100 years
     b.   200 years
     c.   300 years
     d.   400 years

_____ 21. According to Figure 6-1, which of the following took place shortly after the beginning of the rule of Augustus?
     a.   The Pax Romana began.
     b.   The Pax Romana ended.
     c.   Christianity became the official religion of the Roman Empire.
     d.   Rome fell.

_____ 22. According to Figure 6-1, when did Diocletian divide the Roman Empire into two parts?
   a. during the Pax Romana
   b. after Christianity became the official religion
   c. before Constantine granted freedom of religion
   d. when Rome fell

_____ 23. In Roman government, who represented the rights of plebeians?
   a. senators
   b. patricians
   c. tribunes
   d. consuls

_____ 24. After the deaths of the Gracchus brothers, the Roman republic experienced
   a. a series of civil wars.
   b. a stable government.
   c. democratic reforms.
   d. peace and prosperity.

_____ 25. In the fields of art and literature, Romans were greatly influenced by the culture of
   a. Carthage.
   b. Greece.
   c. Gaul.
   d. Palestine.

_____ 26. During the empire, the Roman legal system contributed to
   a. the outbreak of civil war.
   b. further conquests.
   c. the downfall of the emperor.
   d. unity and stability.

_____ 27. Which of the following statements generally describes Rome's attitude toward the Jews of Palestine?
   a. Romans tolerated the Jews' religion.
   b. Romans forced Jews to convert to Christianity.
   c. Romans insisted that Jews worship Roman gods.
   d. Romans forbade Jews to worship.

_____ 28. Jesus proclaimed that his mission was to
   a. overthrow Roman rule.
   b. reject the Ten Commandments.
   c. bring spiritual salvation to believers.
   d. lead the Jews out of Palestine.

_____ 29. The Pax Romana ended in A.D. 180, after the death of
   a. Julius Caesar.
   b. Constantine.
   c. Diocletian.
   d. Marcus Aurelius.

_____ 30. Which of the following places did Constantine make the center of power for the Roman Empire?
   a. Jerusalem
   b. Carthage
   c. Constantinople
   d. Rome

_____ 31. How did the wealth acquired from winning an empire affect Rome?
   a. It benefited the farmers.
   b. It widened the gap between rich and poor.
   c. It provided jobs for people in cities.
   d. It created widespread prosperity.

_____ 32. The decline of the Roman republic followed a century of civil wars fought over the question of
a. which gods to worship.
b. who should hold power.
c. which language to speak.
d. how to keep out invaders.

_____ 33. Roman art and literature blended Roman civilization with that of
a. Gaul.
b. Asia Minor.
c. Carthage.
d. Greece.

_____ 34. Which statement generally describes Rome's attitude toward people of different religions in the empire?
a. Romans persecuted people who believed in one God.
b. Romans tolerated religious differences.
c. Romans forced all people to become Jews.
d. Romans forbade people to worship many gods.

_____ 35. Who tried to restore order to the Roman empire?
a. Caligula and Nero
b. Diocletian and Constantine
c. Attila and Odoacer
d. Hannibal and Mark Antony

_____ 36. Which of the following was not related to the "fall" of Rome?
a. Germanic invasions
b. corrupt officials
c. the assassination of Julius Caesar
d. heavy taxes

Short Answer

37. Describe two positive and two negative ways that winning an empire affected Rome.

38. Explain how the policies of Augustus improved social and economic conditions in the Roman empire.

39. Explain how Roman art and literature blended different traditions.

40. Describe how the basic teachings of Jesus combined Jewish traditions with new beliefs.

41. Describe two of Constantine's actions that had long-lasting effects on Europe.

42. Explain the military, political, and social reasons for the "fall" of Rome.

Read the following excerpt from the Aeneid. *Then answer the questions that follow.*

"'The rest of you, all in your prime,'
   he [Aeneas' father] said,
'Make your escape; you are still hale and strong. . . .
If heaven's lords had wished me a longer span
They would have saved this home for me. I call it
More than enough that once before I saw
My city taken and wrecked, and went on living.
Here is my death bed, here. Take leave of me.
Depart now. I'll find death with my sword arm.
The enemy will oblige; they'll come for spoils.
Burial can be dispensed with. All these years
I've lingered in my [helplessness], at odds
With heaven, since the Father of gods and men
Breathed high winds of thunderbolt upon me
And touched me with his fire.'

'Did you suppose, my father,
That I could tear myself away and leave you?
Unthinkable; how could a father say it?
Now if it please the powers above that nothing
Stand of this great city; if your heart
Is set on adding your own death and ours
To that of Troy, the door's wide open for it:
Pyrrhus [King of Epirus] will be here, splashed
   with Priam's [King of Troy] blood;
He kills the son before his father's eyes,
The father at the altars.

My dear mother [the goddess Aphrodite],
Was it for this, through spears and fire, you brought me,
To see the enemy deep in my house,
To see my son, Ascanius, my father,
And near them both, Creusa [Aeneas' wife],
Butchered in one another's blood? My gear,
Men, bring my gear. The last light calls the conquered.
Give me back to the Greeks. Let me take up
The combat once again. We shall not all die this day unavenged.'"

43. Why did Aeneas return home to Troy when the city was being attacked by Greeks?

44. Why did Aeneas' father refuse to leave the city?

45. What decision did Aeneas make?

46. What does this excerpt from Virgil's poem reveal about Roman values?

Essay
On a separate sheet of paper, write an answer to the following questions.

47. **Making Comparisons** Why was Italy easier to unify than Greece?

48. **Determining Cause and Effect** How did the wealth of the Roman empire cause social problems?

49. **Drawing Conclusions** How did geography help the Romans build a world empire?

50. **Analyzing Information** How did Roman law protect the rights of an accused person?

51. **Analyzing Information** Explain how Roman ideas served as a model for democratic governments.

52. **Drawing Conclusions** Why might a commitment to law and justice be considered Rome's greatest legacy?

CHAPTER 6—ANCIENT ROME AND THE RISE OF CHRISTIANITY (509 B.C.–A.D. 476)
Answer Section

MATCHING

1. ANS: C   DIF: E   REF: 132-133   OBJ: C6S2-1
     TOP: Impact of the individual, Hannibal
2. ANS: B   DIF: E   REF: 134-135   OBJ: C6S2-2
     TOP: Impact of the individual, Julius Ceasar
3. ANS: A   DIF: E   REF: 135   OBJ: C6S2-3
     TOP: Impact of the individual, Augustus
4. ANS: H   DIF: E   REF: 137   OBJ: C6S3-2
     TOP: Art and literature, Aeneid
5. ANS: G   DIF: E   REF: 138, 140   OBJ: C6S3-2
     TOP: Impact of the individual, Ptolemy
6. ANS: D   DIF: E   REF: 142-144   OBJ: C6S3-2
     TOP: Impact of the individual, Jesus
7. ANS: F   DIF: E   REF: 143-144   OBJ: C6S4-2
     TOP: Impact of the individual, Paul
8. ANS: E   DIF: E   REF: 149   OBJ: C6S4-3
     TOP: Impact of the individual, Odoacer

9. ANS: D   DIF: E   REF: 129   OBJ: C6S5-2
     TOP: Social system, Patrician
10. ANS: E   DIF: E   REF: 129   OBJ: C6S1-2
     TOP: Social system, Plebian
11. ANS: C   DIF: E   REF: 142-143   OBJ: C6S1-2
     TOP: Religion, Messiah
12. ANS: A   DIF: E   REF: 144   OBJ: C6S4-3
     TOP: Religion, Martyr
13. ANS: B   DIF: E   REF: 149   OBJ: C6S4-3
     TOP: Political systems, Mercenary

14. ANS: D   DIF: E   REF: 129   OBJ: C6S5-3
     TOP: Political systems, Republic
15. ANS: C   DIF: E   REF: 131   OBJ: C6S1-2
     TOP: Political systems, Roman army
16. ANS: A   DIF: E   REF: 138   OBJ: C6S1-3
     TOP: Technology, Aqueduct
17. ANS: E   DIF: E   REF: 145   OBJ: C6S3-2
     TOP: Religion, Bishop
18. ANS: B   DIF: E   REF: 146   OBJ: C6S4-3
     TOP: Religion, Heresy

MULTIPLE CHOICE

19. ANS: A   DIF: E   REF: 135-136   OBJ: C6S4-3
   TOP: Continuity and change, Pax Romana

20. ANS: C   DIF: E   REF: 147-149   OBJ: C6S2-3
   TOP: Continuity and change, Fall of Rome

21. ANS: A   DIF: A   REF: 135-136   OBJ: C6S5-3
   TOP: Continuity and change, Pax Romana

22. ANS: C   DIF: E   REF: 148   OBJ: C6S2-3
   TOP: Continuity and change, Emperor Diocletian

23. ANS: C   DIF: A   REF: 129   OBJ: C6S5-2
   TOP: Political systems, Plebian

24. ANS: A   DIF: A   REF: 133-134   OBJ: C6S1-2
   TOP: Continuity and change, Civil war

25. ANS: B   DIF: D   REF: 137   OBJ: C6S2-2
   TOP: Art and literature, Greek culture

26. ANS: D   DIF: A   REF: 140   OBJ: C6S3-1
   TOP: Continuity and change, Roman law

27. ANS: A   DIF: D   REF: 141   OBJ: C6S3-3
   TOP: Religion, Jews

28. ANS: C   DIF: D   REF: 142-143   OBJ: C6S4-1
   TOP: Religion, Jesus

29. ANS: D   DIF: D   REF: 136   OBJ: C6S4-2
   TOP: Continuity and change, Pax Romana

30. ANS: C   DIF: E   REF: 148   OBJ: C6S5-1
   TOP: Geography, Emperor Constantine

31. ANS: B   DIF: A   REF: 133   OBJ: C6S5-2
   TOP: Economics, Class system

32. ANS: B   DIF: D   REF: 134   OBJ: C6S2-1
   TOP: Continuity and change, Civil war

33. ANS: D   DIF: D   REF: 137-138   OBJ: C6S2-2
   TOP: Art and literature, Greek culture

34. ANS: B   DIF: A   REF: 141   OBJ: C6S3-1
   TOP: Religion, Religious diversity

35. ANS: B   DIF: D   REF: 147-149   OBJ: C6S4-1
   TOP: Continuity and change, Diocletian and Constantine

36. ANS: C   DIF: A   REF: 149-151   OBJ: C6S5-2
   TOP: Continuity and change, Fall of Rome

SHORT ANSWER

37. ANS:
Winning an empire gave Rome control of busy trade routes and brought great wealth to some Romans. On the other hand, many farmers lost their land, and corruption increased.

DIF: A   REF: 133   OBJ: C6S5-1
TOP: Continuity and change, Economics

38. ANS:
Augustus created a civil service to enforce laws. He allowed self-government in cities and provinces. He ordered a census, set up a postal system, and issued new coins. He also provided jobs by having roads and temples built.

DIF: D   REF: 135   OBJ: C6S2-1
TOP: Continuity and change, Augustus

39. ANS:
Roman artists adapted the realism of Hellenistic works but added their own style by creating images that revealed a person's character. Roman writers imitated Greek styles in prose and poetry, but they used Latin to create their own literature.

DIF: D   REF: 137-138   OBJ: C6S2-3
TOP: Art and literature, Greek culture

40. ANS:
Jesus believed in one God and accepted the Ten Commandments. He defended the law of Moses and the teachings of Jewish prophets. According to his followers, Jesus called himself the Son of God and many believed he was the messiah. He proclaimed that his mission was to bring spiritual salvation and eternal life to others.

DIF: A   REF: 142-143   OBJ: C6S3-1
TOP: Religion, Christianity

41. ANS:
Constantine granted toleration to Christians, which encouraged the rapid growth of Christianity. He built a new capital on the Bosporus, which made the eastern part of the empire the center of power.

DIF: D   REF: 148-149   OBJ: C6S4-2
TOP: Impact of the individual, Constantine

42. ANS:
Germanic invasions weakened the empire. The Roman government became corrupt and authoritarian, thereby losing support of the people. The empire was divided when it was under attack. Heavy taxes caused widespread poverty, and there was a decline in social values such as patriotism.

DIF: D   REF: 149-151   OBJ: C6S4-2
TOP: Continuity and change, Fall of Rome

43. ANS:
Aeneas, out of loyalty, could not leave his father to die. Also, he wanted to help his father, his wife, and his son escape to safety.

DIF: A   REF: 137   OBJ: C6S5-3
TOP: Art and literature, Aeneid

44. ANS:
He said that if the gods had wanted him to live longer they would have saved his home. He had decided to stay and die.

DIF: D   REF: 137   OBJ: C6S3-2
TOP: Art and literature, Aeneid

45. ANS:
Aeneas called for his gear so that he could return to battle.

DIF: D   REF: 137   OBJ: C6S3-2
TOP: Art and literature, Aeneid

46. ANS:
Romans valued family, home, loyalty, and courage.

DIF: D   REF: 130-131, 137-138   OBJ: C6S3-2
TOP: Art and literature, Aeneid

ESSAY

47. ANS:
Italy is a peninsula centrally located in the Mediterranean Sea. It is not broken up into small, isolated valleys like Greece. The Apennine Mountains are less rugged than the mountains of Greece. Italy also has broad, fertile plains that support a growing population.

DIF: D   REF: 128-129   OBJ: C6S3-2
TOP: Geography, Italy, Greece

48. ANS:
A wide gap between rich and poor caused social unrest. Many farmers lost their land because they could not compete with the large estates owned by wealthy Romans.

DIF: D   REF: 133   OBJ: C6S1-1
TOP: Social systems, Class system

49. ANS:
Italy is a peninsula located in the center of the Mediterranean Sea. Rome is located in the center of Italy. The location allowed Romans to expand into Italy, then into lands around the Mediterranean.

DIF: D   REF: 128-134   OBJ: C6S2-1   TOP: Geography, Italy

50. ANS:
    According to Roman law, an accused person was presumed innocent and was allowed to face his or her accuser and to defend himself or herself against a charge. Guilt had to be established clearly through evidence.

    DIF: D   REF: 140   OBJ: C6S1-1
    TOP: Political systems, Roman law

51. ANS:
    Common people gained representation and protection of their rights under Roman rule. Rome provided a system of checks on the power of government. Laws were written, and citizens could appeal a judgment against them. Elected officials could veto laws they felt were harmful. Later democratic governments adapted Roman ideas.

    DIF: D   REF: 140   OBJ: C6S3-3
    TOP: Political systems, Roman law

52. ANS:
    Rome developed a system of law that eventually applied to all people under Roman rule. It fostered unity and stability throughout the empire. Roman law became the basis for legal systems in Europe and Latin America.

    DIF: D   REF: 140   OBJ: C6S1-2
    TOP: Political systems, Roman law

CHAPTER 7—CIVILIZATIONS OF THE AMERICAS (1400 B.C.–A.D. 1570)

Matching

Match each term with the correct statement below.
  a. igloo   d. quipu
  b. kiva   e. tribute
  c. potlatch

_____   1. Payment from conquered peoples

_____   2. Knotted, colored strings used for keeping records

_____   3. Large underground chamber used for religious ceremonies

_____   4. Dome-shaped home made from snow and ice

_____   5. Ceremony in which a wealthy host distributes gifts to guests

Match each term with the correct statement below.
  a. Cahokia   d. Teotihuacán
  b. Cuzco   e. Tikal
  c. Tenochtitlán

_____   6. Largest Mayan city

_____   7. City that dominated the Valley of Mexico from A.D. 100 to A.D. 750

_____   8. Aztec capital

_____   9. Capital of Incan empire

_____ 10. Ceremonial center of the Mississippian culture

Match each term with the correct statement below.
  a. Adena   e. Inti
  b. Anasazi   f. Inuits
  c. Hohokams   g. Olmecs
  d. Huitzilopochtli   h. Pachacuti

_____ 11. People of the first American civilization

_____ 12. Aztec sun god

_____ 13. Founder of the Incan empire

_____ 14. Incan sun god

_____ 15. Farming civilization in the desert southwest of North America

_____ 16. Cliff-dwellers of Mesa Verde

_____ 17. Early Mound Builders in the Ohio Valley

_____ 18. Native American culture of the far north

Multiple Choice
Identify the letter of the choice that best completes the statement or answers the question.

_____ 19. The earliest people who migrated to the Americas came from
     a. Europe.   c. Africa.
     b. Asia.   d. Australia.

_____ 20. The first American civilization emerged along the
     a. Mississippi River.   c. desert coast of South America.
     b. Mexican Gulf Coast.   d. Amazon River.

_____ 21. Which of the following civilizations ruled an area that included the Andes Mountains?
     a. Olmecs   c. Aztecs
     b. Mayas   d. Incas

_____ 22. The Incan road system was built primarily for the purpose of allowing
     a. people to travel to religious festivals.
     b. farmers to carry tribute to the Sapa Inca.
     c. armies and news to move rapidly throughout the empire.
     d. traders to come into the empire.

_____ 23. The Incan Chosen Women were trained to
     a. serve the sun god.   c. run the government.
     b. become soldiers.   d. keep official records.

_____ 24. Which of the following reflects the influence of Middle American civilizations on North American cultures?
     a. Iroquois League   c. Cahokia temple mound
     b. potlatch   d. dog sleds

Culture Group	Time Period	Cultural Characteristic	Location
Hohokam	C.A.D. 900–1500	farmers	Arizona
Anasazi	A.D. 900–1300	cliff dwellers	Four Corners
Hopewell	100 B.C.–A.D. 500	Mound Builders	Ohio Valley
Mississippians	A.D. 700–1200	Mound Builders	Illinois

Figure 7-1

_____ 25. Based on Figure 7-1, what did the Hopewell and the Mississippians have in common?
     a. They lived at the same time.
     b. They were Mound Builders.
     c. They lived in the desert southwest.
     d. They were cliff dwellers.

_____ 26. Based on Figure 7-1, the earliest of these culture groups lived in
    a. Arizona.
    b. the Four Corners region.
    c. the Ohio Valley.
    d. Illinois.

_____ 27. Which of the following statements is true according to Figure 7-1?
    a. The Mound Builders lived in Arizona.
    b. The Mississippians disappeared in A.D. 500.
    c. The Hohokam were Mound Builders.
    d. The Anasazi were cliff dwellers.

_____ 28. Which of the culture groups listed in Figure 7-1 had disappeared before the others emerged?
    a. the Hohokam
    b. the Anasazi
    c. the Hopewell
    d. the Mississippian

_____ 29. The first people who migrated to North America came by way of a land bridge across the present-day
    a. Rocky Mountains.
    b. Mississippi River.
    c. Bering Strait.
    d. Yucatán Peninsula.

_____ 30. Mayas developed an accurate solar calendar so they could
    a. plant crops at the proper time.
    b. hold religious ceremonies at the correct moment.
    c. build pyramids on schedule.
    d. record historical events.

_____ 31. Which of the following statements describes Mayan government?
    a. Each city had its own ruling chief.
    b. Only men could rule.
    c. A king ruled all Mayan city-states.
    d. The emperor claimed divine power.

_____ 32. The Incan empire included the
    a. Valley of Mexico.
    b. Yucatán Peninsula.
    c. Andes Mountains.
    d. Mexican Gulf coast.

_____ 33. Peoples conquered by the Incas were
    a. used as slaves.
    b. trained as priests.
    c. sacrificed to the gods.
    d. enlisted in the Incan armies.

_____ 34. Which of the following peoples united their empire with a road system that extended more than 12,000 miles?
    a. Incas
    b. Aztecs
    c. Mayas
    d. Olmecs

_____ 35. Who made the elaborate clothing worn by the Sapa Inca?
    a. the Coya
    b. the Chosen Women
    c. the priests
    d. the guardian spirits of the empire

_____ 36. Native Americans in North America developed different cultures that were influenced by
   a. monotheism.
   b. the Incas.
   c. the environments in which they lived.
   d. the Greeks.

Short Answer

37. Explain how people reached the Americas.

38. Describe four achievements of Mayan civilization.

39. Describe Aztec religious beliefs.

40. Explain how the Incas united their large empire.

41. In what ways did cultures in the desert southwest reflect the influences of Middle American civilizations?

42. What are three conclusions that can be drawn about the Mound Builders based on archaeological evidence?

43. Explain why the culture of the people of the Northwest Coast differed from that of the Inuits.

Read the following excerpt from "The Famous Shrine of Titicaca and Its Fables and Legends" by Garcilaso de la Vega, the son of a Spanish father and a mother who was a member of a royal Incan family. Then on a separate sheet of paper, answer the questions that follow.

> "Among the famous temples in Peru dedicated to a sun there was one that rivaled that of Cuzco in ornamentation and in wealth of gold and silver, on an island known as Titicaca. . . . The Incas say that the Sun put his son and daughter there when he sent them to earth to enlighten the wild and barbarous people who inhabited the land at that time, and to teach them a better way of living. To this fable they add another that antedates [comes before] it by centuries. They say that after the flood the rays of the sun were first seen on the island . . . before they appeared anywhere else. . . .
> The Incas made the other Indians believe that they were the children of the Sun, and with the many good works they carried out they confirmed them in this idea. Because of these two legends, the Incas and all their subjects considered that island a holy site, and for this reason they ordered a rich temple built there."

44. What were the two Incan fables about Titicaca?

45. Why was a temple built at Titicaca?

46. According to the author, how did such stories benefit the Incas?

Essay
On a separate sheet of paper, write an answer to the following questions.

47. **Making Comparisons** How were the religious beliefs of the Incas like those of the Aztecs? How were they different?

48. **Identifying Central Issues** Explain why Native American groups in North America developed diverse cultures.

49. **Recognizing Causes and Effects** Explain how changes in the Earth's climate may have enabled people to migrate throughout the Americas.

50. **Drawing Conclusions** How did archaeologists determine that the Hopewell traded with people from other regions?

51. **Making Comparisons** How did Aztec government differ from that of the Mayas?

52. **Drawing Conclusions** How did the role of the Chosen Women of the Sun reflect the importance of religion to the Incas?

CHAPTER 7—CIVILIZATIONS OF THE AMERICAS (1400 B.C.–A.D. 1570)
Answer Section

MATCHING

1. ANS: E   DIF: E   REF: 160   OBJ: C7S1-3
   TOP: Economics, Tribute
2. ANS: D   DIF: E   REF: 164   OBJ: C7S1-3
   TOP: Economics, Quipu
3. ANS: B   DIF: E   REF: 169   OBJ: C7S2-2
   TOP: Religion, Kiva
4. ANS: A   DIF: E   REF: 171   OBJ: C7S3-1
   TOP: Technology, Igloo
5. ANS: C   DIF: E   REF: 171   OBJ: C7S3-3
   TOP: Social systems, Potlatch

6. ANS: E   DIF: E   REF: 158   OBJ: C7S3-3
   TOP: Geography, Maya
7. ANS: D   DIF: E   REF: 159   OBJ: C7S1-2
   TOP: Geography, Aztec
8. ANS: C   DIF: E   REF: 159   OBJ: C7S1-3
   TOP: Geography, Aztec
9. ANS: B   DIF: E   REF: 164, 166   OBJ: C7S1-3
   TOP: Geography, Inca
10. ANS: A   DIF: E   REF: 169   OBJ: C7S2-2
    TOP: Social systems, Mound Builders

11. ANS: G   DIF: E   REF: 157-158   OBJ: C7S3-2
    TOP: Social systems, Olmecs
12. ANS: D   DIF: E   REF: 162   OBJ: C7S1-2
    TOP: Religion, Aztec sun god
13. ANS: H   DIF: E   REF: 164   OBJ: C7S2-2
    TOP: Impact of the individual, Pachacuti
14. ANS: E   DIF: E   REF: 164   OBJ: C7S1-3
    TOP: Religion, Incan sun god
15. ANS: C   DIF: E   REF: 168   OBJ: C7S2-2
    TOP: Social system, Hohokam
16. ANS: B   DIF: E   REF: 169   OBJ: C7S2-2
    TOP: Social system, Anasazi
17. ANS: A   DIF: E   REF: 169   OBJ: C7S3-1
    TOP: Social system, Mound Builders
18. ANS: F   DIF: E   REF: 171   OBJ: C7S3-1
    TOP: Social systems, Inuit

MULTIPLE CHOICE

19. ANS: B   DIF: E   REF: 156   OBJ: C7S3-2
     TOP: Geography, Migration

20. ANS: B   DIF: E   REF: 157   OBJ: C7S3-3
     TOP: Geography, Mexican Gulf coast

21. ANS: D   DIF: E   REF: 164   OBJ: C7S1-1
     TOP: Geography, Andes Mountains

22. ANS: C   DIF: A   REF: 164,166   OBJ: C7S1-1
     TOP: Technology, Incan road system

23. ANS: A   DIF: E   REF: 167   OBJ: C7S2-1
     TOP: Religion, Incan Chosen Women

24. ANS: C   DIF: A   REF: 169   OBJ: C7S2-2
     TOP: Social system, Mound Builders

25. ANS: B   DIF: A   REF: 169   OBJ: C7S2-3
     TOP: Social system, Mound Builders

26. ANS: C   DIF: D   REF: 169   OBJ: C7S3-1
     TOP: Geography, Mound Builders

27. ANS: D   DIF: E   REF: 169   OBJ: C7S3-2
     TOP: Social systems, Anasazi

28. ANS: C   DIF: A   REF: 167   OBJ: C7S3-2
     TOP: Continuity and change, Mound Builders

29. ANS: C   DIF: E   REF: 156-157   OBJ: C7S3-1
     TOP: Geography, Bering Strait

30. ANS: B   DIF: E   REF: 159   OBJ: C7S3-2
     TOP: Technology, Mayan solar calendar

31. ANS: A   DIF: E   REF: 158   OBJ: C7S1-1
     TOP: Political systems, Maya

32. ANS: C   DIF: A   REF: 164   OBJ: C7S1-2
     TOP: Geography, Andes Mountains

33. ANS: D   DIF: A   REF: 164   OBJ: C7S1-2
     TOP: Social systems, Inca

34. ANS: A   DIF: A   REF: 164, 166   OBJ: C7S2-1
     TOP: Technology, Incan road system

35. ANS: B   DIF: A   REF: 167   OBJ: C7S2-2
     TOP: Social systems, Incan Chosen Women

36. ANS: C   DIF: A   REF: 169, 171   OBJ: C7S2-2
     TOP: Social systems, Environment

SHORT ANSWER

37. ANS:
Hunters from Asia migrated across a land bridge between Siberia and Alaska that was exposed during the last ice age.

DIF: A   REF: 156   OBJ: C7S2-3
TOP: Geography, Bering Strait

38. ANS:
The Mayas created magnificent buildings and carvings, developed a system of hieroglyphic writing, invented an accurate solar calendar, and developed a numbering system that included the concept of zero.

DIF: A   REF: 158-159   OBJ: C7S3-3
TOP: Technology, Mayan civilization

39. ANS:
Priests formed a separate class that performed rituals to prevent natural disasters. The chief god was Huitzilopochtli, the sun god. Aztecs performed human sacrifice. Each day, a human heart was offered to the sun god to give him strength to battle the forces of evil at night and ensure that he would be reborn the next morning.

DIF: A   REF: 162   OBJ: C7S1-1   TOP: Religion, Aztec

40. ANS:
The Incas imposed their own language and religion on all parts of the empire. They created a system of roads that allowed armies and news to move throughout the empire. Relays of runners could carry messages from distant provinces to the capital.

DIF: A   REF: 164, 166   OBJ: C7S1-2
TOP: Social systems, Incan empire

41. ANS:
The Hohokams used irrigation systems similar to those used by Middle American civilizations. They also built similar temples and ball courts.

DIF: A   REF: 168   OBJ: C7S1-3
TOP: Social systems, Hohokam

42. ANS:
The discovery of shells and copper indicates that the Mound Builders' trade extended from the Great Lakes to the Gulf of Mexico. Artifacts show that they were skilled craft workers. The large size of Cahokia suggests a well-ordered society.

DIF: D   REF: 169   OBJ: C7S2-2
TOP: Social systems, Mound Builders

43. ANS:
The people of the Northwest Coast lived in a richer environment than that of the Inuits. Plentiful resources enabled them to build permanent villages with wooden houses. The Inuits became migrating hunters in order to survive in a frozen land.

DIF: A   REF: 169, 171   OBJ: C7S3-1
TOP: Social systems, Inuit, Northewest Coast Indians

44. ANS:
The Incas said that the Sun put his son and daughter there to enlighten people and teach them a better way of living. The Incas also said that after the flood, the rays of the Sun were seen on the island and lake before they appeared anywhere else.

DIF: D   REF: 164-167   OBJ: C7S3-2
TOP: Art and literature, Incan fables

45. ANS:
A temple was built at Titicaca because they believed it was a holy site and they built a temple to honor the Sun.

DIF: A   REF: 164-167   OBJ: C7S3-3
TOP: Religion, Incan fables

46. ANS:
The Incas made other Indians believe that they were the children of the Sun. This probably helped increase their power over subject peoples.

DIF: D   REF: 164-167   OBJ: C7S2-2
TOP: Art and literature, Incan fables

ESSAY

47. ANS:
Like the Aztecs, the Incas worshipped the sun god. In both cultures, priests held an important place in society. The Incas had special female attendants who served the sun god. Aztecs offered human sacrifices to appease the gods.

DIF: D   REF: 162, 167   OBJ: C7S2-2
TOP: Religion, Inca, Aztec

48. ANS:
People adapted to the environments in which they settled. Geographic conditions influenced their ways of life.

DIF: D   REF: 169, 171   OBJ: C7S2-2
TOP: Social systems, Environments

49. ANS:
During the last ice age, water froze into thick sheets. The sea level dropped and exposed a land bridge between Siberia and Alaska. Hunters likely followed animals across the bridge. As the climate warmed, water covered the land bridge. People then migrated eastward and southward across the Americas.

DIF: A   REF: 156-157   OBJ: C7S2-3
TOP: Geography, Migration

50. ANS:
Hopewell mounds contained shells and shark teeth from the Gulf of Mexico. Hopewell ornaments were made of copper that came from the Great Lakes region.

DIF: D   REF: 169   OBJ: C7S3-3
TOP: Economics, Hopewell

51. ANS:
The Aztecs had a single ruler, chosen by nobles and priests. Nobles served as officials of conquered provinces. The Mayas had a ruling chief for each city. Nobles served as military leaders and officials who managed public works, collected taxes, and enforced laws.

DIF: A   REF: 158, 160, 162   OBJ: C7S1-1
TOP: Political systems, Aztec, Maya

52. ANS:
The Chosen Women were selected from each region of the empire. They had years of training to perfect the skills and duties needed to serve the sun god. The choice of a select group of women to carry out religious duties and the long training indicate that religion played a central role in Incan society.

DIF: D   REF: 167   OBJ: C7S3-2
TOP: Religion, Incan Chosen Women

CHAPTER 8—THE RISE OF EUROPE (500–1300)

Matching

Match each term with the correct statement below.

a.	capital	e.	tithe
b.	charter	f.	secular
c.	chivalry	g.	serf
d.	fief	h.	usury

_____ 1. An estate granted to a vassal

_____ 2. A code of conduct adopted by knights in the Middle Ages

_____ 3. A peasant who was bound to the land

_____ 4. Tax the Church required Christians to pay

_____ 5. Worldly

_____ 6. Written document that set out the rights and privileges of a town

_____ 7. Money for investment

_____ 8. Lending money at interest

Match each person with the correct statement below.

a.	an apprentice	e.	a knight
b.	Leif Erikson	f.	a medieval merchant
c.	Charlemagne	g.	a troubadour
d.	a Benedictine monk	h.	a vassal

_____ 9. "From Aachen I shall rule my empire."

_____ 10. "I set up a short-lived colony in North America."

_____ 11. "My first loyalty is to my liege lord."

_____ 12. "It is my duty to be brave, loyal, and true."

_____ 13. "Let me sing you a song, my lady, praising your virtues."

_____ 14. "I have taken vows of obedience, poverty, and chastity."

_____ 15. "My master is teaching me the art of swordmaking."

_____ 16. "Servants, come! Carry these bundles of cloth for sale through the streets."

Multiple Choice
Identify the letter of the choice that best completes the statement or answers the question.

_____ 17. Which of the following groups conquered the former Roman province of Gaul?
    a.   the Christians   c.   the Muslims
    b.   the Franks   d.   the Saxons

_____ 18. Which of the following is credited to Charlemagne?
    a.   the defeat of the Muslims at the Battle of Tours
    b.   the development of feudalism
    c.   the development of banking
    d.   the revival of Latin learning

_____ 19. Under feudalism, lords granted land to vassals in exchange for which of the following?
    a.   food   c.   farm labor
    b.   military service   d.   housing

_____ 20. The manor economy was based on
    a.   trade among many villages.   c.   metalworking.
    b.   farming and self-sufficiency.   d.   herding and weaving.

_____ 21. How did monks and nuns improve life during the Middle Ages?
    a.   They cared for the sick and poor.   c.   They opposed the feudal system.
    b.   They gave land to the peasants.   d.   They excommunicated criminals.

_____ 22. Why did some religious people want to reform the Church during medieval times?
    a.   It declared war on feudalism.
    b.   Its very success had brought problems.
    c.   It had grown weak.
    d.   It had grown too intellectual.

_____ 23. New agricultural technologies in the Middle Ages led to
    a.   the end of Church influence.   c.   increased food production.
    b.   the end of feudalism.   d.   the creation of farmers' guilds.

_____ 24. Which of the following was the most important economic activity in a medieval town?
    a.   trade   c.   livestock raising
    b.   farming   d.   weaving

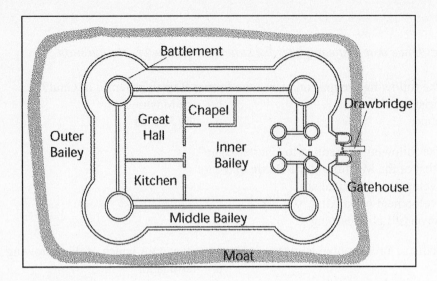

Figure 8-1

____ 25. In Figure 8-1, which of the following suggests that the castle was designed to withstand attack?
- a. the kitchen
- b. the chapel
- c. the battlement
- d. the great hall

____ 26. The moat in Figure 8-1 was used
- a. for recreational purposes.
- b. for drinking water.
- c. for irrigation.
- d. to prevent an enemy from reaching the castle walls.

____ 27. Which of these statements best describes the function of the building in Figure 8-1?
- a. Its main purpose is defense.
- b. It is a center of trade.
- c. It is a center for farming.
- d. It is the center of religious life for many surrounding villages.

____ 28. According to Figure 8-1, from which of the following positions would it be easiest to defend the castle?
- a. the inner bailey
- b. the drawbridge
- c. the middle bailey
- d. the battlements

____ 29. Why was the Battle of Tours significant?
- a. It allowed Muslims to gain control of France.
- b. It resulted in Charles Martel becoming king of France.
- c. It stopped the Muslim advance into Western Europe.
- d. It extended Charlemagne's empire to Spain.

____ 30. Which of the following helped unite Charlemagne's empire?
- a. a strong, efficient government
- b. Magyar attacks
- c. the Treaty of Verdun
- d. Viking attacks

_____ 31. Chivalry governed relations between
    a. serfs and nobles.
    b. noblemen and noblewomen.
    c. lords and vassals.
    d. Christians and non-Christians.

_____ 32. Which group made up the largest part of the population in feudal society?
    a. vassals
    b. peasants
    c. knights
    d. lords

_____ 33. The Church had great power over people during the Middle Ages because
    a. it protected them in times of warfare.
    b. it provided them with education.
    c. it decided who could achieve salvation.
    d. it controlled food production.

_____ 34. What problem did the Cluniac reforms address?
    a. church corruption
    b. feudal warfare
    c. poverty in feudal society
    d. antisemitism in Europe

_____ 35. How did the three-field system contribute to the agricultural revolution that took place during the Middle Ages?
    a. It allowed peasants to produce more crops.
    b. It gave more land to the peasants.
    c. It gave more land to the nobles.
    d. It helped revive religion.

_____ 36. Which of the following groups dominated the economic and political life of towns during the High Middle Ages?
    a. nobles
    b. merchant guilds
    c. knights
    d. the clergy

Short Answer

37. Identify and explain the significance of the Franks and Muslims.

38. Describe how each of the following traditions influenced Charlemagne's rule: Roman, German, and Christian.

39. Identify the responsibilities of the peasant toward the lord and of the lord toward the peasant.

40. Describe three ways the Church shaped medieval life.

41. List three functions performed by monks and nuns during medieval times.

42. List three new technologies or improvements that led to an agricultural revolution in Western Europe.

43. List five economic or social changes that resulted from the growth of trade in the Middle Ages.

Read the following excerpt from a firsthand account of a Viking siege of Paris during the tenth century. Then answer the questions that follow.

"The Northmen [Vikings] came to Paris with 700 sailing ships, not counting those of smaller size which are commonly called barques. At one stretch the Seine was lined with the vessels for more than two leagues [six miles]. . . . The second day after the fleet of the Northmen arrived under the walls of the city, Siegfred, who was then king only in name but who was in command of the expedition, came to the dwelling of the illustrious bishop. He bowed his head and said: 'Gauzelin, have compassion on yourself and on your flock. We beseech you to listen to us, in order that you may escape death. Allow us only the freedom of the city. We will do no harm and we will see to it that whatever belongs either to you or to Odo shall be strictly respected. . . . [I]f you do not listen to my demand, on the morrow our war machines [catapults] will destroy you with poisoned arrows. You will be the prey [victim] of famine and of pestilence [disease] and these evils will renew themselves perpetually every year.' So saying he departed and gathered together his comrades."

44. How do you think the author of this account viewed the Vikings?

45. Based on this account, how do you think the Vikings viewed themselves?

46. Use this account to speculate about the sources of the Vikings' strength. Do you think it was only physical or was there a psychological element involved?

Essay
On a separate sheet of paper, write an answer to the following questions.

47. **Recognizing Causes and Effects** What natural resources helped Western Europe develop into a major population center during the Middle Ages?

48. **Identifying Main Ideas** Give two examples of how the Church influenced the life of women during the Middle Ages.

49. **Making Inferences** How did the physical geography of Western Europe encourage the development of civilization there?

50. **Recognizing Causes and Effects** Describe one long-term and one short-term effect of the agricultural revolution in medieval Europe.

51. **Comparing** The structure of feudal society is sometimes described as a pyramid. Explain why.

52. **Linking Past and Present** How do you think the ideas of chivalry influenced the modern notion of romantic love?

CHAPTER 8—THE RISE OF EUROPE (500–1300)
Answer Section

MATCHING

1. ANS: D   DIF: D   REF: 186   OBJ: C7S2-3
   TOP: Political systems, Feudalism
2. ANS: C   DIF: E   REF: 189   OBJ: C8S2-2
   TOP: Social systems, Chivalry
3. ANS: G   DIF: E   REF: 189   OBJ: C8S2-1
   TOP: Social systems, Peasants
4. ANS: E   DIF: E   REF: 192   OBJ: C8S2-2
   TOP: Religion, Tax
5. ANS: F   DIF: E   REF: 193   OBJ: C8S2-2
   TOP: Political system, Church authority
6. ANS: B   DIF: E   REF: 199   OBJ: C8S3-1
   TOP: Social systems, Medieval town
7. ANS: A   DIF: E   REF: 199   OBJ: C8S3-2
   TOP: Economics, Capital
8. ANS: H   DIF: E   REF: 200   OBJ: C8S4-2
   TOP: Economics, Usury

9. ANS: C   DIF: E   REF: 183-185   OBJ: C8S4-2
   TOP: Impact of the individual, Charlemagne
10. ANS: B   DIF: E   REF: 185   OBJ: C8S4-3
    TOP: Impact of the individual, Vikings
11. ANS: H   DIF: E   REF: 186-188   OBJ: C8S1-3
    TOP: Political systems, Vassal
12. ANS: E   DIF: E   REF: 187   OBJ: C8S1-3
    TOP: Social systems, Chivalry
13. ANS: G   DIF: E   REF: 189   OBJ: C8S2-1
    TOP: Art and literature, Chivalry
14. ANS: D   DIF: E   REF: 192, 194   OBJ: C8S2-2
    TOP: Religion, Benedictine Rule
15. ANS: A   DIF: E   REF: 200   OBJ: C8S2-2
    TOP: Economics, Guilds
16. ANS: F   DIF: E   REF: 201   OBJ: C8S3-1
    TOP: Economics, Medieval town

MULTIPLE CHOICE

17. ANS: B   DIF: E   REF: 183   OBJ: C8S4-3
    TOP: Continuity and change, Franks
18. ANS: D   DIF: E   REF: 184-185   OBJ: C8S4-3
    TOP: Impact of the individual, Charlemagne

19. ANS: B   DIF: E   REF: 186   OBJ: C8S1-2
    TOP: Political systems, Feudalism

20. ANS: B   DIF: A   REF: 189-190   OBJ: C8S1-3
    TOP: Economics, Feudalism

21. ANS: A   DIF: A   REF: 192-193   OBJ: C8S2-1
    TOP: Religion, Monks and nuns

22. ANS: B   DIF: E   REF: 195   OBJ: C8S2-3
    TOP: Religion, Reforms Movements

23. ANS: C   DIF: E   REF: 197-198   OBJ: C8S3-2
    TOP: Technology, Agricultural Revolution

24. ANS: A   DIF: D   REF: 198-199   OBJ: C8S3-3
    TOP: Economics, Medieval town

25. ANS: C   DIF: A   REF: 187, 189   OBJ: C8S4-1
    TOP: Technology, Castles

26. ANS: D   DIF: A   REF: 187, 189   OBJ: C8S4-3
    TOP: Technology, Castles

27. ANS: A   DIF: E   REF: 187, 189   OBJ: C8S2-1
    TOP: Technology, Castles

28. ANS: D   DIF: A   REF: 187, 189   OBJ: C8S2-1
    TOP: Technology, Castles

29. ANS: C   DIF: E   REF: 183   OBJ: C8S2-1
    TOP: Continuity and change, Battle of Tours

30. ANS: A   DIF: A   REF: 184   OBJ: C8S2-1
    TOP: Political systems, Charlemagne

31. ANS: B   DIF: A   REF: 189   OBJ: C8S1-2
    TOP: Social systems, Chivalry

32. ANS: B   DIF: E   REF: 189   OBJ: C8S1-3
    TOP: Social systems, Peasants

33. ANS: C   DIF: A   REF: 195   OBJ: C8S2-2
    TOP: Religion, The Church

34. ANS: A   DIF: A   REF: 195   OBJ: C8S2-3
    TOP: Religion, Cluniac reforms

35. ANS: A   DIF: A   REF: 197   OBJ: C8S3-1
    TOP: Technology, Agricultural Revolution

36. ANS: B   DIF: D   REF: 200   OBJ: C8S3-3
    TOP: Economics, Guilds

SHORT ANSWER

37. ANS:
    The Franks were a Germanic tribe that invaded Western Europe and eventually took control of it. The Muslims, believers in Islam, built a great empire that stretched all the way to Spain and threatened Western Europe.

    DIF: E   REF: 183   OBJ: C8S4-1
    TOP: Continuity and change, Muslims and Franks

38. ANS:
    Roman—Charlemagne tried to turn his capital, Aachen, into a "second Rome" by making it the center of a revival of Latin learning; German—He used a German system of rule. That is, he gave land to powerful nobles and appointed them to rule over it for him. Officials kept an eye on these rulers. Christian—Christianity became the empire's religion and helped to unite it.

    DIF: A   REF: 183-185   OBJ: C8S4-2
    TOP: Political systems, Charlemagne

39. ANS:
    Peasants were responsible for farming the lord's lands, repairing his roads and fences, and fulfilling marriage, inheritance, and other specified payments to the lord. In turn, the lord was responsible for protecting the peasants in times of war and providing them with land to farm for themselves.

    DIF: A   REF: 189-190   OBJ: C8S1-2
    TOP: Social systems, Peasants

40. ANS:
    Possible answers include the following: influenced male and female roles; controlled behavior and morals; served as the focus of social life; provided education; and limited the power of monarchs.

    DIF: A   REF: 191-195   OBJ: C8S1-3
    TOP: Social systems, The Church

41. ANS:
    Answers should include three of the following: took care of the sick and poor; ran schools; provided lodging for travelers; preserved writings of the ancient world; and acted as missionaries for Christianity.

    DIF: A   REF: 192-193   OBJ: C8S2-3
    TOP: Religion, Monks and nuns

42. ANS:
    Answers should include three of the following: iron plows; new harnesses that allowed horses to be used instead of oxen; windmills; making more land available; and the three-field system.

    DIF: A   REF: 197-198   OBJ: C8S3-1
    TOP: Technology, Agricultural Revolution

43. ANS:
    Answers should include five of the following: the development of a money economy; the growth of banking; the development of new business practices, including partnerships, insurance, and bills of exchange; the weakening of serfdom; the growth of guilds; the appearance of a middle class; and new roles for women.

    DIF: A   REF: 198-201   OBJ: C8S3-2
    TOP: Continuity and change, Trade

44. ANS:
The author was intimidated by them.

    DIF: A   REF: 185   OBJ: C8S4-1
    TOP: Continuity and change, Vikings

45. ANS:
Possible answer: The Vikings viewed themselves as fearsome, and this gave them great self-confidence.

    DIF: A   REF: 185   OBJ: C8S4-2
    TOP: Continuity and change, Vikings

46. ANS:
Answers may vary, but many students will probably acknowledge that there was a psychological element involved as well as superior weaponry. Students may also observe that the Vikings were aware that they had an intimidating effect on people and used it as a source of power.

    DIF: A   REF: 185   OBJ: C8S1-2
    TOP: Continuity and change, Vikings

ESSAY

47. ANS:
Forests, rich soil, rivers and seas, and minerals (including iron) all helped Western Europe become a major center of population during the Middle Ages.

    DIF: A   REF: 182   OBJ: C8S1-2
    TOP: Geography, Population expansion

48. ANS:
Answers could include two of the following: It restricted their role in the Church, including forbidding them to preach and hear confessions; it discouraged them from becoming well educated; it limited their social and domestic roles by viewing them as weak and in need of male guidance; it provided them with role models; it protected them; and it allowed them to become nuns. In the early Middle Ages, the Church allowed nuns to preach the Gospel, hear confessions, and to be educated. These rights were later withdrawn.

    DIF: A   REF: 192   OBJ: C8S1-2   TOP: Religion, Women

49. ANS:
Its rich soil enabled it to grow a surplus of crops and encouraged trade and communication; and its rich natural resources, such as lumber and minerals, provided it with valuable raw materials from which to make goods.

    DIF: D   REF: 182, 197-198   OBJ: C8S1-1
    TOP: Geography, Development of civilization

50. ANS:
Short-term effects include increased food production, population growth, and a more varied diet. Long-term effects include a revival in trade, the growth of towns, the growth of banking, the growth of new business practices, the end of serfdom, and the rise of the middle class.

DIF: A   REF: 197-200   OBJ: C8S3-1
TOP: Technology, Agricultural Revolution

51. ANS:
As power increases, fewer and fewer people hold parallel positions. Powerless peasants, who make up most of the population, form the base of the triangle. Above them and greatly less in number are knights. Fewer still are the lords, the level above the knights. Finally at the apex sits the monarch.

DIF: D   REF: 186,188   OBJ: C8S1-1
TOP: Political systems, Feudalism

52. ANS:
Possible answer: The chivalrous idea that women should be protected and cherished is still central to the idea of romantic love. This is expressed in certain courtship rituals, manners, and popular music and literature. Also the idea that a person's beloved has extraordinary gifts and exists apart from the rest of the world also reflects the influence of old chivalrous ideas.

DIF: A   REF: 189   OBJ: C8S4-3
TOP: Social systems, Chivalry

CHAPTER 9—THE HIGH MIDDLE AGES (1050–1450)

Matching

Match each term with the correct statement below.
   a.   scholasticism
   b.   common law
   c.   vernacular
   d.   schism
   e.   crusade

_____   1.   Law that was the same for all people

_____   2.   Holy war

_____   3.   Split

_____   4.   A method of study that uses reason to support Christian beliefs

_____   5.   Everyday language of ordinary people

Match each person with the correct statement below.
   a.   Innocent III
   b.   Isabella
   c.   Joan of Arc
   d.   Thomas Aquinas
   e.   William the Conqueror

_____   6.   Norman king responsible for the *Domesday Book*

_____   7.   Pope who led the Church at the height of its power in the Middle Ages

_____   8.   Ruler who used the Inquisition to help unify Spain

_____   9.   Christian scholar who used reason to examine Christian teaching

_____ 10.   Peasant woman who led French troops to victory against the English in the Hundred Years' War

Match each term with the correct statement below.
   a.   scholasticism
   b.   vernacular
   c.   common law
   d.   crusade
   e.   schism

_____ 11.   This type of law, called _____, is the same for all people.

_____ 12.   A war fought for religious reasons is called a _____.

_____ 13.   A _____, or split, divided the Roman and Byzantine churches.

_____ 14.   A scholarly method that used reason to examine Christian beliefs is known as _____.

_____ 15.   _____ refers to the everyday language of ordinary people.

Match each person with the correct statement below.

a. Christine de Pizan   d. Urban II
b. Edward I   e. Geoffrey Chaucer
c. Gregory VII

____ 16. "What touches all should be approved by all."

____ 17. "I hereby excommunicate Henry IV."

____ 18. "Seize that land from the Turks!"

____ 19. "If daughters were sent to schools like sons, they would learn as well."

____ 20. "My tales give a colorful picture of medieval life."

Multiple Choice
Identify the letter of the choice that best completes the statement or answers the question.

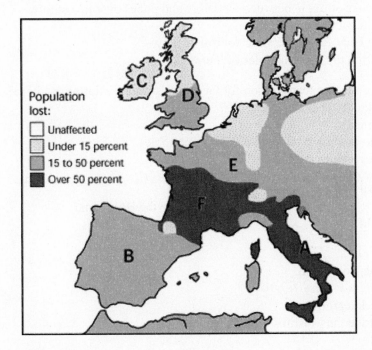

Figure 9-1

____ 21. According to Figure 9-1, which region or regions were most devastated by the Black Death?
a. A and F   c. C and D
b. B   d. E

____ 22. According to Figure 9-1, what percentage of the population died of the Black Death in
Region A?
a. under 15 percent   c. 15 to 50 percent
b. The region was unaffected. d. over 50 percent

_____ 23. According to Figure 9-1, which of the following regions was least affected by the Black Death?
   a. A   c. C
   b. B   d. D

_____ 24. According to Figure 9-1, what percentage of the population died of the Black Death in Region C?
   a. under 15 percent   c. over 50 percent
   b. 15 to 50 percent   d. The region was unaffected.

_____ 25. Why was the Magna Carta important?
   a. It approved money for wars in France.
   b. It asserted that the monarch must obey the law.
   c. It allowed the monarch to abolish Parliament.
   d. It limited the power of the pope.

_____ 26. The Concordat of Worms was
   a. a treaty that ended the struggle between emperors and popes over investiture.
   b. an edict forcing Gregory VII into exile.
   c. a treaty giving the Holy Roman Empire control of Italy.
   d. a document declaring the pope the ruler of the world.

_____ 27. Which of the following was the main reason for Germany's disunity during medieval times?
   a. the growth of trading towns
   b. the physical geography
   c. rulers that failed to control strong and independent nobles
   d. cultural differences among regions

_____ 28. What was the chief goal of the Crusades?
   a. to liberate Spain   c. to free the Holy Land
   b. to conquer England   d. to defeat the Hindus

_____ 29. The Reconquista refers to
   a. the conquest of the Holy Land.
   b. the Christians' defeat at Acre.
   c. the revival of Greek learning.
   d. the campaign to drive the Muslims out of Spain.

_____ 30. Which of the following was a result of the plague in Europe?
   a. economic decline   c. the rebirth of Christianity
   b. political reform   d. the Hundred Years' War

_____ 31. The development of an early jury system took place during the reign of
   a. Urban II.   c. Edward I.
   b. Henry II.   d. William the Conqueror.

_____ 32. A major conflict between the Holy Roman emperors and the popes concerned
   a. who would appoint bishops.   c. who would control England.
   b. the right to succession.   d. the right to wage war.

____ 33. Which of the following was a result of the Crusades?
   a. permanent conquest of the Holy Land by Christians
   b. religious tolerance in Western Europe
   c. increased trade in Western Europe
   d. the reunification of the Roman and Byzantine churches

____ 34. A key feature of Gothic architecture is
   a. towers.
   b. tiny windows.
   c. flying buttresses.
   d. low, heavy roofs.

____ 35. Which of the following best describes the Church during the late Middle Ages?
   a. It provided strong moral leadership.
   b. It wielded great political power.
   c. It grew weak and divided.
   d. It offered great comfort to people during hard times.

____ 36. Why is Joan of Arc remembered?
   a. She led a peasant uprising that ended feudalism.
   b. She led the French to victories against the English in the Hundred Years' War.
   c. She led English troops in the Hundred Years' War.
   d. She drove the English from Calais.

Short Answer

37. Identify three of the following, and tell how they increased their royal power: William the Conqueror, Henry II, the Capetians, Philip Augustus, and Louis IX.

38. List three ideas about government and law that emerged in England that have influenced the modern world. Explain how they did this.

39. Identify the Concordat of Worms and tell what issues it addressed.

40. List three long-term effects of the Crusades.

41. Give two reasons why a revival of learning occurred in the High Middle Ages.

42. Compare the architecture of Gothic and Romanesque churches.

43. List five reasons why the late Middle Ages was a time of decline.

Read the following excerpt from a decree issued by Pope Boniface VIII in 1302. Then answer the questions that follow.

"The apostles said 'behold here are two swords.' Both swords, the spiritual and the secular, are under the power of the Church. One should be wielded for the Church, the other by the Church; the one by the hand of the priest, the other by the hand of kings and knights, but at the will of the priest. One sword moreover ought to be under the other, and the secular authority should be subjected to the spiritual.

The spiritual power has to establish the earthly power, and judge it if it be not good. But if a member of the clergy is accused of a crime he should be judged by the Church. The authority to judge, although exercised through man, is not human but rather divine."

44. What conflict do you suppose led the pope to issue the decree this passage is from? Support your answer with evidence from the document.

45. What do the swords in the document symbolize?

46. According to the document, what is the proper relationship between the Church and the government?

Essay

On a separate sheet of paper, write an answer to the following questions.

47. **Comparing** Compare the Romanesque style of architecture with the Gothic style.

48. **Predicting Consequences** How do you think Western Europe might have developed differently if it had not come in contact with other cultures as a result of the Crusades? Explain.

49. **Making Inferences** How did representative assemblies, including the Great Council and the Estates General, help win popular support for monarchs in England and France?

50. **Linking Past and Present** Pope Urban II described the Seljuk Turks as "an accursed race [that] has violently invaded the lands of those [of Jerusalem and Constantinople] Christians." Compare the attitudes of Europeans toward Muslims during the time of the Crusades to the attitudes today of warring parties toward one another. Try to give an example of a present-day attitude that is similar.

51. **Analyzing Information** How did Thomas Aquinas's *Summa Theologica* reflect a changing view of the universe in medieval Europe?

52. **Recognizing Causes and Effects** Explain how the Black Death undermined people's faith in the Church.

CHAPTER 9—THE HIGH MIDDLE AGES (1050–1450)
Answer Section

MATCHING

1. ANS: B   DIF: D   REF: 207   OBJ: C8S2-2
    TOP: Political systems, Law
2. ANS: E   DIF: E   REF: 214   OBJ: C9S2-3
    TOP: Religion, Crusades
3. ANS: D   DIF: E   REF: 216   OBJ: C9S1-2
    TOP: Continuity and change, Schism
4. ANS: A   DIF: E   REF: 221   OBJ: C9S2-3
    TOP: Religion, Scholasticism
5. ANS: C   DIF: E   REF: 222   OBJ: C9S3-2
    TOP: Art and literature, Vernacular

6. ANS: E   DIF: E   REF: 207   OBJ: C9S4-1
    TOP: Impact of the individual, William the Conqueror
7. ANS: A   DIF: E   REF: 214   OBJ: C9S4-3
    TOP: Impact of the individual, Innocent III
8. ANS: B   DIF: E   REF: 219   OBJ: C9S1-2
    TOP: Impact of the individual, Isabella Queen of Spain
9. ANS: D   DIF: E   REF: 221   OBJ: C9S2-3
    TOP: Impact of the individual, Thomas Aquinas
10. ANS: C   DIF: E   REF: 228   OBJ: C9S3-3
    TOP: Impact of the individual, Joan of Arc

11. ANS: C   DIF: E   REF: 207   OBJ: C9S4-2
    TOP: Political systems, Law
12. ANS: D   DIF: E   REF: 214   OBJ: C9S5-3
    TOP: Religion, Crusades
13. ANS: E   DIF: E   REF: 216   OBJ: C9S1-2
    TOP: Religion, Schism
14. ANS: A   DIF: E   REF: 221   OBJ: C9S2-3
    TOP: Religion, Scholasticism
15. ANS: B   DIF: E   REF: 222   OBJ: C9S3-2
    TOP: Art and literature, Vernacular

16. ANS: B   DIF: E   REF: 208   OBJ: C9S4-1
    TOP: Impact of the individual, Edward I
17. ANS: C   DIF: E   REF: 213   OBJ: C9S4-3
    TOP: Impact of the individual, Gregory VII
18. ANS: D   DIF: E   REF: 216   OBJ: C9S1-2
    TOP: Impact of the individual, Urban II
19. ANS: A   DIF: E   REF: 221   OBJ: C9S2-2
    TOP: Impact of the individual, Christine de Pizan

20. ANS: E DIF: E REF: 223 OBJ: C9S3-2
    TOP: Art and literature, Chaucer

MULTIPLE CHOICE

21. ANS: A DIF: E REF: 225-226 OBJ: C9S4-2
    TOP: Geography, Black Death
22. ANS: D DIF: E REF: 225-226 OBJ: C9S4-3
    TOP: Geography, Black Death
23. ANS: C DIF: A REF: 225-226 OBJ: C9S5-1
    TOP: Geography, Black Death
24. ANS: A DIF: E REF: 225-226 OBJ: C9S5-1
    TOP: Geography, Black Death
25. ANS: B DIF: A REF: 208-209 OBJ: C9S5-1
    TOP: Political systems, Magna Carta
26. ANS: A DIF: E REF: 213 OBJ: C9S5-1
    TOP: Political systems, Concordat of Worms
27. ANS: C DIF: D REF: 212 OBJ: C9S1-2
    TOP: Political systems, Germany
28. ANS: C DIF: A REF: 216 OBJ: C9S2-2
    TOP: Religion, Crusades
29. ANS: D DIF: A REF: 218 OBJ: C9S2-1
    TOP: Religion, Reconquista
30. ANS: A DIF: E REF: 226 OBJ: C9S3-2
    TOP: Economics, Black Death
31. ANS: B DIF: A REF: 207 OBJ: C9S3-4
    TOP: Political systems, Jury
32. ANS: A DIF: A REF: 213 OBJ: C9S5-1
    TOP: Religion, Church power
33. ANS: C DIF: D REF: 217 OBJ: C9S1-2
    TOP: Economics, Crusades
34. ANS: C DIF: A REF: 223 OBJ: C9S2-1
    TOP: Art and literature, Gothic architecture
35. ANS: C DIF: A REF: 226 OBJ: C9S3-2
    TOP: Religion, Church power
36. ANS: B DIF: A REF: 228 OBJ: C9S4-1
    TOP: Impact of the individual, Joan of Arc

SHORT ANSWER

37. ANS:
Answers should include three of the following: William the Conqueror—English king who used a census to increase control over his land and build an efficient system of tax collecting; Henry II—English king who established a royal treasury and expanded the law; Capetians—French rulers from the same family who made the throne hereditary, expanded the lands they ruled, won the support of the Church, and built an effective bureaucracy to collect taxes and impose the law; Philip Augustus—French king who appointed loyal government officials, organized a standing army, collected a national tax, and increased the land he ruled; and Louis IX—French king who created a strong base of support by winning the loyalty of his subjects, expanded the courts, outlawed private wars, and ended serfdom.

DIF: A   REF: 207, 210-211   OBJ: C9S5-2
TOP: Political systems, Monarchs

38. ANS:
Answers should include three of the following: The idea that laws are the same for all people became the basis for English common law; types of early juries were the ancestors of today's grand and trial juries; the Magna Carta established the idea of legal and citizens' rights; and Parliament became the framework for England's legislature and representative government, which later influenced the structure of the U.S. government.

DIF: A   REF: 207-210   OBJ: C9S5-3
TOP: Continuity and change, Law

39. ANS:
The Concordat of Worms was a treaty between the Church and the Holy Roman emperors that established the limits of each of those powers concerning the investiture of church officials.

DIF: D   REF: 213   OBJ: C9S1-1
TOP: Political systems, Concordat of Worms

40. ANS:
Answers should include three of the following: wider world view; increased trade; increased Church power; increased the power of feudal monarchs; and encouraged the growth of a money economy to help undermine serfdom.

DIF: A   REF: 216-218   OBJ: C9S1-2
TOP: Continuity and change, Crusades

41. ANS:
Answers should include two of the following: increased prosperity freed some people from daily toil and allowed them to study; agricultural improvements meant fewer people needed to farm and could follow other career paths, including ones that required education; the Church needed better-educated clergy; rulers needed educated people to run growing bureaucracies; and Greek knowledge was being translated and was reaching Europe.

DIF: A   REF: 220-221   OBJ: C9S2-2
TOP: Continuity and change, Education

42. ANS:
Romanesque churches are low, with thick walls, tiny slits for windows, heavy roofs, and round, squat towers. Gothic churches are graceful with large stained-glass windows and tall spires. Stone arches called flying buttresses support their walls.

   DIF: A   REF: 223-224   OBJ: C9S3-3
   TOP: Art and literature, Gothic and Romanesque architecture

43. ANS:
Answers should include five of the following: the Black Death killed a high percentage of the population; crop failures led to famine; war broke out; the social order broke down; the economy failed; production declined; and the Church lost its authority and was riddled with scandal.

   DIF: D   REF: 225-228   OBJ: C9S4-1
   TOP: Continuity and change, Late Middle Ages

44. ANS:
The pope issued this decree in response to a disagreement over whether a member of the clergy should be tried in a royal court or by the Church.

   DIF: A   REF: 213-214   OBJ: C9S4-3
   TOP: Political systems, Church power

45. ANS:
The swords in the document symbolize authority in general and the authority to judge in particular.

   DIF: A   REF: 213-214   OBJ: C9S5-1
   TOP: Political systems, Church power

46. ANS:
The government should be subject to the authority of the Church.

   DIF: A   REF: 213-214   OBJ: C9S2-2
   TOP: Political systems, Church power

ESSAY

47. ANS:
Romanesque churches are low, with thick walls, tiny slits for windows, heavy roofs, and towers. Gothic churches are graceful, airy structures, with large stained-glass windows and tall spires. Stone arches called flying buttresses support their walls.

   DIF: A   REF: 223-224   OBJ: C9S2-2
   TOP: Art and literature, Gothic and Romanesque architecture

48. ANS:
Possible answer: Europe might never have developed the desire for trade with foreign lands, which led to the age of exploration, the establishment of colonies, and its position for a few centuries as the center of the world.

DIF: A   REF: 217-218   OBJ: C9S2-2
TOP: Continuity and change, Crusades

49. ANS:
They involved more people in the government and gave subjects a sense of power.

DIF: A   REF: 206-208, 210-211   OBJ: C9S4-2
TOP: Political systems, Representative assemblies

50. ANS:
Answers can vary. Students can include examples of attitudes of warring parties in current ethnic conflicts.

DIF: D   REF: 216   OBJ: C9S3-3
TOP: Continuity and change, Crusades

51. ANS:
Answers will vary, but they should indicate that it showed the movement away from a spiritual world that must be taken on faith to a world that can be explored and understood through reason and intellect.

DIF: A   REF: 220-221   OBJ: C9S1-3
TOP: Religion, Thomas Aquinas

52. ANS:
Answers will vary, but they should point to the idea that until the plague the Church was able to provide an explanation for the world and what happened in it that made sense to people. The Black Death, however, blew the Church's world view apart and showed that it did not have all the answers and was not all-powerful.

DIF: D   REF: 225-226, 228   OBJ: C9S3-2
TOP: Religion, Black Death

CHAPTER 10—THE BYZANTINE EMPIRE AND RUSSIA (330–1613)

Matching

Match each term with the correct statement below.
a. icon
b. boyar
c. czar

d. schism
e. autocrat

_____ 1. Ruler with sole authority

_____ 2. A permanent split

_____ 3. A holy image

_____ 4. A landowning noble

_____ 5. An absolute ruler in Russia

Match each person with the correct statement below.
a. Ivan the Great
b. Genghiz Khan
c. Anna Comnena

d. Jadwiga
e. Justinian

_____ 6. Byzantine emperor who developed a law code based on ancient Roman law

_____ 7. A historian of the western world

_____ 8. Ruler who was Russia's first czar

_____ 9. Chief who united the Mongols of central Asia

_____ 10. Polish queen who controlled a large state in Eastern Europe

Match each person with the correct statement below.
a. Theodora
b. Justinian
c. a boyar
d. Ivan the Great

e. a patriarch
f. Muhammad II
g. Jan Sobieski
h. Yaroslav

_____ 11. "As head of the Byzantine Church, I am Christ's co-ruler on Earth."

_____ 12. "I am the highest Church official in Constantinople."

_____ 13. "But I shall stay. I accept the ancient proverb: Royal purple is the best burial sheet."

_____ 14. "From henceforth, this city will be known as Istanbul."

_____ 15. "Under my rule, Kiev has flourished."

_____ 16. "These are my lands. The czar is not my lord."

_____ 17. "In nature I am like all men, but in authority I am like the highest God."

_____ 18. "We've broken the Ottoman's siege of Vienna."

Multiple Choice
Identify the letter of the choice that best completes the statement or answers the question.

_____ 19. Which of the following is a true statement about the Byzantine economy?
- a. It was based on barter.
- b. It was weak.
- c. It was prosperous.
- d. It was controlled by guilds.

_____ 20. The Byzantine empire preserved the cultural heritage of
- a. Greece and Rome.
- b. Russia.
- c. the Mongols.
- d. Western Europe.

_____ 21. Kiev was strongly influenced by the culture of
- a. Rome.
- b. the Byzantine empire.
- c. the Ottoman Turks.
- d. Persia.

_____ 22. What kind of government did Russian rulers develop?
- a. oligarchy
- b. authoritarian or autocratic rule
- c. democracy
- d. theocracy

_____ 23. Which of the following statements best describes the region of Eastern Europe?
- a. a culturally uniform region
- b. an isolated region
- c. a region of many peoples, languages, and cultural traditions
- d. a peaceful region

_____ 24. Which of the following religions had an impact on Poland and Hungary?
- a. Hinduism
- b. Islam
- c. Orthodox Christianity
- d. Roman Catholicism

Figure 10-1

____ 25. According to Figure 10-1, what body of water connects the Sea of Marmara to the Aegean Sea?
  a. Dardanelles
  b. Black Sea
  c. Bosporus
  d. Mediterranean Sea

____ 26. According to Figure 10-1, what is the main reason the Bosporus is an important waterway?
  a. It provides a passage from the Black Sea to the Mediterranean.
  b. It connects the Byzantine empire with the Ottoman empire.
  c. It connects the Black Sea to the Sea of Marmara.
  d. It provides Greece with access to the Black Sea.

____ 27. According to Figure 10-1, what is the narrow body of water connecting the Black Sea to the Sea of Marmara called?
  a. Aegean Sea
  b. Bosporus
  c. Mediterranean Sea
  d. Dardanelles

____ 28. Looking at Figure 10-1, which of the following statements best explains why Constantinople is advantageously located?
  a. It is situated on a crossroads between Europe and Asia.
  b. It is located in the Byzantine empire.
  c. It lies across from the Ottoman empire.
  d. It is near the Sea of Marmara.

____ 29. The Byzantine empire reached its greatest size under
  a. Constantine.
  b. Justinian.
  c. Muhammad II.
  d. Vladimir.

____ 30. Which of the following groups finally conquered the Byzantine empire?
    a. Ottoman Turks   c. Latin Christians
    b. Seljuk Turks   d. Arabs

____ 31. Which of the following statements best describes the style of leadership that emerged in Russia?
    a. cooperative   c. democratic
    b. compromising   d. autocratic

____ 32. Which of the following cities became the capital of Russia under the czars?
    a. Kiev   c. Constantinople
    b. Kulikovo   d. Moscow

____ 33. Which of the following is associated with Ivan the Terrible?
    a. extreme absolute rule   c. written law code
    b. victory over the Golden Horde   d. cooperation with the Mongols

____ 34. Which of the following statements is true?
    a. Most people in Eastern Europe are of French descent.
    b. Eastern Europe is home to many different cultural traditions.
    c. Byzantine culture greatly influenced Poland and Hungary.
    d. The Magyars are the dominant ethnic group in Eastern Europe.

____ 35. Which of the following statements best explains why Eastern European kingdoms were so often invaded?
    a. The rulers were weak.
    b. There were few geographic barriers.
    c. They had no organized government.
    d. The rulers were preoccupied with matters outside of their borders.

____ 36. Which of the following groups of people took refuge in Poland during the late Middle Ages?
    a. Slavs   c. Serbs
    b. Jews   d. Roman Catholics

Short Answer

37. List three ways Justinian tried to restore the glory of Rome to the Byzantine empire.

38. List three ways the Byzantine empire influenced later civilizations, including Russia.

39. Identify and explain the impact of each on early Russia: Slavs, Varangians, and Mongols.

40. Describe how Ivan III became Russia's first czar.

41. List three methods the czars used to secure control of Russia.

42. Explain how geography contributed to Eastern Europe's ethnic diversity.

43. List the four major religions in Eastern Europe and describe where they are located.

Read the following excerpts from histories written by Procopius, a historian who lived during the time of Justinian. Then answer the questions that follow.

From *Buildings*

"Justinian created countless cities which did not exist before. And finding that the belief in God was, before his time, straying into errors and being forced to go in many directions, he completely destroyed all the paths leading to such errors, and brought it about that it stood on the firm foundation of a single faith. Moreover, finding the laws obscure because they had become far more numerous than they should be, and in obvious confusion because they disagreed with each other, he preserved them by cleansing them of the mass of their verbal trickery, and by controlling their discrepancies with the greatest firmness."

From the *Secret History*

"Justinian was dissembling, crafty, hypocritical, secretive by temperament, two-faced; a clever fellow with marvelous ability to conceal his real opinion, and able to shed tears, not from any joy or sorrow, but employing them artfully when required in accordance with the immediate need, lying all the time; not carelessly, however, but confirming his undertakings both with his signature and with the most fearsome oaths, even when dealing with his own subjects."

44. Contrast the picture of Justinian found in each passage.

45. Do you think it's possible that both views of Justinian are truthful? Why or why not?

46. *Buildings* was published while Procopius was alive, but the *Secret History* was published after the author's death. Why do you think this was?

Essay
On a separate sheet of paper, write an answer to the following questions.

47. **Making Generalizations** Make one generalization about Russian rulers. Support the generalization with two facts.

48. **Drawing Conclusions** Explain how geography influenced Eastern European history.

49. **Predicting Consequences** How do you think Russia might have developed differently if it had not been influenced by the Byzantine empire?

50. **Linking Past and Present** How do long-standing ethnic differences still affect the Balkans today?

51. **Synthesizing Information** Why do you think the Byzantine empire was so much more prosperous than the Holy Roman Empire during the Middle Ages?

52. **Drawing Conclusions** Why do you think Eastern Europe has been the site of so much warfare?

CHAPTER 10—THE BYZANTINE EMPIRE AND RUSSIA (330–1613)
Answer Section

MATCHING

1. ANS: E   DIF: E   REF: 236   OBJ: C10S1-1
    TOP: Political systems, Autocrat

2. ANS: D   DIF: E   REF: 237   OBJ: C10S1-2
    TOP: Religion, Schism

3. ANS: A   DIF: E   REF: 237   OBJ: C10S1-4
    TOP: Religion, Icon

4. ANS: B   DIF: E   REF: 242   OBJ: C10S2-3
    TOP: Social systems, Boyar

5. ANS: C   DIF: E   REF: 243   OBJ: C10S2-3
    TOP: Political systems, Czar

6. ANS: E   DIF: E   REF: 236   OBJ: C10S1-1
    TOP: Impact of the individual, Justinian

7. ANS: C   DIF: E   REF: 239   OBJ: C10S1-3
    TOP: History, Anna Comnena

8. ANS: A   DIF: E   REF: 242-243   OBJ: C10S2-3
    TOP: Impact of the individual, Ivan the Great

9. ANS: B   DIF: E   REF: 241   OBJ: C10S2-2
    TOP: Impact of the individual, Genghiz Khan

10. ANS: D   DIF: E   REF: 245   OBJ: C10S3-3
    TOP: Impact of the individual, Queen Jadwiga

11. ANS: B   DIF: E   REF: 236   OBJ: C10S1-1
    TOP: Impact of the individual, Justinian

12. ANS: E   DIF: E   REF: 237   OBJ: C10S1-2
    TOP: Religion, Patriarch

13. ANS: A   DIF: E   REF: 236   OBJ: C10S1-1
    TOP: Impact of the individual, Theodora

14. ANS: F   DIF: E   REF: 238   OBJ: C10S1-3
    TOP: Continuity and change, Fall of Constantinople

15. ANS: H   DIF: E   REF: 241   OBJ: C10S2-1
    TOP: Impact of the individual, Yaroslav

16. ANS: C   DIF: E   REF: 242   OBJ: C10S2-3
    TOP: Social systems, Boyar

17. ANS: D   DIF: E   REF: 242-243   OBJ: C10S2-3
    TOP: Impact of the individual, Ivan the Great

18. ANS: G   DIF: E   REF: 247   OBJ: C10S3-3
    TOP: Impact of the individual, Jan Sobieski

            © Pearson Education, Inc.

MULTIPLE CHOICE

19. ANS: C   DIF: A   REF: 236   OBJ: C10S1-2
     TOP: Economics, Byzantine economy
20. ANS: A   DIF: A   REF: 239   OBJ: C10S1-3
     TOP: Culture, Byzantine heritage
21. ANS: B   DIF: A   REF: 241   OBJ: C10S2-1
     TOP: Culture, Kiev
22. ANS: B   DIF: A   REF: 242-243   OBJ: C10S2-3
     TOP: Political systems, Autocracy
23. ANS: C   DIF: D   REF: 244-245   OBJ: C10S3-1
     TOP: Diversity, Eastern Europe
24. ANS: D   DIF: A   REF: 245, 247   OBJ: C10S3-2
     TOP: Religion, Roman Catholicism
25. ANS: A   DIF: E   REF: 234, 238   OBJ: C10S1-2
     TOP: Geography, Dardanelles
26. ANS: C   DIF: D   REF: 234, 238   OBJ: C10S1-2
     TOP: Geography, Bosporus
27. ANS: B   DIF: E   REF: 234, 238   OBJ: C10S1-2
     TOP: Geography, Bosporus
28. ANS: A   DIF: A   REF: 234,238   OBJ: C10S1-2
     TOP: Geography, Constantinople
29. ANS: B   DIF: A   REF: 236   OBJ: C10S1-1
     TOP: Impact of the individual, Justinian
30. ANS: A   DIF: A   REF: 238-239   OBJ: C10S1-2
     TOP: Continuity and change, Fall of Byzantine empire
31. ANS: D   DIF: D   REF: 242-243   OBJ: C10S2-1
     TOP: Political systems, Autocracy
32. ANS: D   DIF: A   REF: 242   OBJ: C10S2-2
     TOP: Continuity and change, Moscow
33. ANS: A   DIF: E   REF: 243   OBJ: C10S2-3
     TOP: Political systems, Ivan the Terrible
34. ANS: B   DIF: A   REF: 244-245   OBJ: C10S3-1
     TOP: Diversity, Eastern Europe
35. ANS: B   DIF: A   REF: 244   OBJ: C10S3-3
     TOP: Geography, Eastern Europe
36. ANS: B   DIF: A   REF: 245-246   OBJ: C10S3-3
     TOP: Religion, Jews in Poland

SHORT ANSWER

37. ANS:
Justinian reconquered western provinces (North Africa, Italy, and Spain); beautified Constantinople (including constructing Hagia Sophia) to make it worthy of its title, the "New Rome"; and collected and revised ancient Roman laws.

DIF: A   REF: 236   OBJ: C10S1-1
TOP: Impact of the individual, Justinian

38. ANS:
Answers should include three of the following: its scholars preserved and spread ancient Greek classics; its religion, Eastern Orthodox Christianity, spread to Eastern Europe and Russia; it provided Russia with a written script; its art, architecture, and music spread to Eastern Europe and Russia; Justinian's law code influenced law in Eastern and Western Europe; and it established patterns in government, especially the close relationship between the church and state in Russia.

DIF: A   REF: 239   OBJ: C10S1-3
TOP: Continuity and change, Byzantine heritage

39. ANS:
Slavs—among the earliest people to settle Russia who set up farming villages and started trading; Varangians—Vikings from Scandinavia who established a thriving trade with Constantinople and brought Kiev into the Byzantine sphere of influence; and Mongols—nomadic people from central Asia who overran Russia and brought peace to the region but also cut it off from the rest of Europe and delayed its development in the arts and sciences.

DIF: E   REF: 241-242   OBJ: C10S2-1
TOP: Continuity and change, Early Russia

40. ANS:
Ivan III brought a large area of Russia under his military control. Then he began building a framework for absolute political control, which included limiting the power of the land-owning nobles, adopting Byzantine court rituals to legitimize his authority, and giving himself the title of czar.

DIF: A   REF: 242-243   OBJ: C10S2-2
TOP: Political systems, Ivan the Great

41. ANS:
Answers should include three of the following: exercised their military might, centralized political power, made an ally of the Eastern Orthodox church, took privileges away from the boyars, and used terror to frighten people.

DIF: A   REF: 242-243   OBJ: C10S2-3
TOP: Political systems, Czarist power

42. ANS:
    The lack of natural geographic barriers and the presence of rivers made migration into the
    region by many different groups easy.

    DIF: D   REF: 244-245   OBJ: C10S3-1
    TOP: Diversity, Geography of Eastern Europe

43. ANS:
    Roman Catholic Christianity—Poland, Hungary, Czech area, western Balkans; Islam—the
    Balkans; Eastern Orthodox Christianity—the Balkans; Judaism—Poland and Hungary.

    DIF: A   REF: 245-247   OBJ: C10S3-2
    TOP: Religion, Religions of Eastern Europe

44. ANS:
    In the first passage, Procopius praises Justinian, and in the second he reviles him.

    DIF: D   REF: 236   OBJ: C10S1-1
    TOP: Impact of the individual, Justinian

45. ANS:
    Answers might include that it was possible for Justinian to make positive achievements while
    at the same time having a hypocritical nature.

    DIF: D   REF: 236   OBJ: C10S1-1
    TOP: Impact of the individual, Justinian

46. ANS:
    It would have been too dangerous for Procopius to publish the *Secret History* while Justinian
    was alive because the history was so unflattering.

    DIF: A   REF: 236   OBJ: C10S1-1   TOP: History, Justinian

ESSAY

47. ANS:
    Possible answer: Generalization—Russian rulers were power hungry. Facts—they were
    absolute rulers; and they took away the rights of the boyars.

    DIF: A   REF: 242-243   OBJ: C10S2-3
    TOP: Political systems, Russian rulers

48. ANS:
    The lack of natural geographic boundaries encouraged many different groups to migrate to the
    region. It also made the region easy to invade.

    DIF: D   REF: 244   OBJ: C10S3-3
    TOP: Geography, Eastern Europe

49. ANS:
Possible answers: It would not have adopted Byzantine culture or religion; it might have come to be influenced by Western Europe and Roman Catholicism and developed a form of government that was less autocratic.

DIF: A   REF: 241   OBJ: C10S2-1
TOP: Culture, Byzantine heritage

50. ANS:
Rival ethnic groups descended from Slavs who migrated to the region have fought in Bosnia and Kosovo. In part, the conflict can be traced to Ottoman rule and religious differences between the Bosnian Serbs, who are Christians, and the Croats, who are Muslims.

DIF: D   REF: 245   OBJ: C10S3-3   TOP: Diversity, Balkans

51. ANS:
Answers might include that its situation at the center of key trade routes between Europe and Asia played a large role. Also, its cosmopolitan character and open atmosphere invited opportunity.

DIF: A   REF: 234-236   OBJ: C10S1-2
TOP: Economics, Byzantine empire

52. ANS:
Answers might include that antagonisms among its many peoples made the area ripe for conflict; its physical geography made it especially vulnerable to invasion; its location put it at the crossroads of invading armies; its frequently changing political boundaries gave it a fluid quality that invited foreign powers to conquer it.

DIF: D   REF: 244-245   OBJ: C10S3-1
TOP: Geography, Eastern Europe

CHAPTER 11—THE MUSLIM WORLD (622–1629)

Matching

Match each term with the correct statement below.
a. arabesque
b. hajj
c. millet
d. minaret
e. sultan

_____ 1. Pilgrimage to Mecca required of all Muslims who are able

_____ 2. Slender tower of a mosque

_____ 3. Intricate design of curved lines that suggests floral shapes

_____ 4. Turkish ruler

_____ 5. Religious communities of non-Muslims in the Ottoman empire

Match each person with the correct statement below.
a. Akbar
b. al-Khwarizmi
c. Muhammad
d. Sinan
e. Tamerlane

_____ 6. Prophet of Islam

_____ 7. Mongol leader who conquered Persia and Mesopotamia

_____ 8. Muslim mathematician who pioneered the study of algebra

_____ 9. Chief builder of the Mughal dynasty

_____ 10. Ottoman architect who designed the Selimiye Mosque

Match each term with the correct statement below.
a. Abu al-Abbas
b. Abu Bakr
c. al-Khwarizmi
d. Nanak
e. Omar Khayyám
f. Sinan
g. Suleiman
h. Tamerlane

_____ 11. Successor to Muhammad

_____ 12. Founder of the Abbassid dynasty

_____ 13. Mongol leader who invaded Persia and Mesopotamia

_____ 14. Scholar and astronomer who wrote *The Rubáiyát*

_____ 15. Muslim mathematician who pioneered the study of algebra

_____ 16. Indian holy man who established a new religion called Sikhism

_____ 17. Sultan who ruled the Ottoman empire during its golden age

____ 18. Ottoman architect who designed mosques and palaces

Multiple Choice
Identify the letter of the choice that best completes the statement or answers the question.

SPREAD OF ISLAM		
Country	Approximate Date of Introduction of Islam	Approximate Percentage of Muslims Today
Egypt	656	94%
India	1250	11%
Iran (Persia)	656	95%
Morocco	750	99%
Saudia Arabia	610	100%
Spain	750	less tan 1%
Syria	656	90%
Turkey (Asia Minor)	1070	99.8%

Figure 11-1

____ 19. Which of the following statements is true according to Figure 11-1?
   a.   All Egyptians are Muslims.
   b.   Spain has a higher percentage of Muslims than Morocco has.
   c.   Most Indians are Muslims.
   d.   Islam is the major religion in Saudi Arabia.

____ 20. Based on Figure 11-1, Islam was introduced in Syria before it was introduced in
   a.   Egypt.   c.   Saudi Arabia.
   b.   Iran.   d.   Morocco.

____ 21. Based on Figure 11-1, in less than 50 years, Islam had spread from Saudi Arabia to
   a.   Egypt.   c.   Morocco.
   b.   India.   d.   Turkey.

____ 22. Which of the following statements is accurate according to Figure 11-1?
   a.   Islam is the major religion in India.
   b.   Most Spaniards are Muslims.
   c.   Iran has a higher percentage of Muslims than Egypt has.
   d.   All Syrians are Muslims.

____ 23. Which of the following beliefs is held by Muslims, Jews, and Christians?
   a.   belief in reincarnation   c.   belief in one God
   b.   belief in Jesus as the messiah d.   belief in Muhammad

____ 24. The split between Sunni and Shiite Muslims began with disagreement over
   a. the choice of a caliph.
   b. a belief in one God.
   c. acceptance of the Quran.
   d. the required pilgrimage to Mecca.

____ 25. Which of the following words best describes Muslim trade?
   a. extensive   c. forbidden
   b. restricted   d. unsuccessful

____ 26. Which of the following results followed the Muslim invasions of India?
   a. Trade between India and the Muslim world decreased.
   b. Many Hindus converted to Buddhism.
   c. Sultans introduced Muslim traditions of government to India.
   d. Hindu princes united against Muslim invaders.

____ 27. A religion that blended Muslim and Hindu beliefs is
   a. Urdu.   c. Sufi.
   b. Buddhism.   d. Sikhism.

____ 28. The Ottoman and Safavid empires shared the Muslim tradition of
   a. the caste system.   c. the Sharia.
   b. nonviolence.   d. religious intolerance.

____ 29. Before Muhammad became the prophet of Islam, he was a
   a. priest.   c. ruler.
   b. merchant.   d. soldier.

____ 30. According to the Five Pillars of Islam, every Muslim must
   a. read the Bible.   c. believe in many gods.
   b. give alms.   d. obey official priests.

____ 31. Avicenna is known for developing
   a. a medical encyclopedia.
   b. a mathematics textbook.
   c. standards for the scientific study of history.
   d. accurate calculations of the Earth's circumference.

____ 32. Which of the following events created a Muslim empire in India?
   a. the fall of the Gupta empire
   b. the establishment of the Delhi sultanate
   c. the invasion by Tamerlane
   d. the conquest by Mahmud

____ 33. Sikhism blended the beliefs of Islam with those of
   a. Christianity.   c. Buddhism.
   b. Judaism.   d. Hinduism.

____ 34. Which of the following rulers strengthened the Mughal empire by promoting religious harmony through tolerance?
   a. Babur
   b. Akbar
   c. Jahangir
   d. Aurangzeb

____ 35. Which of the following statements describes the Ottoman and Safavid empires?
   a. Both were ruled by a caliph.
   b. Both persecuted non-Muslims.
   c. Both preserved peace.
   d. Both based their government on Muslim traditions.

____ 36. Ottoman and Safavid artists were influenced by
   a. Persian styles.
   b. Byzantine styles.
   c. Greek styles.
   d. Hindu styles.

Short Answer

37. List the five basic duties of Muslims, also known as the Five Pillars of Islam.

38. Explain three reasons for the rapid spread of Islam.

39. Describe two ways in which religion influenced Muslim arts.

40. List at least three advances in medicine made by Muslim physicians.

41. Explain why Muslim and Hindu cultures clashed.

42. Explain how Akbar's policies promoted religious harmony in Mughal India.

43. Describe ways in which culture flourished under Suleiman and Abbas.

Read the following excerpts from the Quran. Then answer the questions that follow.

"In the name of the Merciful and Compassionate God. That is the Book! there is no doubt therein; a guide to the pious [religious], who believe in the unseen, and are steadfast in prayer, and of what we have given them expend [spend] in alms [charity]; who believe in what is revealed to thee, and what was revealed before thee, and of the hereafter they are sure. These are in guidance from their Lord, and these are the prosperous. . . .

God, there is no God but He! He will surely assemble you on the resurrection day, there is no doubt therein. . . .

But whoso rebels against God and His Apostle, and transgresses His bounds, He will make him enter into fire, and dwell therein for aye; and for him is shameful woe. . . .

The likeness of those who expend their wealth in God's way is as the likeness of a grain that grows to seven ears, in every ear a hundred grains; for God will double unto whom he pleases; for God both embraces and knows. . . .

Kind speech and pardon are better than almsgiving, followed by annoyance, and God is rich and clement [merciful]. . . .

Then fear God as much as ye can! and hear, and obey, and expend in alms, it is better for yourselves."

44. According to the first verses of the excerpt, what is the purpose of the Quran?

45. What rewards are promised to those who obey the Quran?

46. According to the Quran, what will happen to those who rebel against God and Muhammad?

Essay
On a separate sheet of paper, write an answer to the following questions.

47. **Identifying Central Issues** Why is the Quran important to Muslims?

48. **Making Comparisons** How did Muslim and Hindu beliefs differ?

49. **Making Comparisons** What are the similarities among Islamic, Jewish, and Christian teachings?

50. **Drawing Conclusions** How did the spread of Islam create an international trade network?

51. **Drawing Conclusions** Explain how Islam became both a religion and a way of life.

52. **Making Comparisons** Describe the similarities and differences between Sunni and Shiite Muslims.

CHAPTER 11—THE MUSLIM WORLD (622–1629)
Answer Section

MATCHING

1. ANS: B   DIF: E   REF: 254   OBJ: C11S1-2
   TOP: Religion, Five Pillars of Islam
2. ANS: D   DIF: E   REF: 259   OBJ: C11S2-3
   TOP: Religion, Minaret
3. ANS: A   DIF: E   REF: 263   OBJ: C11S3-2
   TOP: Art and literature, Arabesque
4. ANS: E   DIF: E   REF: 259   OBJ: C11S2-3
   TOP: Political systems, Sultan
5. ANS: C   DIF: E   REF: 273   OBJ: C11S5-2
   TOP: Religion, Millet

6. ANS: C   DIF: E   REF: 252-253   OBJ: C11S1-1
   TOP: Religion, Muhammad
7. ANS: E   DIF: E   REF: 260   OBJ: C11S2-3
   TOP: Impact of the individual, Tamerlane
8. ANS: B   DIF: E   REF: 265   OBJ: C11S3-3
   TOP: Impact of the individual, Al-Khwarizmi
9. ANS: A   DIF: E   REF: 269-271   OBJ: C11S4-3
   TOP: Impact of the individual, Akbar
10. ANS: D   DIF: E   REF: 273   OBJ: C11S5-2
    TOP: Art and literature, Sinan

11. ANS: B   DIF: E   REF: 256   OBJ: C11S2-1
    TOP: Impact of the individual, Abu Bakr
12. ANS: A   DIF: E   REF: 259   OBJ: C11S2-2
    TOP: Impact of the individual, Abu al-Abbas
13. ANS: H   DIF: E   REF: 260   OBJ: C11S2-3
    TOP: Impact of the individual, Tamerlane
14. ANS: E   DIF: E   REF: 263-265   OBJ: C11S3-2
    TOP: Impact of the individual, Omar Khayyam
15. ANS: C   DIF: E   REF: 265   OBJ: C11S3-3
    TOP: Impact of the individual, Al-Khwarizmi
16. ANS: D   DIF: E   REF: 269   OBJ: C11S4-2
    TOP: Religion, Sikhism
17. ANS: G   DIF: E   REF: 272-273   OBJ: C11S5-1
    TOP: Impact of the individual, Suleiman
18. ANS: F   DIF: E   REF: 273   OBJ: C11S5-2
    TOP: Impact of the individual, Sinan

MULTIPLE CHOICE

19. ANS: D   DIF: A   REF: 257-258   OBJ: C11S2-1
    TOP: Religion, Spread of Islam
20. ANS: D   DIF: E   REF: 257-258   OBJ: C11S2-1
    TOP: Religion, Spread of Islam
21. ANS: A   DIF: E   REF: 257-258   OBJ: C11S2-1
    TOP: Religion, Spread of Islam
22. ANS: C   DIF: A   REF: 257-258   OBJ: C11S2-1
    TOP: Religion, Spread of Islam
23. ANS: C   DIF: D   REF: 262   OBJ: C11S1-2
    TOP: Religion, Monotheistic religions
24. ANS: A   DIF: D   REF: 257-258   OBJ: C11S2-2
    TOP: Religion, Sunni and Shiites
25. ANS: A   DIF: A   REF: 262   OBJ: C11S3-1
    TOP: Global interaction, Muslim trade
26. ANS: C   DIF: D   REF: 267-268   OBJ: C11S4-1
    TOP: Global interaction, Muslim invasion of India
27. ANS: D   DIF: A   REF: 269   OBJ: C11S4-1
    TOP: Religion, Sikhism
28. ANS: C   DIF: A   REF: 272-275   OBJ: C11S5-2
    TOP: Culture, Ottomans and Safavids
29. ANS: B   DIF: E   REF: 253   OBJ: C11S1-1
    TOP: Impact of the individual, Muhammad
30. ANS: B   DIF: A   REF: 254   OBJ: C11S1-2
    TOP: Religion, Five Pillars of Islam
31. ANS: A   DIF: A   REF: 266   OBJ: C11S3-3
    TOP: Impact of the individual, Avicenna
32. ANS: B   DIF: A   REF: 267   OBJ: C11S4-1
    TOP: Political systems, Delhi sultanate
33. ANS: D   DIF: A   REF: 257-258   OBJ: C11S4-2
    TOP: Religion, Sikhism
34. ANS: B   DIF: A   REF: 269-271   OBJ: C11S4-3
    TOP: Impact of the individual, Akbar
35. ANS: D   DIF: A   REF: 272-275   OBJ: C11S5-2
    TOP: Culture, Ottomans and Safavids
36. ANS: A   DIF: A   REF: 273   OBJ: C11S5-3
    TOP: Art and literature, Persian influence

SHORT ANSWER

37.   ANS:
The Five Pillars of Islam are: (1) Believe in one God, (2) Pray daily, (3) Give charity to the poor, (4) Fast from sunrise to sunset during the month of Ramadan, and (5) Make a pilgrimage to Mecca.

DIF: A   REF: 254   OBJ: C11S1-2
TOP: Religion, Five Pillars of Islam

38.   ANS:
Arabs were able to spread Islam because the Byzantine and Persian empires were weak, and people in the Fertile Crescent welcomed Arab conquerors. The Arabs had superior fighting methods. Their common faith united them in victory.

DIF: D   REF: 257-258   OBJ: C11S2-1
TOP: Religion, Spread of Islam

39.   ANS:
The Quran banned the worship of idols, so Muslim artists were forbidden to portray God or human figures in religious art. They developed intricate floral patterns and calligraphy to decorate mosques and art objects.

DIF: A   REF: 263   OBJ: C11S3-2
TOP: Art and literature, Influence of Islam

40.   ANS:
Muslim physicians pioneered a study of measles and smallpox, wrote a medical encyclopedia about the diagnosis and treatment of diseases, developed a way to treat cataracts, and mixed bitter medicines into sweet-tasting syrups.

DIF: A   REF: 266   OBJ: C11S3-3
TOP: Science, Muslim advances in medicine

41.   ANS:
Hindus believed in many gods and many sacred texts. They divided people into groups based on caste and honored Brahmans as priests. They included music and dance in religious celebrations. Muslims believed in one God and one sacred text. They taught that all people were equal. They had no priests, and they condemned the practice of celebrating religious events with music and dance.

DIF: D   REF: 268   OBJ: C11S4-2
TOP: Religion, Hindu-Muslim differences

42.   ANS:
Akbar opened government jobs to all Hindus and treated Hindu princes as partners in ruling the empire. He married a Hindu. He ended taxes on non-Muslims. He consulted leaders of many religions.

DIF: A   REF: 269-271   OBJ: C11S4-3
TOP: Impact of the individual, Akbar

43. ANS:
Under Suleiman, Ottoman artists produced detailed miniatures and illuminated manuscripts. The architecture of Sinan rivaled that of the Byzantine empire. Writers adapted Persian and Arab models to produce Turkish works. Abbas welcomed artists, poets, and scholars to the court. Palace workshops produced porcelains, clothes, and rugs.

   DIF: D   REF: 273, 275   OBJ: C11S5-3
   TOP: Culture, Suleiman and Abbas

44. ANS:
The Quran is a guide for believers.

   DIF: D   REF: 254   OBJ: C11S1-2   TOP: Religion, Quran

45. ANS:
God will make them prosperous and assemble them on resurrection day.

   DIF: D   REF: 254   OBJ: C11S1-2   TOP: Religion, Quran

46. ANS:
They will be punished in hell.

   DIF: D   REF: 254   OBJ: C11S1-2   TOP: Religion, Quran

ESSAY

47. ANS:
Muslims believe that the Quran contains the word of God as revealed to Muhammad. They consider it the final authority on all matters and a complete guide to life.

   DIF: D   REF: 254   OBJ: C11S1-3   TOP: Religion, Quran

48. ANS:
Hindus recognized many sacred texts and worshiped many gods. They divided people based on the caste system and honored Brahmans as a priestly group. They also celebrated religious occasions with music and dance. Muslims believed in one God and one sacred text. They taught the equality of all believers. They had no priests and condemned music and dance in religious celebrations.

   DIF: A   REF: 268   OBJ: C11S4-2
   TOP: Religion, Hindu-Muslim differences

49. ANS:
Muslims, Christians, and Jews all believe in one God. Muslims recognize many of the same prophets as Christians and Jews. They accept the idea of heaven and hell.

   DIF: A   REF: 253   OBJ: C11S1-2
   TOP: Religion, Religious teachings

50. ANS:
Muslim merchants built trade as they spread Islam to Africa, China, and India. A common language and religion enabled Muslims to establish a global network.

DIF: D   REF: 262   OBJ: C11S3-1
TOP: Global interaction, Muslim trade

51. ANS:
Muslims consider the Quran a complete guide to life. The Islamic system of law, the Sharia, is based on the Quran. The Sharia does not separate religious matters from criminal or civil law.

DIF: D   REF: 254-255   OBJ: C11S1-3
TOP: Religion, Islam as way of life

52. ANS:
The Sunnis and Shiites split over the issue of choosing a caliph. Sunnis viewed the caliph as a political leader, not a religious authority. Shiites believed that only a descendant of Muhammad could be a caliph. Both Sunnis and Shiites believe in one God. They follow the Quran and make the hajj to Mecca. They differ over matters of religious practices, law, and daily life.

DIF: D   REF: 257-258   OBJ: C11S2-2
TOP: Religion, Sunni and Shiites

CHAPTER 12—KINGDOMS AND TRADING STATES OF AFRICA (750 B.C.–A.D. 1586)

Matching

Match each term with the correct statement below.

a.	Benin	e.	Great Zimbabwe
b.	Ethiopia	f.	Nubia
c.	Gao	g.	Sahara
d.	Ghana	h.	Timbuktu

_____ 1. World's largest desert

_____ 2. Ancient kingdom located along the fertile land of the upper Nile

_____ 3. Kingdom of the Soninke people located between the Niger and Senegal rivers

_____ 4. Center for trade and learning in Mali

_____ 5. Capital of Songhai

_____ 6. Kingdom in the rain forests of the Guinea coast

_____ 7. Christian kingdom in the mountains of East Africa

_____ 8. Capital of inland empire whose name means "great stone buildings"

Match each term with the correct statement below.

a.	desertification	d.	mansa
b.	griot	e.	savanna
c.	lineage		

_____ 9. Grassy plains

_____ 10. Process by which a desert spreads

_____ 11. King of Mali

_____ 12. Group of households who claimed a common ancestor

_____ 13. Professional poet who preserved traditional West African stories

Match each term with the correct statement below.

a.	Augustine	d.	Sonni Ali
b.	Lalibela	e.	Sundiata
c.	Piankhi		

_____ 14. Nubian king who conquered Egypt

_____ 15. Influential Christian thinker of the late Roman empire who was bishop of Hippo

_____ 16. Founder of the Mali empire

_____ 17. Soldier-king who made Songhai the largest kingdom in West Africa

_____ 18. Ethiopian ruler who had churches carved into the mountains

Multiple Choice
Identify the letter of the choice that best completes the statement or answers the question.

_____ 19. The Nubian capital of Meroë was an important producer of

    a.   salt.   c.   gold.

    b.   iron.   d.   silk.

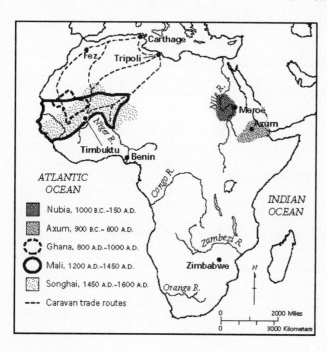

Figure 12-1

_____ 20. According to Figure 12-1, the earliest African kingdoms developed

    a.   in East Africa.   c.   along the Zambezi River.

    b.   in West Africa.   d.   along the northwest coast.

_____ 21. Based on Figure 12-1, which African kingdom controlled the largest area?

    a.   Songhai   c.   Axum

    b.   Ghana   d.   Nubia

_____ 22. Which of the following statements is accurate according to Figure 12-1?

    a.   Caravan trade routes were located in southwest Africa.

    b.   Caravan trade routes connected West African kingdoms with cities in North Africa.

    c.   Caravan trade routes linked North African kingdoms with South African kingdoms.

    d.   Caravan trade routes crossed the Congo River.

____ 23. According to Figure 12-1, which kingdom controlled caravan trade routes in A.D. 900?
    a. Axum
    b. Ghana
    c. Mali
    d. Songhai

____ 24. Which of the following rulers made a hajj that resulted in trading and diplomatic ties between Mali and other Muslim states?
    a. Amina
    b. Sundiata
    c. Mansa Musa
    d. Sonni Ali

____ 25. Axum prospered partly because it had a port on the
    a. Mediterranean Sea.
    b. Indian Ocean.
    c. Atlantic Ocean.
    d. Red Sea.

____ 26. King Ezana of Axum strengthened ties with the Mediterranean world by
    a. converting to Christianity.
    b. making a hajj to Mecca.
    c. observing Jewish holidays.
    d. following traditional religious beliefs.

____ 27. What group of people developed expert knowledge of the natural world by adapting to life in the Kalahari?
    a. Hausa
    b. Khoisan
    c. Almoravids
    d. Phoenicians

____ 28. Which of the following practices represents an adaptation to the environment?
    a. reaching decisions by consensus
    b. believing in a supreme being
    c. creating stylized masks
    d. using slash-and-burn agriculture

____ 29. Which of the following statements describes a patrilineal culture?
    a. The husband joined his wife's family in her village.
    b. Inheritance was traced through the mother's side.
    c. Kinship ties came through the father's side.
    d. Sisters made their sons available to help their brothers.

____ 30. The griots of West Africa preserved
    a. oral traditions.
    b. written records.
    c. woven cloth.
    d. religious statues.

____ 31. Which of the following leaders set up a Muslim dynasty in Songhai?
    a. Mansa Musa
    b. Sundiata
    c. Sonni Ali
    d. Askia Muhammad

____ 32. Which of the following kingdoms had a port on the Red Sea?
    a. Ghana
    b. Mali
    c. Axum
    d. Nubia

____ 33. What religious tradition did the Axumites pass on to the Ethiopians?
    a. Christianity
    b. Islam
    c. Hinduism
    d. Buddhism

_____ 34. Monsoon winds aided trade between East Africa and
   a. West Africa.   c. India.
   b. the Mediterranean.   d. Egypt.

_____ 35. Khoisan people adapted to the Kalahari environment by
   a. practicing slash-and-burn agriculture.
   b. becoming nomadic cattle herders.
   c. gathering roots and hunting small game.
   d. trading surplus fish for grain.

_____ 36. Which of the following terms refers to people who trace their inheritance and descent through the mother's side?
   a. a nuclear family   c. a clan
   b. a joint family   d. a matrilineal culture

Short Answer

37. Explain how desertification influenced migration patterns in Africa.

38. List three early civilizations that influenced North Africa.

39. Explain why gold and salt dominated Sahara trade.

40. Describe the results of Mansa Musa's hajj.

41. Describe the religious traditions that influenced Ethiopia.

42. Compare matrilineal and patrilineal cultures.

43. Describe two ways in which African societies preserved their histories and values.

Read the following excerpt from Sundiata: An Epic of Old Mali, *by Djibril Tamsir Niane. Then answer the questions that follow.*

"Sogolon's son [Sundiata] had a slow and difficult childhood. At the age of three he still crawled along on all-fours while children of the same age were already walking. He had nothing of the great beauty of his father Naré Maghan. He had a head so big that he seemed unable to support it; he also had large eyes which would open wide whenever anyone entered his mother's house. He was taciturn [not talkative] and used to spend the whole day just sitting in the middle of the house. . . .

One day Naré Maghan made Mari Djata [Sundiata] come to him and he spoke to the child as one speaks to an adult. '. . . I am growing old and soon I shall be no more among you, but before death takes me off I am going to give you the present each king gives his successor. In Mali every prince has his own griot. . . . Balla Fasséké here, will be your griot. Be inseparable friends from this day forward. From his mouth you will hear the history of your ancestors, you will learn the art of governing Mali according to the principles which our ancestors have bequeathed [handed down] to us. I have served my term and done my duty too. I have done everything which a king of Mali ought to do. I am handing an enlarged kingdom over to you and I leave you sure allies. May your destiny be accomplished.'"

44. What difficulties did Sundiata have as a child?

45. Why did Naré Maghan give his son a griot?

46. According to Naré Maghan, what was Sundiata's destiny?

Essay
On a separate sheet of paper, write an answer to the following questions.

47. **Synthesizing Information** Did Africa's geographic features aid or hinder migrations of people? Explain.

48. **Making Comparisons** How were religious beliefs in Africa similar to those of other peoples?

49. **Drawing Conclusions** What archaeological evidence suggested that Great Zimbabwe was part of a trade network?

50. **Analyzing Information** How did African art strengthen social bonds within a community?

51. **Recognizing Causes and Effects** How did prosperous trading cities grow up along Africa's east coast?

52. **Drawing Conclusions** Why did the ways of life of African societies differ from place to place?

CHAPTER 12—KINGDOMS AND TRADING STATES OF AFRICA (750 B.C.–A.D. 1586)
Answer Section

MATCHING

1. ANS: G   DIF: E   REF: 280-281   OBJ: C12S1-1
   TOP: Geography, Sahara
2. ANS: F   DIF: E   REF: 281-282   OBJ: C12S1-2
   TOP: Geography, Nubia
3. ANS: D   DIF: E   REF: 285   OBJ: C12S2-2
   TOP: Geography, Ghana
4. ANS: H   DIF: E   REF: 287   OBJ: C12S2-2
   TOP: Culture, Timbuktu
5. ANS: C   DIF: E   REF: 287   OBJ: C12S2-2
   TOP: Geography, Songhai
6. ANS: A   DIF: E   REF: 288   OBJ: C12S2-3
   TOP: Geography, Benin
7. ANS: B   DIF: E   REF: 290   OBJ: C12S3-1
   TOP: Geography, Ethiopia
8. ANS: E   DIF: E   REF: 291-292   OBJ: C12S3-3
   TOP: Geography, Great Zimbabwe

9. ANS: E   DIF: E   REF: 280-281   OBJ: C12S1-1
   TOP: Geography, Savanna
10. ANS: A   DIF: E   REF: 281   OBJ: C12S1-1
    TOP: Geography, Desertification
11. ANS: D   DIF: E   REF: 285   OBJ: C12S2-2
    TOP: Political systems, Mansa
12. ANS: C   DIF: E   REF: 295   OBJ: C12S4-2
    TOP: Social systems, Lineage
13. ANS: B   DIF: E   REF: 296-297   OBJ: C12S4-3
    TOP: Art and literature, Griot

14. ANS: C   DIF: E   REF: 282   OBJ: C12S1-2
    TOP: Impact of the individual, Piankhi
15. ANS: A   DIF: E   REF: 146   OBJ: C12S3-1
    TOP: Religion, Augustine
16. ANS: E   DIF: E   REF: 285   OBJ: C12S2-2
    TOP: Impact of the individual, Sundiata
17. ANS: D   DIF: E   REF: 287   OBJ: C12S2-2
    TOP: Impact of the individual, Sonni Ali
18. ANS: B   DIF: E   REF: 290   OBJ: C12S3-1
    TOP: Impact of the individual, Lalibela

MULTIPLE CHOICE

19. ANS: B   DIF: A   REF: 282   OBJ: C12S1-2
    TOP: Technology, Meroë
20. ANS: A   DIF: A   REF: 289-292   OBJ: C12S1-3
    TOP: Geography, East Africa
21. ANS: A   DIF: E   REF: 287   OBJ: C12S2-2
    TOP: Geography, Songhai
22. ANS: B   DIF: A   REF: 284   OBJ: C12S2-1
    TOP: Geography, Gold-salt trade routes
23. ANS: B   DIF: A   REF: 285   OBJ: C12S2-1
    TOP: Geography, Gold-salt trade routes
24. ANS: C   DIF: A   REF: 286-287   OBJ: C12S2-3
    TOP: Impact of the individual, Mansa Musa
25. ANS: D   DIF: A   REF: 289-290   OBJ: C12S3-1
    TOP: Geography, Axum
26. ANS: A   DIF: D   REF: 290   OBJ: C12S3-2
    TOP: Religion, Axum
27. ANS: B   DIF: D   REF: 293   OBJ: C12S4-1
    TOP: Environment, Khoisan
28. ANS: D   DIF: E   REF: 294   OBJ: C12S4-1
    TOP: Environment, Slash-and-burn agriculture
29. ANS: C   DIF: D   REF: 295   OBJ: C12S4-2
    TOP: Social systems, Patrilineal
30. ANS: A   DIF: E   REF: 296-297   OBJ: C12S4-3
    TOP: Art and literature, Griot
31. ANS: D   DIF: A   REF: 287   OBJ: C12S2-3
    TOP: Impact of the individual, Askia Muhammad
32. ANS: C   DIF: A   REF: 289   OBJ: C12S3-1
    TOP: Geography, Axum
33. ANS: A   DIF: A   REF: 290   OBJ: C12S3-2
    TOP: Religion, Ethiopia
34. ANS: C   DIF: A   REF: 291   OBJ: C12S3-3
    TOP: Geography, Monsoon winds
35. ANS: C   DIF: D   REF: 293   OBJ: C12S4-1
    TOP: Environment, Khoisan
36. ANS: D   DIF: E   REF: 295   OBJ: C12S4-2
    TOP: Social systems, Matrilineal

SHORT ANSWER

37. ANS:
   Changes in the climate caused the Sahara region to dry out, and desertification destroyed cropland and pastureland in North Africa. People migrated to the Mediterranean coast and to savanna and rain forest regions.

   DIF: A   REF: 281   OBJ: C12S1-1
   TOP: Geography, Desertification

38. ANS:
   Egyptian, Roman, and Arabian civilizations influenced North Africa.

   DIF: E   REF: 283   OBJ: C12S1-3
   TOP: Global interaction, North Africa

39. ANS:
   Gold, which was plentiful in West African kingdoms, was sold in North Africa and Europe. From the Sahara, West Africans received salt, which they needed to prevent dehydration—especially in tropical areas. Salt was scarce in savanna regions.

   DIF: A   REF: 284   OBJ: C12S2-1
   TOP: Geography, Gold-salt trade

40. ANS:
   Mansa Musa created trading and diplomatic ties with Muslim states. He brought Muslim scholars to Mali. News of Mali's wealth created European interest in African gold.

   DIF: A   REF: 286-287   OBJ: C12S2-2
   TOP: Impact of the individual, Mansa Musa

41. ANS:
   Ethiopians gained Christian traditions from their Axumite ancestors. They adapted East African religious traditions. They also observed Jewish holidays, based on the traditional belief that they were descendants of King Solomon.

   DIF: A   REF: 290   OBJ: C12S3-2   TOP: Religion, Ethiopia

42. ANS:
   In matrilineal cultures, inheritance and descent are traced through the mother's side. The husband joins his wife's family in her village. In patrilineal cultures, kinship ties are traced through the father's side. A bride moves into her husband's village and becomes part of his family.

   DIF: A   REF: 295   OBJ: C12S4-2
   TOP: Social systems, Family patterns

43. ANS:
Some African societies left written records of their past. Others handed down oral traditions, which preserved histories and folk tales.

DIF: A   REF: 297   OBJ: C12S4-3
TOP: Art and literature, African literary traditions

44. ANS:
Sundiata still crawled at the age of three. He was not handsome or talkative.

DIF: D   REF: 285   OBJ: C12S2-2
TOP: Impact of the individual, Sundiata

45. ANS:
Naré Maghan gave Sundiata a griot to help him learn the history of his ancestors.

DIF: D   REF: 285   OBJ: C12S2-2   TOP: Culture, Sundiata

46. ANS:
Sundiata's destiny was to govern Mali.

DIF: D   REF: 285   OBJ: C12S2-2
TOP: Impact of the individual, Sundiata

ESSAY

47. ANS:
Africa's deserts and rain forests were barriers to movement of people and goods. River travel between the coast and the interior was hindered by rapids and cataracts. However, major rivers and the Great Rift Valley aided travel within the interior.

DIF: A   REF: 281   OBJ: C12S1-1
TOP: Geography, Migration

48. ANS:
Like Hindus, Greeks, or Romans, Africans worshiped many gods. They identified the forces of nature with divine spirits. Like the Chinese, many Africans believed that the spirits of their ancestors were present on Earth.

DIF: D   REF: 295-297   OBJ: C12S4-2
TOP: Religion, African religious beliefs

49. ANS:
Beads from India and porcelain from China were discovered among the ruins of Great Zimbabwe.

DIF: D   REF: 292   OBJ: C12S3-3
TOP: Global interaction, Great Zimbabwe

50. ANS:
Patterns identified the makers and users of the works of art. The patterns might indicate the work of a particular clan or a possession of royalty.

DIF: D   REF: 297   OBJ: C12S4-3
TOP: Art and literature, African artistic traditions

51. ANS:
Arab and Asian immigrants set up trading communities on Africa's east coast. Monsoon winds enabled trading vessels to sail between Africa and India. Trade helped local rulers build strong city-states.

DIF: D   REF: 290-291   OBJ: C12S3-3
TOP: Continuity and change, East African trade cities

52. ANS:
Bantu-speaking peoples migrated across Africa and adapted to the environment of places they settled. They also learned different ways of life through trade with other societies.

DIF: D   REF: 293   OBJ: C12S4-1
TOP: Geography, Bantu migrations

CHAPTER 13—SPREAD OF CIVILIZATIONS IN EAST ASIA (500–650)

Matching

Match each term with the correct statement below.
a. archipelago
b. haiku
c. hangul
d. pagoda
e. shogun

_____ 1. Multistoried temple with eaves that turn up at the corners

_____ 2. Alphabet made up of symbols representing the sounds of spoken Korean

_____ 3. Chain of islands

_____ 4. Supreme military commander in Japan

_____ 5. Three-line poem consisting of 17 syllables

Match each person with the correct statement below.
a. Genghiz Khan
b. Minamoto Yoritomo
c. Murasaki Shikibu
d. Sejong
e. Tang Taizong

_____ 6. Tang ruler who became the most admired of all Chinese emperors

_____ 7. Mongol chieftain who became the world's most successful conqueror

_____ 8. Korean ruler who replaced the Chinese writing system with a Korean alphabet

_____ 9. Heian writer who created *The Tale of Genji*

_____ 10. Japanese military commander who set up the Kamakura shogunate

Match each person with the correct statement below.
a. Kublai Khan
b. Li Bo
c. Sejong
d. Shotoku
e. Tokugawa Ieyasu
f. Wu Zhao
g. Yi Song-gye
h. Zheng He

_____ 11. Tang empress who restored a system of uniform government to China

_____ 12. Tang poet whose works celebrated harmony with nature

_____ 13. Mongol emperor who established the Yuan dynasty

_____ 14. Chinese admiral who explored Southeast Asia and East Africa

_____ 15. Korean general who set up the Choson dynasty

_____ 16. Korean king who replaced the Chinese writing system with hangul

_____ 17. Japanese prince who sent nobles to study in China

_____ 18. Daimyo who founded a shogunate that imposed central government control on all of Japan

Multiple Choice
Identify the letter of the choice that best completes the statement or answers the question.

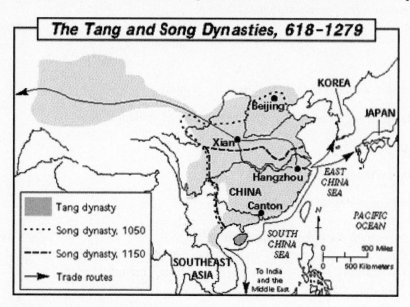

Figure 13-1

_____ 19. Based on Figure 13-1, which city was a center for overland and water trade routes?
   a. Beijing   c. Hangzhou
   b. Xian   d. Canton

_____ 20. Which of the following conclusions is supported by Figure 13-1?
   a. China had no foreign trade during the Tang and Song dynasties.
   b. China carried out foreign trade with Japan and Korea during the period from 618 to 1279.
   c. Water routes provided the only means of trade with China.
   d. China's overland trade routes did not extend to foreign lands.

_____ 21. According to Figure 13-1, overland trade routes extended from
   a. Hangzhou to Central Asia.   c. Korea to Xian.
   b. Beijing to Canton.   d. Canton to India.

_____ 22. Which of the following statements is accurate according to Figure 13-1?
   a. The Song dynasty gained territory between 1050 and 1150.
   b. The Tang empire was larger than that of the Song.
   c. The Song empire included Korea and Japan.
   d. The Tang dynasty ruled all of Southeast Asia.

_____ 23. Mongol rule in China was a time of
   a. peace and order.   c. restricted trade.
   b. violence and oppression.   d. widespread poverty.

_____ 24. Ming rulers promoted trade with Southeast Asia and India through the voyages of
    a.   Marco Polo.   c.   Wu Zhao.
    b.   Genghiz Khan.   d.   Zheng He.

_____ 25. Because of Korea's geography, most people met their need for protein by
    a.   farming.   c.   herding.
    b.   fishing.   d.   trading.

_____ 26. Which of the following cultures had the greatest influence on Korea?
    a.   Chinese   c.   European
    b.   Japanese   d.   African

_____ 27. Which of the following influences did Japan adopt from China?
    a.   Shinto   c.   kana
    b.   civil service   d.   pagoda architecture

_____ 28. Heian women influenced Japanese culture by
    a.   studying the Chinese language.
    b.   producing important works of literature.
    c.   supervising family estates.
    d.   training in the military arts.

_____ 29. Which of the following statements reflects a Confucian value that influenced Tang and Song dynasties?
    a.   Merchants had lower social status than peasants.
    b.   Only the gentry could hold government office.
    c.   Girls were valued more highly than boys.
    d.   Position in government was based on military service.

_____ 30. The Mongol conquest of China resulted in
    a.   increased contact between China and the western world.
    b.   a revival of Chinese arts and literature.
    c.   a lack of political stability.
    d.   persecution of Muslims and Christians.

_____ 31. Korea's landscape consists mainly of
    a.   rain forests.   c.   plains.
    b.   deserts.   d.   mountains.

_____ 32. Which of the following Chinese influences did the Japanese reject?
    a.   law code   c.   civil service system
    b.   tea ceremony   d.   pagoda architecture

_____ 33. The most important works of Japanese literature during the Heian period were produced by
    a.   Buddhist monks.   c.   peasants.
    b.   noblewomen.   d.   Confucian scholars.

_____ 34. Who held the real power in Japan's feudal society?
    a.   the emperor   c.   samurai
    b.   women   d.   the shogun

_____ 35. The Tokugawa shoguns created an orderly society by
    a. ending feudalism.
    b. forbidding trade.
    c. giving peasants greater freedom.
    d. imposing central government control on all Japan.

_____ 36. Which of the following Japanese cultural traditions was a new form of drama influenced by the rise of towns in the 1600s?
    a. tea ceremony   c. kabuki
    b. No plays   d. haiku

Short Answer

37. Describe two themes that influenced painting in Tang and Song China.

38. Explain why foreign influences on Chinese culture increased under Mongol rule.

39. Explain how geography affected Korea's economy and culture.

40. Describe two ways that Korea's culture differed from that of China.

41. List three ways that Japan's government during the 600s and 700s was similar to that of Tang China.

42. List three changes that took place in Japan under Tokugawa rule.

43. Explain how Zen Buddhism influenced Japanese culture.

Read the following excerpt from the writings of Marco Polo. Then answer the questions that follow.

"I shall now speak of how the Emperor Kublai Khan shows great charity and care to the poor in the city of Kanbulu. Whenever he hears of a family who had once lived in comfort but who have been reduced to poverty because of misfortunes, or who are unable to work for a living or raise grain because of illness, then he gives that family all they need for one year. At the customary time, such people present themselves before the officers who manage this department of the Emperor's expenses, and who live in a palace in which that business is taken care of. . . . In a similar way the Emperor provides clothing for his poor, which he can do because all subjects are expected to provide him with one-tenth of all the wool, silk, and hemp they produce. . . .

I should also comment on the order and regularity shown by people of all classes when they present themselves before the Emperor. When they approach within half a mile of the place where he happens to be, they show their respect for his noble character by acting humble, calm, and quiet, so much so that not the least noise or any person's voice can be heard. . . . Men also take with them handsome white leather boots, and just before they enter the reception hall of the court, they put on these white boots, and give the boots in which they had walked to the servants to take care of. This practice is observed so that they will not soil the beautiful carpets, which are unusually made of silk and gold, and exhibit a variety of colors."

44. According to Marco Polo, how did Kublai Khan treat the poor?

45. Describe two ways that people showed respect for the emperor.

46. Based on this excerpt, what conclusions might Europeans have drawn about the relationship between Kublai Khan and the Chinese people?

Essay
On a separate sheet of paper, write an answer to the following questions.

47. **Identifying Main Ideas** Explain how Tang and Song societies reflected Confucian traditions.

48. **Recognizing Causes and Effects** How did the Tokugawa shoguns end feudal warfare in Japan?

49. **Making Comparisons** How was the culture of Korea like that of China?

50. **Drawing Conclusions** How did the geography of Japan both protect and isolate it from foreign influences?

51. **Making Comparisons** Describe the similarities and differences between Tang and Song China.

52. **Analyzing Information** Did feudalism strengthen or weaken Japanese society? Explain.

CHAPTER 13—SPREAD OF CIVILIZATIONS IN EAST ASIA (500–650)
Answer Section

MATCHING

1. ANS: D DIF: E REF: 307 OBJ: C13S1-3
   TOP: Art and literature, Pagoda
2. ANS: C DIF: E REF: 315 OBJ: C13S3-3
   TOP: Culture, Hangul
3. ANS: A DIF: E REF: 316 OBJ: C13S4-1
   TOP: Geography, Archipelago
4. ANS: E DIF: E REF: 320 OBJ: C13S5-1
   TOP: Political systems, Shogun
5. ANS: B DIF: E REF: 325 OBJ: C13S5-3
   TOP: Art and literature, Haiku

6. ANS: E DIF: E REF: 302-303 OBJ: C13S1-1
   TOP: Impact of the individual, Tang Taizong
7. ANS: A DIF: E REF: 308-309 OBJ: C13S2-1
   TOP: Impact of the individual, Genghiz Khan
8. ANS: D DIF: E REF: 315 OBJ: C13S3-3
   TOP: Impact of the individual, Sejong
9. ANS: C DIF: E REF: 319 OBJ: C13S4-3
   TOP: Art and literature, Murasaki Shikibu
10. ANS: B DIF: E REF: 320 OBJ: C13S5-1
   TOP: Impact of the individual, Minamoto Yoritomo

11. ANS: F DIF: E REF: 302 OBJ: C13S1-1
   TOP: Impact of the individual, Wu Zhao
12. ANS: B DIF: E REF: 307 OBJ: C13S1-3
   TOP: Art and literature, Li Bo
13. ANS: A DIF: E REF: 310 OBJ: C13S2-2
   TOP: Impact of the individual, Kublai Khan
14. ANS: H DIF: E REF: 311-312 OBJ: C13S2-4
   TOP: Impact of the individual, Zheng He
15. ANS: G DIF: E REF: 315 OBJ: C13S3-3
   TOP: Impact of the individual, Yi Song-gye
16. ANS: C DIF: E REF: 315 OBJ: C13S3-3
   TOP: Impact of the individual, Sejong
17. ANS: D DIF: E REF: 318 OBJ: C13S4-2
   TOP: Global interaction, Japan looks to China
18. ANS: E DIF: E REF: 322 OBJ: C13S5-2
   TOP: Impact of the individual, Tokugawa Ieyasu

MULTIPLE CHOICE

19. ANS: C DIF: A REF: 304 OBJ: C13S1-1
    TOP: Geography, Hangzhou
20. ANS: B DIF: D REF: 304 OBJ: C13S1-1
    TOP: Global interaction, Chinese foreign trade
21. ANS: A DIF: E REF: 304 OBJ: C13S1-1
    TOP: Global interaction, Chinese foreign trade
22. ANS: B DIF: A REF: 304 OBJ: C13S1-1
    TOP: Geography, Tang and Song empires
23. ANS: A DIF: A REF: 309 OBJ: C13S2-2
    TOP: Political systems, Mongol China
24. ANS: D DIF: A REF: 311-312 OBJ: C13S2-3
    TOP: Global interaction, Zheng He
25. ANS: B DIF: E REF: 313 OBJ: C13S3-1
    TOP: Geography, Korean diet
26. ANS: A DIF: E REF: 313-314 OBJ: C13S3-2
    TOP: Global interaction, China influences Korea
27. ANS: D DIF: A REF: 318 OBJ: C13S4-2
    TOP: Global interaction, Pagoda architecture
28. ANS: B DIF: A REF: 319 OBJ: C13S4-3
    TOP: Culture, Heian women
29. ANS: A DIF: D REF: 304 OBJ: C13S1-2
    TOP: Social systems, Merchants in Confucian society
30. ANS: A DIF: A REF: 310 OBJ: C13S2-2
    TOP: Global interaction, Mongol China
31. ANS: D DIF: E REF: 313 OBJ: C13S3-1
    TOP: Geography, Korean landscape
32. ANS: C DIF: A REF: 318 OBJ: C13S4-2
    TOP: Global interaction, Selective borrowing
33. ANS: B DIF: A REF: 319 OBJ: C13S4-2
    TOP: Art and literature, Heian women
34. ANS: D DIF: E REF: 320 OBJ: C13S5-1
    TOP: Political systems, Shogun
35. ANS: D DIF: D REF: 322 OBJ: C13S5-2
    TOP: Political systems, Tokugawa shoguns
36. ANS: C DIF: A REF: 323-325 OBJ: C13S5-3
    TOP: Art and literature, Kabuki

SHORT ANSWER

37. ANS:
Tang and Song artists tried to achieve balance and harmony in their paintings. Landscape painters sought to capture the spiritual essence of the natural world.

DIF: A   REF: 306-307   OBJ: C13S1-3
TOP: Art and literature, Chinese painting

38. ANS:
Political stability set the stage for economic growth. Trade across Eurasia flourished under the protection of the Mongols. Mongol rulers welcomed foreign visitors to China. They promoted contact with Europe, and they tolerated a variety of beliefs.

DIF: A   REF: 309-310   OBJ: C13S2-2
TOP: Global interaction, Mongol China

39. ANS:
Since much of Korea is mountainous, people depended on the sea for most of the protein in their diet. Korea's location provided cultural and technological links to China and Japan.

DIF: A   REF: 313-314   OBJ: C13S3-1
TOP: Geography, Korean economy and culture

40. ANS:
The Korean language is unrelated to Chinese. Koreans evolved their own ways of life before Chinese influence reached the Korean peninsula.

DIF: A   REF: 313   OBJ: C13S3-3
TOP: Global interaction, Korean culture

41. ANS:
Like Chinese emperors, Japanese rulers claimed absolute power. They strengthened the central government. The Japanese bureaucracy and law code were related to those of Tang China.

DIF: A   REF: 318   OBJ: C13S4-2
TOP: Global interaction, Japanese government

42. ANS:
The Tokugawas imposed central government control on all Japan; they brought order and unity to Japan; and they promoted trade and economic prosperity.

DIF: A   REF: 322-323   OBJ: C13S5-2
TOP: Political systems, Tokugawa shoguns

43. ANS:
Zen Buddhists emphasized devotion to nature and enlightenment through precise performance of everyday tasks. Japanese cultural traditions, such as landscape gardening and the tea ceremony, reflected Zen values.

DIF: A   REF: 323   OBJ: C13S5-3
TOP: Culture, Zen Buddhism

44. ANS:
Kublai Khan provided food and clothing to those in need.

DIF: A   REF: 310   OBJ: C13S2-2
TOP: Social systems, Kublai Khan

45. ANS:
People acted humble, calm, and quiet so that they would not disturb the emperor. Men replaced their street boots with white leather boots when they entered the court so that they would not soil the carpets.

DIF: A   REF: 310   OBJ: C13S2-2
TOP: Social systems, Kublai Khan

46. ANS:
Europeans who read Marco Polo's accounts probably would conclude that Kublai Khan's relationship with the Chinese people was based on mutual respect.

DIF: D   REF: 310   OBJ: C13S2-2
TOP: Social systems, Kublai Khan

ESSAY

47. ANS:
Tang and Song societies used the civil service system to recruit officials trained in Confucian philosophy. They regarded merchants as a low class. In Song times, the custom of footbinding reinforced the subordinate position of women.

DIF: D   REF: 304-306   OBJ: C13S1-2
TOP: Social systems, Confucian society

48. ANS:
The Tokugawas created a strong central government, imposed controls on the daimyo, upheld a strict moral code, and developed a rigid social order.

DIF: D   REF: 322-323   OBJ: C13S5-2
TOP: Political systems, Tokugawa shoguns

49. ANS:
Koreans borrowed Confucian teachings, Buddhism, and styles of art, literature, and architecture from the Chinese. They also modified Chinese ideas and inventions, such as civil service and porcelain making.

DIF: A   REF: 314-315   OBJ: C13S3-2
TOP: Culture, China influences Korea

50. ANS:
The seas that surround Japan isolated it from foreign influences. Japan was too far away for China to conquer, yet it was close enough to learn from China and Korea. The Japanese could choose to accept or reject foreign influences.

DIF: D   REF: 316-317   OBJ: C13S4-1
TOP: Geography, Japan and foreign influences

51. ANS:
    Both the Tang and Song dynasties established a strong central government and a well-ordered society. They encouraged foreign trade and artistic achievements. The Song ruled longer than the Tang, but they controlled less territory and faced the constant threat of invasions.

    DIF: D   REF: 302-304   OBJ: C13S1-1
    TOP: Continuity and change, Tang and Song dynasties

52. ANS:
    During the feudal age, Japanese society was dominated by warrior lords who competed against one another. Lesser warriors pledged loyalty to their overlord. Japan became a war-torn land. Japanese society lacked unity and central authority.

    DIF: D   REF: 320-322   OBJ: C13S5-1
    TOP: Political systems, Feudalism in Japan

CHAPTER 14—THE RENAISSANCE AND REFORMATION (1300–1650)

Matching

Match each term with the correct statement below.

a. annul
b. gravity
c. patron

d. perspective
e. theocracy

_____ 1. Person who provides financial support

_____ 2. Artistic technique that creates a three-dimensional appearance

_____ 3. Government run by church leaders

_____ 4. To cancel

_____ 5. The force that keeps the planets in orbit around the sun

Match each person with the correct statement below.

a. John Calvin
b. Henry VIII
c. Leonardo da Vinci

d. Lorenzo de' Medici
e. Niccolò Machiavell

_____ 6. Wealthy merchant and patron of the arts

_____ 7. Italian painter and inventor

_____ 8. Author of *The Prince*

_____ 9. Religious reformer who believed in predestination

_____ 10. King who established the Church of England

Match each term with the correct statement below.

a. heliocentric
b. humanism
c. indulgence

d. predestination
e. recant

_____ 11. Intellectual movement that focused on worldly subjects rather than on religious issues

_____ 12. A lessening of punishment for sins

_____ 13. To give up one's views

_____ 14. The idea that God determined long ago who would achieve salvation

_____ 15. Centered around the sun

Match each person with the correct statement below.

a. Copernicus   d. Newton
b. Dürer   e. Petrarch
c. Luther

_____ 16. Humanist and author of *Sonnets to Laura*

_____ 17. Painter who brought the Italian Renaissance to Germany

_____ 18. German monk who attacked indulgences

_____ 19. Scholar who believed the sun was at the center of the universe

_____ 20. Scientist who discovered the law of gravity

Multiple Choice

Identify the letter of the choice that best completes the statement or answers the question.

_____ 21. The artists of the Renaissance focused on
     a. humanistic concerns.   c. the universe.
     b. the spiritual world.   d. the Catholic Church.

_____ 22. Why is Albrecht Dürer often compared to Leonardo da Vinci?
     a. He spoke several languages.
     b. He had wide-ranging interests.
     c. He painted many scenes of peasants.
     d. He studied art in Spain.

_____ 23. The development of printing in Europe led to
     a. religious tolerance.
     b. increased competition with China.
     c. increased literacy.
     d. increased corruption in the Roman Catholic Church.

_____ 24. Luther criticized the Roman Catholic Church for
     a. selling indulgences.   c. translating the Bible into German.
     b. preaching forgiveness.   d. believing in the Bible.

_____ 25. Which of the following was a result of the Catholic Reformation?
     a. witch hunts
     b. increased tolerance for religious minorities
     c. the end of the Protestant religion
     d. the spread of Calvinism

_____ 26. Copernicus proposed which of the following?
     a. The sun travels around the Earth.
     b. The Earth travels around the sun.
     c. Gravity keeps the planets in orbit around the sun.
     d. The Earth is the center of the universe.

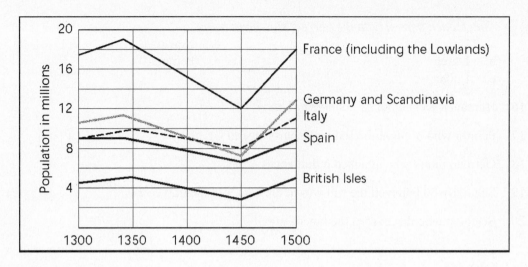

Figure 14-1

_____ 27. Which of the following had a population of about 13 million in the year 1500 according to Figure 14-1?
  a. France and the Lowlands
  b. Germany and Scandinavia
  c. Spain
  d. Italy

_____ 28. According to Figure 14-1, what was the population of the British Isles in 1400?
  a. 5 million
  b. 3 million
  c. 4 million
  d. 15 million

_____ 29. Which country, or group of countries, had a population of 8 million in 1450 according to Figure 14-1?
  a. France and the Lowlands
  b. Italy
  c. Germany and Scandinavia
  d. Spain

_____ 30. What was the population of Italy in 1500 according to Figure 14-1?
  a. 9.5 million
  b. 12 million
  c. 10 million
  d. 11 million

_____ 31. Which of the following contributed to the birth of the Renaissance in Italy?
  a. a new translation of the Bible
  b. a wealthy and powerful merchant class
  c. the development of oil painting
  d. the rise of Protestantism

_____ 32. Which of the following best explains why the Renaissance occurred in northern Europe later than it did in Italy?
  a. There was little interest in the arts in northern Europe.
  b. The Black Death delayed economic growth in northern Europe.
  c. Few people were educated in northern Europe.
  d. Northern Europe was a region of peasants.

____ 33. Which of the following was an effect of the printing revolution in the 1500s?
   a. the spread of new ideas
   b. decreased funding for the arts
   c. increased competition with China
   d. the beginning of compulsory education

____ 34. Luther believed that
   a. good deeds were necessary for salvation.
   b. the Pope was the sole religious authority.
   c. the Bible was a hoax.
   d. salvation could be achieved through faith alone.

____ 35. How did Henry VIII react when the Pope refused to annul his marriage?
   a. He started a war.
   b. He took over the English church.
   c. He started the Reformation.
   d. He imposed fines on the Roman Catholic Church.

____ 36. Which of the following stressed the use of experiments and observation in seeking knowledge?
   a. Bacon
   b. Descartes
   c. Aristotle
   d. Petrarch

Short Answer

37. List three ways the Renaissance differed from the Middle Ages.

38. Choose one writer or artist from the Italian Renaissance and describe how Renaissance ideas influenced his or her work.

39. Identify three of the following and describe how they contributed to the Renaissance in northern Europe: Dürer, Bruegel, Rubens, Sir Thomas More, the van Eycks, Erasmus, Shakespeare, Cervantes, or Rabelais.

40. Explain why the development of printing is described as a "revolution."

41. List three ways the Catholic Church responded to the Protestant Reformation.

42. Explain why the theory of Copernicus was so strongly opposed by the Church and scholars.

43. Compare the scientific method to the traditional way of seeking knowledge. How were they different?

Read the following excerpt from the decrees of the Council of Trent in 1566. Then answer the questions that follow.

"1. If anyone saith, that faith alone is enough for salvation; let him be condemned.
2. If anyone saith, that man is truly absolved; let him be condemned.
3. If anyone saith, that a man is predestined for salvation; let him be condemned.
4. If anyone saith, that nothing besides faith is commanded in the Gospel; that other things are neither commanded nor prohibited; let him be condemned.
5. If anyone saith, that the sacraments are not necessary for salvation and that men obtain salvation through faith alone; let him be condemned."

44. Which of the decrees criticize Luther's ideas?

45. Which of Calvin's ideas were criticized in this excerpt from the Council of Trent?

46. Based on these decrees, what do you think the future held in store for relations between Catholics and Protestants?

Essay
On a separate sheet of paper, write an answer to the following questions.

47. **Recognizing Causes and Effects** Why was economic prosperity a necessary precondition for the Renaissance?

48. **Making Inferences** How did the new scientific method threaten the Catholic Church?

49. **Comparing** Compare the subjects of the paintings of the northern Renaissance with those of the Italian Renaissance. How were they different?

50. **Asking Questions** List three questions you could ask Pope Paul III that would help determine the stand of the Catholic Church on the ideas of Luther and the Protestant Reformation.

51. **Recognizing Causes and Effects** Explain why Henry VIII broke with the Roman Catholic Church and what social and religious changes occurred as a result.

52. **Identifying Main Ideas** What Renaissance ideas are reflected in Descartes's statement "I think, therefore I am"?

CHAPTER 14—THE RENAISSANCE AND REFORMATION (1300–1650)
Answer Section

MATCHING

1. ANS: C   DIF: E   REF: 337   OBJ: C14S1-1
   TOP: Art and literature, Patron

2. ANS: D   DIF: E   REF: 339   OBJ: C14S1-3
   TOP: Art and literature, Perspective

3. ANS: E   DIF: E   REF: 350   OBJ: C14S3-1
   TOP: Political systems, Theocracy

4. ANS: A   DIF: E   REF: 352   OBJ: C14S4-2
   TOP: Religion, Henry VIII

5. ANS: B   DIF: E   REF: 358   OBJ: C14S5-3
   TOP: Science, Gravity

6. ANS: D   DIF: E   REF: 337   OBJ: C14S1-1
   TOP: Impact of the individual, Lorenzo de' Medici

7. ANS: C   DIF: E   REF: 339   OBJ: C14S1-3
   TOP: Impact of the individual, Leonardo da Vinci

8. ANS: E   DIF: E   REF: 341   OBJ: C14S1-3
   TOP: Art and literature, Niccolò Machiavelli

9. ANS: A   DIF: E   REF: 350   OBJ: C14S3-3
   TOP: Religion, John Calvin

10. ANS: B   DIF: E   REF: 352   OBJ: C14S4-2
    TOP: Impact of the individual, Henry VIII

11. ANS: B   DIF: E   REF: 337-338   OBJ: C14S1-2
    TOP: Culture, Humanism

12. ANS: C   DIF: E   REF: 346   OBJ: C14S3-1
    TOP: Religion, Indulgence

13. ANS: E   DIF: E   REF: 347   OBJ: C14S3-2
    TOP: Religion, Martin Luther

14. ANS: D   DIF: E   REF: 350   OBJ: C14S3-3
    TOP: Religion, Predestination

15. ANS: A   DIF: E   REF: 356   OBJ: C14S5-1
    TOP: Science, Heliocentric model of the universe

16. ANS: E   DIF: E   REF: 338   OBJ: C14S1-3
    TOP: Impact of the individual, Petrarch

17. ANS: B   DIF: E   REF: 342   OBJ: C14S2-1
    TOP: Impact of the individual, Dürer

18. ANS: C   DIF: E   REF: 346-347   OBJ: C14S3-2
    TOP: Impact of the individual, Luther

19. ANS: A   DIF: E   REF: 356   OBJ: C14S5-1
    TOP: Impact of the individual, Copernicus

20. ANS: D   DIF: E   REF: 358   OBJ: C14S5-3
    TOP: Impact of the individual, Newton

MULTIPLE CHOICE

21. ANS: A   DIF: D   REF: 338-339   OBJ: C14S1-1
    TOP: Art and literature, Humanist concerns
22. ANS: B   DIF: A   REF: 342   OBJ: C14S2-2
    TOP: Impact of the individual, Albrecht Dürer
23. ANS: C   DIF: A   REF: 345   OBJ: C14S2-3
    TOP: Technology, Printing revolution
24. ANS: A   DIF: A   REF: 347   OBJ: C14S3-2
    TOP: Impact of the individual, Martin Luther
25. ANS: A   DIF: D   REF: 354   OBJ: C14S4-3
    TOP: Religion, Witch hunts
26. ANS: B   DIF: E   REF: 356   OBJ: C14S5-1
    TOP: Science, Heliocentric model of the universe
27. ANS: B   DIF: A   REF: 342   OBJ: C14S1-2
    TOP: Continuity and change, European populations
28. ANS: C   DIF: A   REF: 342   OBJ: C14S1-2
    TOP: Continuity and change, Population of Britain
29. ANS: B   DIF: A   REF: 336-337   OBJ: C14S1-2
    TOP: Continuity and change, Population of Italy
30. ANS: D   DIF: A   REF: 336-337   OBJ: C14S1-2
    TOP: Continuity and change, Population of Italy
31. ANS: B   DIF: A   REF: 336   OBJ: C14S1-2
    TOP: Continuity and change, Birth of Renaissance
32. ANS: B   DIF: E   REF: 342   OBJ: C14S2-1
    TOP: Culture, Northern Renaissance
33. ANS: A   DIF: A   REF: 345   OBJ: C14S2-3
    TOP: Technology, Printing revolution
34. ANS: D   DIF: D   REF: 347-348   OBJ: C14S3-2
    TOP: Religion, Martin Luther
35. ANS: B   DIF: E   REF: 352   OBJ: C14S4-1
    TOP: Impact of the individual, Henry VIII
36. ANS: A   DIF: A   REF: 357-358   OBJ: C14S5-2
    TOP: Science, Scientific method

SHORT ANSWER

37. ANS:
    Answers should include three of the following: It was a period of cultural rebirth; it was a period of great creativity; its thinkers explored the realm of human experience, rather than religious issues; and it was a time when human achievement was emphasized.

    DIF: A   REF: 336-338   OBJ: C14S1-1
    TOP: Continuity and change, Renaissance and Middle Ages

38. ANS:
    Answers should include one of the following: Leonardo da Vinci—great realism from study of nature; Michelangelo —his *David* recalls harmony and grace of classical forms; Raphael—blended Christian and classical styles; Castiglione—focused on the qualities of the ideal human in terms of the classical model of balance; and Machiavelli—focused on individual and on realities of use of power.

    DIF: A   REF: 339-341   OBJ: C14S1-3
    TOP: Art and literature, Influence of Renaissance

39. ANS:
    Answers should include three of the following: Durër—painter who brought Italian Renaissance ideas to Germany; the van Eycks—Flemish painters who developed oil paint and a realistic style of painting that focused on the common person; Bruegel—Flemish painter whose realistic painting of peasant life influenced later artists; Rubens—Flemish painter who created larger-scale paintings; Erasmus—Dutch humanist who translated the Bible into Greek and worked toward Church reform; Sir Thomas More—English humanist who wrote *Utopia* and used his writing to press for social and economic reforms; Rabelais—French humanist and writer who used characters in his novels to offer his own ideas on education and religion; Shakespeare—great English poet and playwright whose plays focus on the powerful forces that affect humanity; and Cervantes—Spanish writer who wrote *Don Quixote.*

    DIF: E   REF: 342-345   OBJ: C14S2-2
    TOP: Impact of the individual, Northern Renaissance

40. ANS:
    The printing revolution brought huge changes. The availability of books increased access to knowledge and exposed people to new ideas. This, in turn, influenced thought and affected movements for change.

    DIF: A   REF: 345   OBJ: C14S2-3
    TOP: Technology, Printing revolution

41. ANS:
    Answers should include three of the following: appointed reformers to key posts within the papacy, established the Council of Trent, stepped up the Inquisition, recognized a new religious order to spread the Catholic faith, and reformed convents and monasteries.

    DIF: A   REF: 353-354   OBJ: C14S4-3
    TOP: Religion, Catholic Reformation

42. ANS:
It challenged the whole system of human knowledge upon which the medieval world was grounded.

DIF: A   REF: 356   OBJ: C14S5-1
TOP: Continuity and change, Heliocentric model of the universe

43. ANS:
The new scientific method relied on observation and experimentation, while the traditional way relied on subjective observations and conclusions inherited from the classical world.

DIF: A   REF: 357-358   OBJ: C14S5-2
TOP: Science, Scientific method

44. ANS:
Luther's emphasis on faith to obtain salvation was criticized in Decree 1. Decrees 4 and 5 also coincide with some of Luther's teachings.

DIF: D   REF: 348, 353   OBJ: C14S3-2
TOP: Religion, Council of Trent

45. ANS:
Calvin's idea of predestination was criticized in Decree 3.

DIF: D   REF: 350, 353   OBJ: C14S3-3
TOP: Religion, Council of Trent

46. ANS:
Based on these decrees, relations between Protestants and Catholics during and after the Reformation would be filled with distrust, animosity, and intolerance.

DIF: A   REF: 353   OBJ: C14S4-3
TOP: Religion, Council of Trent

ESSAY

47. ANS:
It provided the financial resources to support the artists and thinkers.

DIF: A   REF: 336-337   OBJ: C14S2-1
TOP: Economics, Renaissance

48. ANS:
The scientific method, based on objective data, undermined Church teachings, which were rooted in ancient biblical and classical beliefs and based on subjective experiences and observations.

DIF: D   REF: 356   OBJ: C14S5-2
TOP: Religion, Scientific method and the Catholic Church

49. ANS:
    The northern Renaissance focused on realistic depictions of daily life, while the Italian Renaissance emphasized classical and biblical themes.

    DIF: A   REF: 339-340, 342   OBJ: C14S2-3
    TOP: Art and literature, Renaissance paintings

50. ANS:
    Questions will vary, but should show an understanding of Luther's ideas, especially those regarding salvation; his attitude toward the Church and its practices; and the role of the Bible, priests, and the pope in Catholicism, as well as other aspects of the Protestant Reformation.

    DIF: D   REF: 348, 353-354   OBJ: C14S4-3
    TOP: Religion, Catholic Reformation

51. ANS:
    Henry VIII wanted to annul his marriage so that he could marry a different woman, in the hopes that she would bear him a male heir. Angry when the pope refused to grant the annulment, Henry took the English church from the pope's control and created the Church of England. Many loyal Catholics refused to take an oath accepting the new church and were executed for treason. Henry also closed Catholic convents and monasteries and seized their land and wealth, giving them to nobles to win their support. The new church, however, kept most Catholic forms of worship.

    DIF: A   REF: 351-352   OBJ: C14S4-2
    TOP: Religion, English Reformation

52. ANS:
    Students' answers will vary but should point to the relation between Descartes's statement and the Renaissance emphasis on the individual as the source of knowledge.

    DIF: D   REF: 358   OBJ: C14S5-2   TOP: Science, Descartes

CHAPTER 15—THE FIRST GLOBAL AGE: EUROPE AND ASIA (1415–1796)

Matching

Match each term with the correct definition below.
a. astrolabe
b. caravel
c. cartographer
d. circumnavigate
e. sepoy

_____ 1. A mapmaker

_____ 2. A ship with square and triangular sails

_____ 3. A device used to measure the angle of the sun and the stars above the horizon

_____ 4. To sail around the world

_____ 5. An Indian soldier

Match each person with the correct statement below.
a. Afonso de Albuquerque
b. Christopher Columbus
c. Henry the Navigator
d. Ferdinand Magellan
e. Trung Trac

_____ 6. Portuguese ruler who encouraged ocean exploration

_____ 7. Navigator who wanted to reach Asia by sailing west from Europe

_____ 8. Navigator who wanted to find a sea route through the Americas to the Indies

_____ 9. One of two rulers who drove the Chinese out of Vietnam

_____ 10. Military leader who ended Muslim control of Indian Ocean trade

Match each person with the correct statement below.
a. Christopher Columbus
b. a cartographer
c. Qianlong
d. Vasco da Gama
e. a sepoy

_____ 11. "This trip around the tip of Africa to the rich lands of India has made me a wealthy man."

_____ 12. "I'll name this new land I've drawn 'America.'"

_____ 13. "I am sure as the sun sets that I can reach the Indies by sailing west."

_____ 14. "The British East India Company pays my wages."

_____ 15. "Your country's barbarian merchants have benefited from the blessings of our civilization."

Match each place with the correct statement below.

a. China
b. Britain
c. India

d. Philippines
e. Portugal

_____ 16. This country led overseas exploration.

_____ 17. Magellan reached these islands.

_____ 18. This civilization greatly influenced Southeast Asia.

_____ 19. This country dominated trade in India in the late 1700s.

_____ 20. This civilization strictly controlled European trading rights.

Multiple Choice

Identify the letter of the choice that best completes the statement or answers the question.

_____ 21. Which of the following best explained why European rulers encouraged ocean exploration?
   a. They wanted to find new trade routes.
   b. They wanted to conquer new lands.
   c. They wanted to spread Islam.
   d. They wanted to test new navigational tools.

_____ 22. Which of the following statements accurately describes trade in Southeast Asia?
   a. Travel was not influenced by the monsoon winds.
   b. Women were successful merchants and rulers in some ports.
   c. Most of the spices traded were destined for markets in Europe.
   d. Indian traditions did not spread to the region as a result of trade.

_____ 23. The Khmer empire was influenced by
   a. India.
   b. China.
   c. Japan.
   d. England.

_____ 24. How did Portugal gain control of trade in Southeast Asia?
   a. They used military force.
   b. They established ties with local rulers.
   c. They paid money for trading rights.
   d. They agreed to share their navigational know-how with rulers of the region.

_____ 25. In the 1600s, the Portuguese lost control of trade in the Indian Ocean to the
   a. French.
   b. Spanish.
   c. Dutch.
   d. English.

_____ 26. The Ming and Qing dynasties followed which of the following policies regarding foreign trade?
   a. They restricted foreign trade.
   b. They encouraged foreign trade.
   c. They allowed foreign trade in all of China's coastal cities.
   d. They forbade foreign trade entirely.

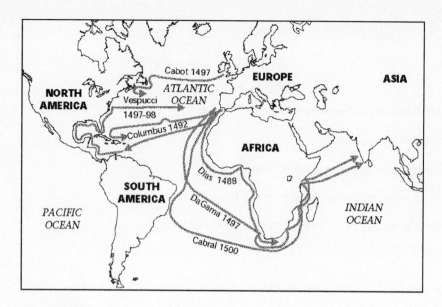

Figure 15-1

_____ 27. According to Figure 15-1, which European power took the lead in sending out voyages of exploration?
   a. France
   b. Portugal
   c. England
   d. the Dutch

_____ 28. According to Figure 15-1, which of the following explorers sailed around Africa to India?
   a. Dias
   b. Da Gama
   c. Columbus
   d. Cabot

_____ 29. Which of the following generalizations is supported by Figure 15-1?
   a. The English were the first to reach North America.
   b. Early explorers were searching for gold and other treasures in Africa.
   c. The Dutch were the last power to take to the oceans for riches.
   d. Portugal and Spain took the lead in sending out voyages of exploration.

_____ 30. According to Figure 15-1, what explorer first crossed the Atlantic?
   a. Da Gama
   b. Columbus
   c. Cabot
   d. Cabral

_____ 31. How did Prince Henry change the course of Portugal's history?
   a. Portugal became a Muslim country.
   b. Portugal led the way in exploration.
   c. Portugal became the first country to circumnavigate the world.
   d. Portugal became a gold-rich country.

_____ 32. Which of the following best describes Southeast Asia?
   a. a region completely dominated by China
   b. a completely isolated region
   c. a region composed of a mainland and scattered islands
   d. a region located between China and Japan

_____ 33. Which of the following controlled Vietnam?
    a. India
    b. Britain
    c. Portugal
    d. China

_____ 34. Who took over control of the spice trade from the Portuguese?
    a. the Dutch
    b. the English
    c. the Spanish
    d. the French

_____ 35. Korea was similar to China in that it
    a. encouraged contacts with outsiders.
    b. discouraged contacts with outsiders.
    c. killed all foreigners in its territory.
    d. was part of a vast trade network.

_____ 36. Which of the following was true of Japan under the Tokugawa shoguns?
    a. It had good trade relations with the Europeans.
    b. It was isolated from the rest of the world.
    c. It was a haven for Christians.
    d. It was the center of a flourishing Pacific trade.

Short Answer

37. List three reasons European nations encouraged overseas exploration.

38. Describe the role of Portugal and the role of Spain in conquering the world's oceans.

39. Explain why early trade patterns in Southeast Asia can be described as "global."

40. List three ways India influenced the development of civilization in Southeast Asia.

41. Compare the methods the Portuguese and the Dutch used to control the spice trade in Asia.

42. Describe China's attitude toward foreigners.

43. Identify three reasons why Japan closed its doors to the outside world.

Read the following excerpt from a writing by historian Trevor Cairns describing early navigation methods. Then answer the questions that follow.

"A piece of wood was thrown from the ship into the sea, with a thin rope attached to it. As the ship sailed on, the wood remained bobbing in the water at about the same place; the rope unwound as the ship sailed by and away from the wood. By leaving the wood, or "log" as English sailors called it, in the water for a minute . . . the seaman would know how far the ship had traveled in that time, and so work out how far it had traveled in an hour. . . . [i]f a knot were tied in the rope every one-sixtieth of a mile, all a sailor had to do was to count the knots as he pulled in the rope, and he would know how many miles per hour his ship was traveling."

44. Based on this excerpt, where did the use of the term *knots* to measure the speed of a ship originate?

45. How did tying knots in the rope make the job of figuring out how far a ship had traveled easier?

46. What do you think was a drawback to this method of calculating distance?

Essay
On a separate sheet of paper, write an answer to the following questions.

47. **Drawing Conclusions** Describe how trade contributed to Southeast Asia's cultural diversity.

48. **Comparing** How has Japan's position in the global trade network changed from the time of Tokugawa rule to the present?

49. **Synthesizing Information** Explain how the phrase "gold, God, and glory" relates to the time of ocean exploration.

50. **Predicting Consequences** What do you think were the consequences of the isolationist policies of East Asia?

51. **Recognizing Causes and Effects** How did trade help the Europeans gain political control of parts of Southeast Asia, including the Philippines, and India?

52. **Linking Past and Present** How are the effects of isolationist policies after the 1500s in East Asia still being felt in the region today?

CHAPTER 15—THE FIRST GLOBAL AGE: EUROPE AND ASIA (1415–1796)
Answer Section

MATCHING

1. ANS: C   DIF: E   REF: 365   OBJ: C15S1-1
   TOP: Technology, Cartographer
2. ANS: B   DIF: E   REF: 365, 367   OBJ: C15S1-2
   TOP: Technology, Caravel
3. ANS: A   DIF: E   REF: 365,367   OBJ: C15S1-1
   TOP: Technology, Astrolabe
4. ANS: D   DIF: E   REF: 368   OBJ: C15S1-3
   TOP: Global interaction, Circumnavigate
5. ANS: E   DIF: E   REF: 376   OBJ: C15S3-3
   TOP: Power and conflict, Sepoy

6. ANS: C   DIF: E   REF: 365   OBJ: C15S1-2
   TOP: Impact of the individual, Henry the Navigator
7. ANS: B   DIF: E   REF: 365-367   OBJ: C15S1-3
   TOP: Impact of the individual, Christopher Columbus
8. ANS: D   DIF: E   REF: 367-368   OBJ: C15S1-3
   TOP: Impact of the individual, Ferdinand Magellan
9. ANS: E   DIF: E   REF: 372   OBJ: C15S2-3
   TOP: Impact of the individual, Trung Trac
10. ANS: A   DIF: E   REF: 373   OBJ: C15S3-1
    TOP: Impact of the individual, Alphonse de Albuquerque

11. ANS: D   DIF: E   REF: 365   OBJ: C15S1-2
    TOP: Impact of the individual, Vasco da Gama
12. ANS: B   DIF: E   REF: 365   OBJ: C15S1-3
    TOP: Technology, Cartographer
13. ANS: A   DIF: E   REF: 365-367   OBJ: C15S1-3
    TOP: Impact of the individual, Christopher Columbus
14. ANS: E   DIF: E   REF: 376   OBJ: C15S3-3
    TOP: Power and conflict, Sepoy
15. ANS: C   DIF: E   REF: 378-379   OBJ: C15S4-1
    TOP: Impact of the individual, Qianlong

16. ANS: E   DIF: E   REF: 365   OBJ: C15S1-2
    TOP: Global interaction, Overseas exploration
17. ANS: D   DIF: E   REF: 367-368   OBJ: C15S3-2
    TOP: Global interaction, Magellan
18. ANS: C   DIF: E   REF: 370-372   OBJ: C15S2-2
    TOP: Global interaction, Southeast Asia
19. ANS: B   DIF: E   REF: 376   OBJ: C15S3-3
    TOP: Global interaction, Trade in India

20. ANS: A   DIF: E   REF: 377   OBJ: C15S4-1
    TOP: Global interaction, China limits trade

MULTIPLE CHOICE

21. ANS: A   DIF: A   REF: 364   OBJ: C15S1-1
    TOP: Global interaction, Quest for trade routes
22. ANS: B   DIF: D   REF: 370   OBJ: C15S2-1
    TOP: Social systems, Women in Southeast Asia
23. ANS: A   DIF: A   REF: 371   OBJ: C15S2-3
    TOP: Global interaction, Khmer empire
24. ANS: A   DIF: A   REF: 373   OBJ: C15S3-1
    TOP: Global interaction, Portuguese in Southeast Asia
25. ANS: C   DIF: A   REF: 374   OBJ: C15S3-2
    TOP: Continuity and change, Dutch in Southeast Asia
26. ANS: A   DIF: E   REF: 377-378   OBJ: C15S4-1
    TOP: Global interaction, China limits trade
27. ANS: B   DIF: A   REF: 365   OBJ: C15S1-3
    TOP: Global interaction, Portugal
28. ANS: B   DIF: E   REF: 365   OBJ: C15S1-3
    TOP: Global interaction, Da Gama
29. ANS: D   DIF: A   REF: 365-366   OBJ: C15S1-3
    TOP: Global interaction, Early voyages of exploration
30. ANS: B   DIF: E   REF: 365-366   OBJ: C15S1-3
    TOP: Global interaction, Columbus
31. ANS: B   DIF: A   REF: 365   OBJ: C15S1-2
    TOP: Impact of the individual, Henry the Navigator
32. ANS: C   DIF: A   REF: 369   OBJ: C15S2-1
    TOP: Geography, Southeast Asia
33. ANS: D   DIF: E   REF: 372   OBJ: C15S2-3
    TOP: Power and conflict, Vietnam
34. ANS: A   DIF: A   REF: 374   OBJ: C15S3-1
    TOP: Continuity and change, Dutch in Southeast Asia
35. ANS: B   DIF: A   REF: 380   OBJ: C15S4-2
    TOP: Global interaction, Korea and isolation
36. ANS: B   DIF: E   REF: 380-381   OBJ: C15S4-3
    TOP: Global interaction, Japan and isolation

SHORT ANSWER

37. ANS:
Reasons include the following: They wanted to find an all-water trade route to Asia that bypassed the Mediterranean; they wanted to fulfill an old desire to crusade against the Muslims and spread Christianity; and they wanted to satisfy their sense of curiosity about other lands and their spirit of adventure.

DIF: A   REF: 364-365   OBJ: C15S1-1
TOP: Global interaction, Motives for overseas exploration

38. ANS:
Portugal was the first to finance ocean exploration. A Portuguese explorer, Da Gama, was the first to find an all-water route to Asia. Another Portuguese explorer, Magellan, was the first to circumnavigate the globe. Spain sponsored Columbus, who crossed the Atlantic and reached the Americas.

DIF: A   REF: 365-366   OBJ: C15S1-3
TOP: Global interaction, Portugal and Spain

39. ANS:
Trade linked East Africa and the Middle East to India, Southeast Asia, and China.

DIF: A   REF: 369-370   OBJ: C15S2-1
TOP: Global interaction, Southeast Asian trade patterns

40. ANS:
India influenced Southeast Asia in the following areas: religion (Hinduism, Buddhism, and Islam all spread to Southeast Asia from India), writing, law, government, art, architecture, and farming.

DIF: A   REF: 370-371   OBJ: C15S2-2
TOP: Global interaction, India and Southeast Asia

41. ANS:
Both the Portuguese and the Dutch used military force to control the spice trade; however, the Dutch forged closer ties with local rulers than the Portuguese did.

DIF: A   REF: 373-374   OBJ: C15S3-1
TOP: Global interaction, Asian spice trade

42. ANS:
China viewed foreigners, including western merchants, as barbarians from inferior cultures.

DIF: A   REF: 377   OBJ: C15S4-1
TOP: Global interaction, China limits trade

43. ANS:
Japan was afraid that foreigners might invade it, it wanted to discourage Christian missionaries, and it wanted to isolate its own Christians, whom it suspected of disloyalty.

DIF: D   REF: 380-381   OBJ: C15S4-3
TOP: Global interaction, Japan and isolation

44. ANS:
It originated in reference to the knots sailors tied in the rope used to measure the distance a ship traveled.

DIF: A   REF: 365   OBJ: C15S1-2
TOP: Technology, Navigation methods

45. ANS:
A sailor had only to count the knots that had unwound into the water over the course of one minute in order to determine how many miles the ship was traveling in one hour. This was easier than measuring how far the ship had traveled in one minute and then multiplying to determine the number of miles per hour.

DIF: A   REF: 365   OBJ: C15S1-2
TOP: Technology, Navigation methods

46. ANS:
This method of determining the speed of a ship depended on the log's remaining in one place. If there were currents, the logs would move and this would throw the calculations off.

DIF: D   REF: 365   OBJ: C15S1-2
TOP: Technology, Navigation methods

ESSAY

47. ANS:
Indian traders brought new religions and ideas in government, law, and the arts, which were widely adopted in the region. Frequently, such as in the instance of the kingdom of Pagan and the Khmer empire, Indian influences blended with other traditions to create distinct cultures.

DIF: A   REF: 370-372   OBJ: C15S2-2
TOP: Diversity, Southeast Asian trade

48. ANS:
Japan was isolated and at the fringes of global trade patterns during Tokugawa rule. Today, it is one of the centers of world trade.

DIF: D   REF: 381   OBJ: C15S4-3
TOP: Continuity and change, Japan and global trade

49. ANS:
Countries encouraged exploration out of a competitive sense of wanting to be the "first," because they wanted riches, and because they hoped to spread Christianity.

DIF: A   REF: 364-365   OBJ: C15S1-1
TOP: Global interaction, Motives for overseas exploration

50. ANS:
Answers will vary but should point to the link between isolationist policies and the relatively isolated positions of China and North Korea in global trade today.

DIF: A   REF: 377-380   OBJ: C15S4-3
TOP: Continuity and change, Isolationism

51. ANS:
It allowed them to establish contact and a military presence in the area. As a result, they could easily take over from weak local rulers when the opportunity arose.

DIF: A   REF: 374-375   OBJ: C15S3-3
TOP: Global interaction, Europeans in Southeast Asia

52. ANS:
Answers will vary but should hint at the fact that isolationist policies hindered economic development in China and Korea and contributed to the relative isolation that still characterizes those regions today.

DIF: D   REF: 377-380   OBJ: C15S4-3
TOP: Continuity and change, Isolationism

CHAPTER 16—THE FIRST GLOBAL AGE: EUROPE, THE AMERICAS, AND AFRICA (1492–1750)

Matching

Match each term with the correct statement below.
a. Boer
b. capitalism
c. conquistador
d. creole
e. encomienda
f. Pilgrim
g. tariff
h. viceroy

_____ 1. Spanish conqueror

_____ 2. Representative who ruled a Spanish province in the king's name

_____ 3. The right to demand labor or tribute from Native Americans in a particular area

_____ 4. American-born descendant of Spanish settlers

_____ 5. English Protestant who rejected practices of the Church of England

_____ 6. Dutch farmer in southern Africa

_____ 7. Investment of money to make a profit

_____ 8. Tax on imported goods

Match each term with the correct statement below.
a. mestizo
b. Middle Passage
c. inflation
d. plantation
e. viceroy

_____ 9. Person appointed to rule a Spanish province in the king's name

_____ 10. Large estate run by an owner or overseer

_____ 11. Person of mixed Spanish and Native American descent

_____ 12. Part of a trade network that sent enslaved people from Africa to the Americas

_____ 13. Economic cycle that involves a rise in prices linked to a sharp increase in available money

Match each person with the correct statement below.
a. Bartolomé de Las Casas
b. Samuel de Champlain
c. Moctezuma
d. Shaka
e. Usman dan Fodio

_____ 14. Aztec emperor

_____ 15. Spanish priest who worked to end abuses against Native Americans

_____ 16. Founder of Quebec

_____ 17. Fulani scholar who set up an Islamic state in West Africa

_____ 18. Zulu leader who waged war against nearby peoples in southern Africa

Multiple Choice
Identify the letter of the choice that best completes the statement or answers the question.

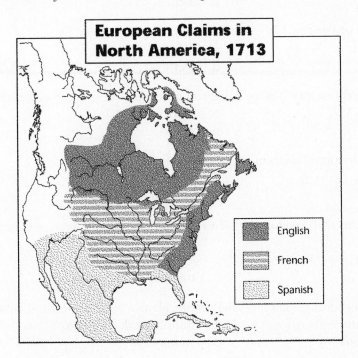

Figure 16-1

_____ 19. Which of the following statements is accurate according to Figure 16-1?
   a. In 1713, English claims included most of North America.
   b. In 1713, French claims included most of the major rivers in North America.
   c. In 1713, Spanish claims included northern lands in North America.
   d. Most lands in North America were unclaimed in 1713.

_____ 20. According to Figure 16-1, the land along the east coast of North America was
   a. claimed by Spain.   c. claimed by England.
   b. claimed by France.   d. unclaimed.

_____ 21. Which of the following statements is accurate according to Figure 16-1?
   a. In 1713, England's claims in North America were separated by those of France.
   b. In 1713, Spain claimed most of North America's major rivers.
   c. In 1713, lands along North America's eastern coast were unclaimed.
   d. In 1713, France claimed the lands along the northwest coast of North America.

_____ 22. According to Figure 16-1, lands in the central region of North America were
   a. claimed by England.   c. claimed by Spain.
   b. claimed by France.   d. unclaimed.

_____ 23. Spanish explorers traveled to the Americas to find
    a. slave labor.   c. horses.
    b. gold.   d. furs.

_____ 24. Which of the following places was influenced by Portuguese culture?
    a. Mexico   c. Cuba
    b. Brazil   d. Peru

_____ 25. As a result of the Treaty of Paris of 1763, North America was dominated by
    a. France.   c. Britain.
    b. Spain.   d. Portugal.

_____ 26. Which of the following represents a Native American influence on European colonists?
    a. horses   c. Christianity
    b. corn   d. disease

_____ 27. By the 1500s, the most important element of African trade with Europeans was
    a. ivory.   c. hides.
    b. gold.   d. enslaved Africans.

_____ 28. Many of the new kingdoms that developed in West Africa in the early modern age were influenced by
    a. Islamic reforms.   c. Calvinist reforms.
    b. Catholic reforms.   d. traditional African beliefs.

_____ 29. Who began a vast global exchange that included people, plants, technologies, and cultures?
    a. Samuel de Champlain   c. Bartolomé de las Casas
    b. Christopher Columbus   d. Hernan Cortés

_____ 30. Which of the following statements accurately describes the economic policy of mercantilism?
    a. It downplayed the role of government in stimulating economic growth.
    b. It discouraged the establishment of overseas colonies.
    c. It encouraged trade by abolishing laws that regulated trade.
    d. It was based on a belief that a nation's real wealth was measured in its gold and silver treasure.

_____ 31. Which of the following resulted from encounters between the Spanish and Native Americans?
    a. Spanish treasures flowed into the Americas.
    b. The Native American population declined.
    c. Native Americans defeated Spanish conquerors.
    d. Spanish explorers treated Native Americans with respect.

_____ 32. The culture that developed in Brazil blended Native American and African influences with those of
    a. Spain.   c. England.
    b. France.   d. Portugal.

____ 33. The Treaty of Paris of 1763 resulted in
   a. French control of eastern North America.
   b. Spanish control of Canada.
   c. British control of eastern North America.
   d. Portuguese control of Peru.

____ 34. Which of the following did Europeans learn from Native Americans?
   a. Christian traditions
   b. use of horses
   c. hunting and trapping of forest animals
   d. use of metal helmets and armor

____ 35. European traders sent Africans to the Americas to
   a. start new colonies.   c. spread Islam.
   b. trade with Native Americans. d. work as slaves on plantations.

____ 36. Which of the following statements describes Europe's middle class during the 1500s and 1600s?
   a. They enjoyed a comfortable life.
   b. They had to sell off their land.
   c. They lived in poverty.
   d. They raised new crops from the Americas.

Short Answer

37. Explain three reasons why the Spanish were able to conquer the Aztec and Incan empires.

38. Explain two ways that Spain supplied workers to make the sugar plantations profitable.

39. Describe how the Treaty of Paris of 1763 affected British and French claims in the Americas.

40. List two ways that the Atlantic slave trade affected Africa.

41. Identify two groups that battled for power in southern Africa.

42. Explain how the voyages of Columbus led to a global exchange.

43. Describe three ways that European powers strengthened their economies in the 1500s and 1600s.

Read the following excerpt from an account by a British doctor named Falconbridge who traveled on a slave ship across the Atlantic. Then answer the questions that follow.

"The men negroes on being brought aboard are immediately fastened two by two by handcuffs on their wrists and by irons on their legs. They are frequently stowed [packed] so close as to admit of no other posture than lying on their sides. . . . Neither will the height between decks . . . permit them . . . an erect posture. . . .

The negroes are far more violently affected by seasickness than Europeans. It frequently ends in death, especially among the women. The exclusion [lack] of fresh air is amongst the most unbearable of their sufferings. Many ships have ventilators [openings], but whenever the sea is rough and the rain heavy, it becomes necessary to shut these and every other means by which air is admitted. The fresh air being thus excluded, the negroes' rooms very soon become unbearably hot. The confined air being breathed repeatedly and the foul smells soon produce sickness and fevers which result in the death of a great number of the slaves. . . .

The slaves were so crowded that they had to lie one upon another. This causes such a death rate among them that, without meeting very stormy weather or having a longer voyage than usual, nearly half of them died before the ship arrived at the West Indies."

44. According to this account, why was it necessary for slaves to lie on their sides in the ship?

45. Why did Dr. Falconbridge consider a lack of fresh air among the most unbearable sufferings of the slaves?

46. According to Dr. Falconbridge, what was the usual death rate on a slave ship?

Essay
On a separate sheet of paper, write an answer to the following questions.

47. **Recognizing Causes and Effects** What were the results of the first Spanish encounters with Native Americans?

48. **Drawing Conclusions** What was the impact of the Atlantic slave trade on Africa?

49. **Analyzing Information** What role did the Catholic Church play in governing Spain's American empire?

50. **Drawing Conclusions** How did Columbus begin a global exchange?

51. **Drawing Conclusions** How did cultural blending affect ways of life throughout the Americas?

52. **Making Comparisons** How did government in the English colonies differ from that in French or Spanish colonies?

CHAPTER 16—THE FIRST GLOBAL AGE: EUROPE, THE AMERICAS, AND AFRICA (1492–1750)
Answer Section

MATCHING

1. ANS: C   DIF: E   REF: 386   OBJ: C16S1-2
   TOP: Global interaction, Conquistador
2. ANS: H   DIF: E   REF: 389   OBJ: C16S2-1
   TOP: Political systems, Viceroy
3. ANS: E   DIF: E   REF: 390   OBJ: C16S2-1
   TOP: Economics, Encomienda
4. ANS: D   DIF: E   REF: 390-391   OBJ: C16S2-2
   TOP: Social systems, Creole
5. ANS: F   DIF: E   REF: 395   OBJ: C16S3-2
   TOP: Religion, Pilgrim
6. ANS: A   DIF: E   REF: 402   OBJ: C16S4-3
   TOP: Global interaction, Boer
7. ANS: B   DIF: E   REF: 404   OBJ: C16S5-1
   TOP: Economics, Capitalism
8. ANS: G   DIF: E   REF: 406   OBJ: C16S5-1
   TOP: Economics, Tariff

9. ANS: E   DIF: E   REF: 389   OBJ: C16S2-1
   TOP: Political systems, Viceroy
10. ANS: D   DIF: E   REF: 390   OBJ: C16S2-1
    TOP: Economics, Plantation
11. ANS: A   DIF: E   REF: 391   OBJ: C16S2-2
    TOP: Social systems, Mestizo
12. ANS: B   DIF: E   REF: 399-400   OBJ: C16S4-1
    TOP: Global interaction, Middle Passage
13. ANS: C   DIF: E   REF: 404   OBJ: C16S5-1
    TOP: Economics, Inflation

14. ANS: C   DIF: E   REF: 387   OBJ: C16S1-2
    TOP: Impact of the individual, Moctezuma
15. ANS: A   DIF: E   REF: 390   OBJ: C16S2-2
    TOP: Impact of the individual, Bartolomé de las Casas
16. ANS: B   DIF: E   REF: 394   OBJ: C16S3-1
    TOP: Impact of the individual, Samuel de Champlain
17. ANS: E   DIF: E   REF: 401   OBJ: C16S4-2
    TOP: Impact of the individual, Usman dan Fodio
18. ANS: D   DIF: E   REF: 402   OBJ: C16S4-3
    TOP: Impact of the individual, Shaka

MULTIPLE CHOICE

19. ANS: B   DIF: A   REF: 394, 396   OBJ: C16S3-1
    TOP: Geography, New France

20. ANS: C   DIF: E   REF: 395-396   OBJ: C16S3-2
    TOP: Geography, English colonies

21. ANS: A   DIF: A   REF: 396   OBJ: C16S3-1
    TOP: Geography, British-French rivalries

22. ANS: B   DIF: E   REF: 394, 396   OBJ: C16S3-2
    TOP: Geography, New France

23. ANS: B   DIF: E   REF: 386   OBJ: C16S1-1
    TOP: Global interaction, Spanish explorers

24. ANS: B   DIF: A   REF: 393   OBJ: C16S2-3
    TOP: Global interaction, Brazil

25. ANS: C   DIF: A   REF: 396   OBJ: C16S3-3
    TOP: Continuity and change, Treaty of Paris of 1763

26. ANS: B   DIF: A   REF: 397   OBJ: C16S3-3
    TOP: Diversity, Native American legacy

27. ANS: D   DIF: A   REF: 398   OBJ: C16S4-1
    TOP: Global interaction, African slave trade

28. ANS: A   DIF: A   REF: 401-402   OBJ: C16S4-3
    TOP: Continuity and change, West Africa

29. ANS: B   DIF: A   REF: 403-404   OBJ: C16S5-1
    TOP: Impact of the individual, Christopher Columbus

30. ANS: D   DIF: D   REF: 406   OBJ: C16S5-1
    TOP: Economics, Mercantilism

31. ANS: B   DIF: A   REF: 388   OBJ: C16S1-3
    TOP: Global interaction, Native Americans

32. ANS: D   DIF: A   REF: 393   OBJ: C16S2-3
    TOP: Diversity, Culture of Brazil

33. ANS: C   DIF: A   REF: 396   OBJ: C16S3-3
    TOP: Continuity and change, Treaty of Paris of 1763

34. ANS: C   DIF: A   REF: 397   OBJ: C16S3-3
    TOP: Diversity, Native American legacy

35. ANS: D   DIF: A   REF: 399   OBJ: C16S4-1
    TOP: Global interaction, African slave trade

36. ANS: A   DIF: D   REF: 406   OBJ: C16S5-1
    TOP: Social systems, Middle class

SHORT ANSWER

37. ANS:
The Spaniards had horses and superior weapons. They were aided by enemies of the Aztecs and Incas. The Indians were weakened and demoralized by disease.

DIF: A   REF: 388   OBJ: C16S1-2
TOP: Global interaction, Conquest of the Americas

38. ANS:
Under the encomienda system, conquistadors enslaved Native Americans to work on plantations. Spanish settlers imported African slaves to work as field hands.

DIF: A   REF: 390   OBJ: C16S2-2
TOP: Economics, Sugar plantations

39. ANS:
By the terms of the Treaty of Paris, France ceded Canada and its lands east of the Mississippi River to Britain. Britain returned France's sugar-producing islands in the Caribbean.

DIF: A   REF: 396   OBJ: C16S3-3
TOP: Continuity and change, Treaty of Paris of 1763

40. ANS:
Many Africans died as a result of brutal conditions on slave ships. The populations of West African states were depleted. New states, whose way of life depended on slave trade, rose in West Africa.

DIF: A   REF: 400   OBJ: C16S4-2
TOP: Global interaction, African slave trade

41. ANS:
Dutch farmers, called Boers, battled the Zulus, a powerful African group, for control of southern Africa.

DIF: A   REF: 402   OBJ: C16S4-3
TOP: Power and conflict, Southern Africa

42. ANS:
When Columbus returned to Spain in 1493, he brought plants, animals, and people from the Americas. When he returned to the Americas, he took European settlers, plants, and animals. This exchange led to a global movement of people, ideas, and technologies.

DIF: A   REF: 403-404   OBJ: C16S5-1
TOP: Global interaction, Columbian Exchange

43. ANS:
European powers adopted the policy of mercantilism by which colonies existed for the benefit of the parent country. Europeans regulated trade with their colonies, sold monopolies to industries or trading companies, and imposed tariffs to protect their industries from competition.

DIF: A   REF: 406   OBJ: C16S5-1
TOP: Economics, Mercantilism

44. ANS:
The slaves were packed close together between decks. There was not enough space for them to sit or stand.

DIF: A   REF: 399-400   OBJ: C16S4-1
TOP: Social systems, African slave trade

45. ANS:
Rooms became unbearably hot. Foul air produced sickness and fever, which resulted in the deaths of many slaves.

DIF: A   REF: 399-400   OBJ: C16S4-1
TOP: Social systems, African slave trade

46. ANS:
Nearly half of the enslaved people died.

DIF: A   REF: 399-400   OBJ: C16S4-1
TOP: Social systems, African slave trade

ESSAY

47. ANS:
The Spanish seized Native American resources, enslaved the people, forced them to convert to Christianity, and introduced diseases that wiped out Native American populations.

DIF: D   REF: 389-390   OBJ: C16S1-3
TOP: Global interaction, Spanish and Native Americans

48. ANS:
As a result of the slave trade, West Africa lost much of its population. Some African societies and small states disappeared. New states, whose way of life depended upon the slave trade, rose in West Africa during the 1600s and 1700s.

DIF: D   REF: 400   OBJ: C16S4-2
TOP: Continuity and change, African slave trade

49. ANS:
    Church leaders served as royal officials and helped regulate activities of Spanish settlers in the Americas. Missionaries worked to emphasize loyalty to the king of Spain and to introduce Spanish culture to Native Americans.

    DIF: D   REF: 389-390   OBJ: C16S2-1
    TOP: Political systems, Catholic Church

50. ANS:
    Columbus brought people, plants, and animals from the Americas to Europe. He also took European settlers, plants, and animals to the Americas. This exchange sparked a vast movement of people, ideas, and technologies.

    DIF: D   REF: 403-404   OBJ: C16S5-1
    TOP: Global interaction, Columbian Exchange

51. ANS:
    European settlers learned Native American styles of building. They adopted canoes and Native American foods. They taught their religion to Native Americans and introduced horses to the Americas. Africans contributed their farming methods, cooking styles, crops, and music. Africans combined Christian beliefs with their own to create new religions.

    DIF: D   REF: 391   OBJ: C16S2-3
    TOP: Diversity, Cultural blending

52. ANS:
    Compared with French and Spanish colonists, English settlers had a large degree of self-government. Each colony elected a representative assembly that advised the royal governor and made decisions on local matters.

    DIF: D   REF: 395-396   OBJ: C16S3-2
    TOP: Political systems, Colonial governments

CHAPTER 17—THE AGE OF ABSOLUTISM (1550–1800)

Matching

Match each term with the correct statement below.
a. absolute monarch
b. balance of power
c. divine right
d. habeas corpus
e. limited monarchy

_____ 1. A ruler who has complete authority over government and the lives of the people

_____ 2. The belief that authority to rule comes directly from God

_____ 3. A distribution of military and economic power that prevents any one nation from dominating

_____ 4. Principle stating that a person cannot be held in prison without being charged with a crime

_____ 5. Government in which a constitution or legislative body limits the monarch's power

Match each person with the correct statement below.
a. Catherine the Great
b. Miguel de Cervantes
c. James I
d. Maria Theresa
e. Richelieu

_____ 6. Author of *Don Quixote*

_____ 7. French cardinal who strengthened the central government by destroying the power of the nobles

_____ 8. First Stuart king of England

_____ 9. First woman to rule the Hapsburg lands

_____ 10. Empress of Russia who began state-supported education for boys and girls

Match each person with the correct statement below.
a. Catherine the Great
b. Oliver Cromwell
c. Elizabeth I
d. Frederick the Great
e. Louis XIV
f. Molière
g. Peter the Great
h. Philip II

_____ 11. King of Spain who advanced Catholic power throughout the world

_____ 12. Queen of England who encouraged sea captains to plunder Spanish treasure ships

_____ 13. French king who built a palace at Versailles

_____ 14. French actor-playwright who produced comedies that made fun of French society

_____ 15. Leader of the Roundheads in the English Civil War

_____ 16. King of Prussia who used the army to strengthen the nation's power

_____ 17. Ruler of Russia who carried out social and economic reforms to modernize the country

____ 18. Ruler of Russia who seized territory from Poland

Multiple Choice
Identify the letter of the choice that best completes the statement or answers the question.

____ 19. Which of the following people is best known for his portraits of Spanish nobles during Spain's golden century?

    a. Richelieu   c. Miguel de Cervantes

    b. El Greco   d. Lope de Vega

____ 20. By the Edict of Nantes in 1598, Henry IV of France granted religious toleration to

    a. Catholics.   c. Jews.

    b. Muslims.   d. Huguenots.

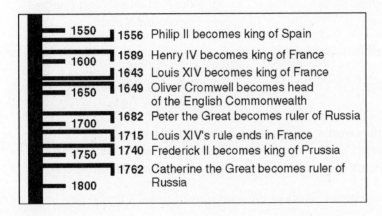

Figure 17-1

____ 21. Based on Figure 17-1, which of the following events happened first?

    a. Louis XIV became king of France.

    b. Frederick II became king of Prussia.

    c. Oliver Cromwell became head of England.

    d. Peter the Great became ruler of Russia.

____ 22. According to Figure 17-1, which of the following people ruled during the same time as Louis XIV?

    a. Henry IV   c. Frederick II

    b. Peter the Great   d. Catherine the Great

____ 23. According to Figure 17-1, which of the following events happened first?

    a. Catherine the Great became ruler of Russia.

    b. Oliver Cromwell became head of the English Commonwealth.

    c. Peter the Great became ruler of Russia.

    d. Louis XIV became king of France.

_____ 24. According to Figure 17-1, Oliver Cromwell became head of England during the same time that
   a. Louis XIV ruled France.
   b. Philip II ruled Spain.
   c. Frederick II ruled Prussia.
   d. Catherine the Great ruled Russia.

_____ 25. Which of the following resulted from the Thirty Years' War?
   a. German states were united.
   b. The Hapsburgs gained power.
   c. France lost territory to Spain and Germany.
   d. The Netherlands and Switzerland became independent states.

_____ 26. During the 1700s, which of the following countries battled for control of the German states?
   a. Prussia and Austria
   b. Britain and France
   c. the Netherlands and England
   d. Spain and Russia

_____ 27. Peter the Great forced Russians to accept social reforms that would make their culture more like that of
   a. Native Americans.
   b. Chinese.
   c. Western Europeans.
   d. Ottoman Turks.

_____ 28. As a result of Peter the Great's war against Sweden, Russia gained
   a. a warm-water port.
   b. land along the Black Sea.
   c. the Bering Strait.
   d. land along the Baltic Sea.

_____ 29. Which of the following people mocked the traditions of Spain's feudal past in his novel *Don Quixote*?
   a. El Greco
   b. Diego Velázquez
   c. Lope de Vega
   d. Miguel de Cervantes

_____ 30. In the late 1500s, France was torn apart by religious wars between Catholics and
   a. Muslims.
   b. Jews.
   c. Huguenots.
   d. Calvinists.

_____ 31. French styles of art, culture, manners, and customs became the standard for European taste as a result of the reign of
   a. Henry IV.
   b. Louis XIII.
   c. Louis XIV.
   d. Louis XV.

_____ 32. The Stuart kings' claims to absolute power were challenged by
   a. the Tudors.
   b. Parliament.
   c. the Cavaliers.
   d. the Church of England.

_____ 33. Which of the following was divided into many small states as a result of the Thirty Years' War?
   a. France
   b. Spain
   c. Germany
   d. the Netherlands

____ 34. Why did Prussia battle Austria during the 1700s?
    a.   to compete for overseas empires   c.   to end the aggression of Louis XIV
    b.   to gain control of German states   d.   to honor an alliance with the Dutch

____ 35. Peter the Great fought the Ottoman Turks for the purpose of
    a.   building St. Petersburg.
    b.   defining their common border with Qing China.
    c.   winning lands along the Baltic Sea.
    d.   gaining a warm-water port on the Black Sea.

____ 36. Which of the following statements describes what happened to Poland in 1795 as a result of actions by Russia, Austria, and Prussia?
    a.   Poland became a strong European power.
    b.   Poland disappeared from the map of Europe.
    c.   Poland seized territory from Russia.
    d.   Poland formed an alliance with Austria.

Short Answer

37. Explain three ways that Philip II strengthened the power of the monarchy in Spain.

38. Explain three reasons why Spanish power declined in the 1600s.

39. Describe three ways that Henry IV laid the foundation for absolutism in France.

40. List the successes and failures of Louis XIV.

41. What were four results of the Thirty Years' War?

42. Describe how the balance of power affected Europe in the late 1700s.

43. Explain why Poland vanished from the map of Europe in the late 1700s.

Read the following description of Versailles written by Duc de Saint-Simon. Then answer the questions that follow.

"As for the King [Louis XIV] himself, nobody ever approached his magnificence. His buildings, who could number them? At the same time, who was there who did not deplore [dislike] the pride . . . the bad taste seen in them? He built nothing useful or ornamental [decorative] in Paris, except the Pont Royal, and that simply by necessity; so that . . . Paris is inferior to many cities in Europe. St. Germains, a lovely spot, with a marvellous view, rich forest, terraces, gardens, and water he abandoned for Versailles; the dullest and most ungrateful of all places, without prospect, without wood, without water, without soil; for the ground is all shifting sand or swamp, the air accordingly bad.

. . . He built at Versailles, on, on, without any general design, the beautiful and the ugly . . . all jumbled together. His own apartments and those of the Queen are inconvenient to the last degree, dull, close, stinking. The gardens astonish by their magnificence, but cause regret by their bad taste. . . . The abundance of water, forced up and gathered together from all parts, is rendered green, thick, muddy; it disseminates [gives off] humidity, unhealthy and evident; and an odor still more so. . .
.

But the supply of water for the fountains was . . . [always inadequate] in spite of those seas of reservoirs which had cost so many millions to establish and to form upon the shifting sand and marsh. Who could have believed it? This defect became the ruin of the infantry which was turned out to do the work."

44. How does Saint-Simon describe the location that Louis XIV chose for his palace?

45. Why, according to Saint-Simon, were the gardens at Versailles in bad taste?

46. Based on this excerpt, what was Saint-Simon's opinion of Louis XIV?

Essay
On a separate sheet of paper, write an answer to the following questions.

47. **Recognizing Causes and Effects** Why did Poland disappear from the map of Europe in the late 1700s?

48. **Recognizing Causes and Effects** What economic problems caused the decline of Spanish power in the 1600s?

49. **Drawing Conclusions** How did the Glorious Revolution provide England with the beginnings of a limited monarchy?

50. **Recognizing Causes and Effects** What political and social changes resulted from the English Civil War?

51. **Drawing Conclusions** How did Peter the Great accomplish his goal of modernizing Russia?

CHAPTER 17—THE AGE OF ABSOLUTISM (1550–1800)
Answer Section

MATCHING

1. ANS: A   DIF: E   REF: 413   OBJ: C17S1-1
    TOP: Political systems, Absolute monarch
2. ANS: C   DIF: E   REF: 413   OBJ: C17S1-1
    TOP: Political systems, Divine right
3. ANS: B   DIF: E   REF: 420   OBJ: C17S2-3
    TOP: Political systems, Balance of power
4. ANS: D   DIF: E   REF: 426   OBJ: C17S3-3
    TOP: Social systems, Habeas corpus
5. ANS: E   DIF: E   REF: 426   OBJ: C17S3-3
    TOP: Political systems, Limited monarchy

6. ANS: B   DIF: E   REF: 415   OBJ: C17S1-2
    TOP: Impact of the individual, Miguel de Cervantes
7. ANS: E   DIF: E   REF: 417   OBJ: C17S2-1
    TOP: Impact of the individual, Richelieu
8. ANS: C   DIF: E   REF: 422   OBJ: C17S3-1
    TOP: Impact of the individual, James I
9. ANS: D   DIF: E   REF: 429   OBJ: C17S4-2
    TOP: Impact of the individual, Maria Theresa
10. ANS: A   DIF: E   REF: 434-435   OBJ: C17S5-3
    TOP: Impact of the individual, Catherine the Great

11. ANS: H   DIF: E   REF: 413-414   OBJ: C17S1-1
    TOP: Impact of the individual, Philip II
12. ANS: C   DIF: E   REF: 421   OBJ: C17S1-1
    TOP: Impact of the individual, Elizabeth I
13. ANS: E   DIF: E   REF: 417-419   OBJ: C17S2-2
    TOP: Impact of the individual, Louis XIV
14. ANS: F   DIF: E   REF: 418   OBJ: C17S2-2
    TOP: Art and literature, Molière
15. ANS: B   DIF: E   REF: 423-424   OBJ: C17S3-2
    TOP: Impact of the individual, Oliver Cromwell
16. ANS: D   DIF: E   REF: 430   OBJ: C17S4-2
    TOP: Impact of the individual, Frederick the Great
17. ANS: G   DIF: E   REF: 431-432   OBJ: C17S5-1
    TOP: Impact of the individual, Peter the Great
18. ANS: A   DIF: E   REF: 434-435   OBJ: C17S5-3
    TOP: Impact of the individual, Catherine the Great

MULTIPLE CHOICE

19. ANS: B　　　　DIF: A　　　REF: 414-415　　　OBJ: C17S1-2
    TOP: Art and literature, El Greco

20. ANS: D　　　　DIF: A　　　REF: 417　　　　OBJ: C17S2-1
    TOP: Religion, Edict of Nantes

21. ANS: A　　　　DIF: A　　　REF: 417　　　　OBJ: C17S2-2
    TOP: Political systems, Louis XIV

22. ANS: B　　　　DIF: A　　　REF: 431　　　　OBJ: C17S3-2
    TOP: Political systems, Peter the Great

23. ANS: D　　　　DIF: E　　　REF: 417　　　　OBJ: C17S2-2
    TOP: Political systems, Louis XIV

24. ANS: A　　　　DIF: A　　　REF: 423　　　　OBJ: C17S3-2
    TOP: Political systems, Oliver Cromwell

25. ANS: D　　　　DIF: A　　　REF: 428　　　　OBJ: C17S4-1
    TOP: Continuity and change, Thirty Years' War

26. ANS: A　　　　DIF: A　　　REF: 429-430　　　OBJ: C17S4-3
    TOP: Power and conflict, German states

27. ANS: C　　　　DIF: A　　　REF: 431-432　　　OBJ: C17S5-1
    TOP: Global interaction, Peter the Great

28. ANS: D　　　　DIF: A　　　REF: 433　　　　OBJ: C17S5-2
    TOP: Power and conflict, Expansion under Peter

29. ANS: D　　　　DIF: A　　　REF: 415　　　　OBJ: C17S1-2
    TOP: Art and literature, Don Quixote

30. ANS: C　　　　DIF: A　　　REF: 416　　　　OBJ: C17S2-1
    TOP: Religion, Huguenots

31. ANS: C　　　　DIF: A　　　REF: 418　　　　OBJ: C17S2-3
    TOP: Culture, Louis XIV

32. ANS: B　　　　DIF: A　　　REF: 421-422　　　OBJ: C17S3-1
    TOP: Political systems, Stuarts

33. ANS: C　　　　DIF: E　　　REF: 428　　　　OBJ: C17S4-1
    TOP: Continuity and change, Thirty Years' War

34. ANS: B　　　　DIF: A　　　REF: 429-430　　　OBJ: C17S4-3
    TOP: Power and conflict, German states

35. ANS: D　　　　DIF: A　　　REF: 433　　　　OBJ: C17S5-2
    TOP: Power and conflict, Expansion under Peter

36. ANS: B　　　　DIF: A　　　REF: 435　　　　OBJ: C17S5-3
    TOP: Continuity and change, Partition of Poland

SHORT ANSWER

37. ANS:
Philip II centralized royal power and made all parts of the government responsible to him. He became an absolute monarch. As a result of the concept of divine right, Philip also became guardian of the Catholic Church.

DIF: A   REF: 413   OBJ: C17S1-1
TOP: Impact of the individual, Philip II

38. ANS:
Overseas wars drained Spain's wealth. Treasure from the Americas caused Spain to neglect farming and commerce and led to soaring inflation. The government placed heavy taxes on the middle class and drove out Muslims and Jews.

DIF: A   REF: 415   OBJ: C17S1-3
TOP: Economics, Spanish decline

39. ANS:
The government of Henry IV reached into every area of French life. He built a royal bureaucracy that administered every aspect of life in France. He also reduced the influence of the nobles.

DIF: A   REF: 417   OBJ: C17S2-2
TOP: Political systems, Henry IV

40. ANS:
Louis XIV succeeded in building royal power, expanding the economy, strengthening the army, and making French culture the standard for European taste. His excessive spending and wars drained the economy and led rival rulers to join forces against France. Louis's treatment of the Huguenots caused France to lose many hard-working and prosperous subjects.

DIF: A   REF: 420   OBJ: C17S2-3
TOP: Impact of the individual, Louis XIV

41. ANS:
As a result of the Thirty Years' War, France gained territory from Spain and Germany. The Hapsburgs lost power. The Netherlands and Switzerland became independent states. Germany was divided into many separate states.

DIF: A   REF: 428   OBJ: C17S4-1
TOP: Continuity and change, Thirty Years' War

42. ANS:
Prussia fought Austria for control of the German states. France and Britain competed for overseas empires. In some cases, conflicts spread to North America and to Asia.

DIF: A   REF: 429-430   OBJ: C17S4-3
TOP: Global interaction, Balance of power

43. ANS:

Polish rulers did not become absolute monarchs. Their weak government could not stand up to Russia, Prussia, and Austria. Those three countries partitioned Poland among themselves. By 1795, Poland no longer existed as an independent kingdom.

DIF: A   REF: 435   OBJ: C17S5-3
TOP: Continuity and change, Partition of Poland

44. ANS:

He called Versailles dull and ungrateful. He said it lacked wood, water, and soil because the ground was shifting sand or swamp. The air was bad.

DIF: A   REF: 418-419   OBJ: C17S2-2
TOP: Geography, Versailles

45. ANS:

The water was green, thick, and muddy, and it smelled bad.

DIF: A   REF: 418-419   OBJ: C17S2-2   TOP: Culture, Versailles

46. ANS:

Saint-Simon thought that Louis XIV wasted money on a palace that was built in bad taste. He criticized the king for neglecting Paris and for choosing a location that was unsuitable for a palace. He indicated that the building of Versailles had resulted in the ruin of the infantry that was required to build the reservoirs.

DIF: D   REF: 418-419   OBJ: C17S2-2
TOP: Impact of the individual, Louis XIV

ESSAY

47. ANS:

In the 1770s, and twice in the 1790s, Austria, Prussia, and Russia partitioned Poland. By 1795 the independent kingdom of Poland no longer existed.

DIF: A   REF: 435   OBJ: C17S5-3
TOP: Continuity and change, Partition of Poland

48. ANS:

Overseas wars drained Spain's wealth. Treasure from the Americas caused Spain to neglect farming and commerce and led to soaring inflation. Heavy taxes weakened the middle class. The expulsion of Muslims and Jews deprived the economy of skilled artisans and merchants.

DIF: D   REF: 415   OBJ: C17S1-3
TOP: Economics, Spanish decline

49. ANS:
The Glorious Revolution put William and Mary on the English throne, but they were required to accept the Bill of Rights. The Bill limited the power of the monarchy and restated the traditional rights of English citizens. After the Glorious Revolution, English rulers had to obey the law and govern in partnership with Parliament.

DIF: D   REF: 421   OBJ: C17S3-3
TOP: Continuity and change, Glorious Revolution

50. ANS:
As a result of the English Civil War, England became a commonwealth headed by Oliver Cromwell. The monarchy, the House of Lords, and the Church of England were abolished. Puritan influences resulted in the closing of theaters. Jews were welcomed back to England.

DIF: D   REF: 423-424   OBJ: C17S3-2
TOP: Continuity and change, English Civil War

51. ANS:
Peter the Great imported western technology and improved education by setting up academies for the study of mathematics, science, and engineering. He forced noblemen to shave their beards and wear Western European clothes. He held parties at which men and women were expected to dance together. Peter executed those who resisted his reforms.

DIF: D   REF: 431-432   OBJ: C17S5-1
TOP: Continuity and change, Modernization of Russia

CHAPTER 18—THE ENLIGHTENMENT AND THE AMERICAN REVOLUTION (1707–1800)

Matching

Match each term with the correct statement below.
a. constitutional government
b. enlightened despot
c. natural laws
d. natural rights
e. physiocrat

_____ 1. According to Hobbes and Locke, human nature was governed by _____.

_____ 2. Life, liberty, and property are examples of _____.

_____ 3. A(n) _____ believed that natural laws could be used to define economic systems.

_____ 4. Joseph II was a(n) _____ because he used Enlightenment ideas to bring about political and social change.

_____ 5. The powers of a(n) _____ are defined and limited by law.

Match each person with the correct statement below.
a. Johann Sebastian Bach
b. Denis Diderot
c. Thomas Paine
d. Jean-Jacques Rousseau
e. Robert Walpole

_____ 6. Editor of the controversial *Encyclopedia*

_____ 7. Philosopher who believed that people were basically good

_____ 8. German composer of religious music for choirs and organ

_____ 9. Whig leader often called Britain's first prime minister

_____ 10. Author of pamphlet encouraging Americans to declare independence from Britain

Match each term with the correct statement below.
a. baroque
b. oligarchy
c. laissez faire
d. salon
e. social contract

_____ 11. An agreement by which people give up their natural state for an organized society

_____ 12. A policy that allows businesses to operate without government interference

_____ 13. A government in which the ruling power belongs to a few people

_____ 14. A social gathering in which artists and thinkers exchange ideas

_____ 15. A grand and complex artistic style

Match each person with the correct statement below.

a. Voltaire
b. Adam Smith
c. Jean-Jacques Rousseau

d. Baron de Montesquieu
e. Thomas Paine

_____ 16. "In order to have liberty, it is necessary that the powers of the government be separated."

_____ 17. "I do not agree with a word you say, but I will defend to the death your right to say it."

_____ 18. "Man is born free, but is everywhere in chains."

_____ 19. "There should be no government regulations on trade."

_____ 20. "It is against all reason to suppose that this Continent can long remain subject to any external power."

Multiple Choice

Identify the letter of the choice that best completes the statement or answers the question.

_____ 21. Montesquieu believed the purpose of the separation of powers was to
a. make government more efficient.
b. protect the liberties of the people.
c. strengthen the monarchy.
d. promote reform.

_____ 22. Which of the following is a true statement about European peasants during the Enlightenment?
a. Their life changed greatly.
b. Most moved to the cities.
c. The Enlightenment had little effect on their life.
d. They acquired material wealth.

_____ 23. Which of the following helped Britian become a global power in the 1700s?
a. its rich resources
b. its strong navy
c. its favorable climate
d. its position next to mainland Europe

_____ 24. Which of the following groups had the right to vote in Britain in the 1700s?
a. all citizens over 21
b. male property owners
c. male citizens over 21
d. males and females who belonged to the aristocracy

_____ 25. Trade within the colonies of the British empire was controlled by
a. Great Britain
b. smugglers
c. wealthy landowners and merchants
d. colonial assemblies

_____ 26. The statement "No taxation without representation" was partly influenced by the thinking of
   a. Adam Smith
   b. John Locke
   c. Baron de Montesquieu
   d. Thomas Hobbes

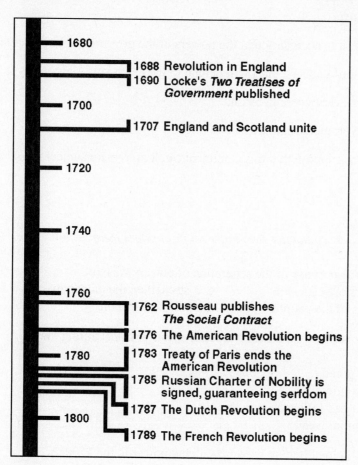

Figure 18-1

_____ 27. Which event in Figure 18-1 suggests that the American Revolution had a global impact?
   a. England and Scotland unite
   b. the French Revolution
   c. the Russian Charter of Nobility is signed
   d. the Treaty of Paris

_____ 28. According to Figure 18-1, how many years passed between the publication of Locke's *Two Treatises of Government* and the end of the American Revolution?
   a. 75
   b. 100
   c. 93
   d. 90

_____ 29. According to Figure 18-1, in what year did the French Revolution begin?
   a. 1780
   b. 1789
   c. 1785
   d. 1790

_____ 30. Which event in Figure 18-1 best supports the generalization that Enlightenment reforms lagged behind in some parts of Europe?
   a.   The Russian Charter of Nobility is signed.
   b.   The Dutch Revolution begins.
   c.   The French Revolution begins.
   d.   The American Revolution begins.

_____ 31. Thinkers during the Age of Reason challenged the established social order by
   a.   calling for an end to government.
   b.   denying the existence of heaven.
   c.   calling for a just society based on reason.
   d.   supporting peasant rebellions.

_____ 32. Joseph II adopted Enlightenment ideas
   a.   to gain more power.
   b.   to make his government more efficient.
   c.   to end superstition in his kingdom.
   d.   to improve the life of his people.

_____ 33. The Tory party in Britain was made up primarily of
   a.   landowning aristocrats.   c.   middle-class merchants.
   b.   wealthy business leaders.   d.   peasants.

_____ 34. Which of the following was a new feature of English government in the late 1700s?
   a.   an absolute monarch   c.   a cabinet
   b.   divine rule   d.   all adults had the right to vote

_____ 35. American resentment of British rule increased after 1763 over
   a.   a lack of religious freedom.
   b.   taxation without representation in Parliament.
   c.   a lack of tea.
   d.   the right to free speech.

_____ 36. The Declaration of Independence clearly reflects the ideas of
   a.   Catherine the Great.   c.   George III.
   b.   John Locke.   d.   Thomas Hobbes.

Short Answer

37. Explain why the Enlightenment is sometimes called the Age of Reason and link it to the Scientific Revolution of the 1500s and 1600s.

38. Give a brief description of each of these thinkers' beliefs: Locke, Montesquieu, Voltaire, Rousseau.

39. Contrast the economic philosophy of the physiocrats with that of the mercantilists.

40. Describe how the artistic tastes of aristocrats differed from those of the middle class.

41. List three factors that helped Britain become a global power in the 1700s.

42. List the three new institutions that became part of England's changing government in the 1700s and briefly describe their functions.

43. Identify three causes of the American Revolution.

Read the following excerpts from Mary Wollstonecraft's book A Vindication of the Rights of Woman, *in which she challenges statements by Jean-Jacques Rousseau. Then answer the questions that follow.*

> Rousseau: "The education of women should be always relative to men. To please, to be useful to us, to make us love them, to render [make] our lives easy and agreeable; these are the duties of women at all times, and what they should be taught in infancy."
> Wollstonecraft: "Woman was not created merely to be the solace [comfort] of man. . . . On this . . . error has all the false system been erected, which robs [all women of their] dignity. . . ."
> Rousseau: "Girls must be subject all their lives to the most constant and severe restraint [control] . . . that they may the more readily learn to submit to the will of others. . . ."
> Wollstonecraft: "How can a woman believe that she was made to submit to man—a being like herself, her equal?"

44. What did Rousseau consider the duty of a woman to be?

45. How would Wollstonecraft describe the relationship between men and women in an ideal society?

46. Based on what you know concerning Rousseau's philosophy about government and society, do you think the beliefs he expresses here are consistent with those ideas or not?

Essay

On a separate sheet of paper, write an answer to the following questions.

47. **Synthesizing Information** Why was Locke's belief that governments exist to serve the people considered a radical idea?

48. **Predicting Consequences** How did King George III and his advisers help bring about the American Revolution?

49. **Identifying Main Ideas** Why was the Enlightenment called the Age of Reason?

50. **Linking Past and Present** List three Enlightenment ideas that are now identified as American ideals.

51. **Defending a Position** Assume the role of either a philosopher who supports Enlightenment ideas or a church official who supports the old order. Briefly describe your position on reform for a just society.

52. **Applying Information** Explain how John Locke's political ideas could be used to justify the American Revolution.

CHAPTER 18—THE ENLIGHTENMENT AND THE AMERICAN REVOLUTION (1707–1800)
Answer Section

MATCHING

1. ANS: C   DIF: E   REF: 446   OBJ: C18S1-1
    TOP: Social systems, Natural laws

2. ANS: D   DIF: E   REF: 447   OBJ: C18S1-2
    TOP: Social systems, Natural rights

3. ANS: E   DIF: E   REF: 450   OBJ: C18S1-3
    TOP: Economics, Physiocrat

4. ANS: B   DIF: E   REF: 452   OBJ: C18S2-2
    TOP: Political systems, Enlightened despot

5. ANS: A   DIF: E   REF: 457   OBJ: C18S3-2
    TOP: Political systems, Constitutional government

6. ANS: B   DIF: E   REF: 449   OBJ: C18S1-3
    TOP: Impact of the individual, Denis Diderot

7. ANS: D   DIF: E   REF: 449   OBJ: C18S1-3
    TOP: Impact of the individual, Jean-Jacques Rousseau

8. ANS: A   DIF: E   REF: 453   OBJ: C18S2-3
    TOP: Impact of the individual, Johann Sebastian Bach

9. ANS: E   DIF: E   REF: 458   OBJ: C18S3-2
    TOP: Impact of the individual, Robert Walpole

10. ANS: C   DIF: E   REF: 460   OBJ: C18S4-1
    TOP: Impact of the individual, Thomas Paine

11. ANS: E   DIF: E   REF: 447   OBJ: C18S1-2
    TOP: Social systems, Social contract

12. ANS: C   DIF: E   REF: 450   OBJ: C18S1-3
    TOP: Economics, Laissez faire

13. ANS: B   DIF: E   REF: 458   OBJ: C18S3-3
    TOP: Political systems, Oligarchy

14. ANS: D   DIF: E   REF: 451-452   OBJ: C18S2-1
    TOP: Social systems, Salon

15. ANS: A   DIF: E   REF: 453   OBJ: C18S2-3
    TOP: Art and literature, Baroque

16. ANS: D   DIF: E   REF: 447   OBJ: C18S1-2
    TOP: Political systems, Separation of powers

17. ANS: A   DIF: E   REF: 447-449   OBJ: C18S1-2
    TOP: Social systems, Freedom of speech

18. ANS: C   DIF: E   REF: 449   OBJ: C18S1-3
    TOP: Impact of the individual, Jean-Jacques Rousseau

19. ANS: B   DIF: E   REF: 450   OBJ: C18S1-3
    TOP: Economics, Laissez faire
20. ANS: E   DIF: E   REF: 460   OBJ: C18S4-1
    TOP: Impact of the individual, Thomas Paine

MULTIPLE CHOICE

21. ANS: B   DIF: A   REF: 447   OBJ: C18S1-2
    TOP: Political systems, Separation of powers
22. ANS: C   DIF: A   REF: 455   OBJ: C18S2-4
    TOP: Social systems, European peasants
23. ANS: B   DIF: E   REF: 456-457   OBJ: C18S3-1
    TOP: Global interaction, Britain's rise to global power
24. ANS: B   DIF: A   REF: 459   OBJ: C18S3-3
    TOP: Political systems, Suffrage in Britain
25. ANS: A   DIF: A   REF: 460-461   OBJ: C18S4-1
    TOP: Global interaction, British colonies
26. ANS: B   DIF: D   REF: 447, 461-463
    OBJ: C18S4-2   TOP: Political systems, American Revolution
27. ANS: B   DIF: A   REF: 463   OBJ: C18S4-3
    TOP: Global interaction, American Revolution
28. ANS: C   DIF: E   REF: 447, 461   OBJ: C18S1-2
    TOP: Impact of the individual, John Locke
29. ANS: B   DIF: E   REF: 463   OBJ: C18S4-3
    TOP: Global interaction, French Revolution
30. ANS: A   DIF: A   REF: 452   OBJ: C18S2-4
    TOP: Continuity and change, Enlightenment reforms
31. ANS: C   DIF: A   REF: 451   OBJ: C18S2-1
    TOP: Social systems, Age of Reason
32. ANS: D   DIF: A   REF: 452   OBJ: C18S2-2
    TOP: Social systems, Joseph II
33. ANS: A   DIF: A   REF: 457-458   OBJ: C18S3-2
    TOP: Political systems, Tory party
34. ANS: C   DIF: A   REF: 458   OBJ: C18S3-1
    TOP: Political systems, Cabinet system
35. ANS: B   DIF: D   REF: 461   OBJ: C18S4-2
    TOP: Power and conflict, American Revolution
36. ANS: B   DIF: D   REF: 461   OBJ: C18S4-3
    TOP: Political systems, Declaration of Independence

SHORT ANSWER

37. ANS:

The thinkers of the time believed that you could use reason to discover the natural laws that underlie a just society. The Enlightenment's faith in reason to solve social problems grew out of the successes of science during the Scientific Revolution.

DIF: A   REF: 446   OBJ: C18S1-1
TOP: Social systems, Age of Reason

38. ANS:

Locke believed people were born with natural rights and that they formed governments to protect these rights. People have the right to overthrow a government that fails to protect their natural rights. Montesquieu believed that the separation of powers was the best way to protect liberty. Voltaire believed that freedom of speech and thought were essential rights. Rousseau believed that people are basically good but become corrupted by society. People in an ideal society would put the collective good over their own interests.

DIF: A   REF: 446-449   OBJ: C18S1-2
TOP: Impact of the individual, Enlightenment thinkers

39. ANS:

Physiocrats believed government should not interfere with trade, they supported free trade, and they believed real wealth came from making the land more productive. Mercantilists called for the acquisition of gold and silver wealth through trade. They believed trade should be supported through government regulation to achieve a favorable trade balance.

DIF: D   REF: 406, 450   OBJ: C18S1-3
TOP: Economics, Physiocrat

40. ANS:

Aristocrats favored art and architecture either in the classical tradition, the grand, ornate style of the baroque, or the elegant style of the rococo. The middle class, however, had simpler tastes and preferred art that reflected the reality of their daily lives.

DIF: A   REF: 453-455   OBJ: C18S2-3
TOP: Art and literature, Aristocrats and middle class

41. ANS:

Answers should include three of the following: an island location, a strong navy, success in war, a favorable business climate, the union of England and Scotland.

DIF: E   REF: 456-457   OBJ: C18S3-1
TOP: Global interaction, Britain's rise to global power

42. ANS:
    Political parties—advanced the interests of the groups in political power (landed aristocrats and wealthy business people); cabinet—helped the king rule; prime minister—headed the cabinet and acted as chief official of the government.

    DIF: A   REF: 457-458   OBJ: C18S3-2
    TOP: Political systems, British government

43. ANS:
    Answers should include three of the following: British taxes on the colonies without representation in the Parliament, tightening British control of colonial trade, growing sense of distinct American identity, punitive measures against the colonies for rebellious acts.

    DIF: A   REF: 460-461   OBJ: C18S4-2
    TOP: Power and conflict, American Revolution

44. ANS:
    Their duty is to serve men.

    DIF: A   REF: 449   OBJ: C18S2-1
    TOP: Social systems, Rousseau

45. ANS:
    Men and women would have an equal relationship in an ideal society.

    DIF: A   REF: 249-250, 449   OBJ: C18S2-1
    TOP: Social systems, Women's rights

46. ANS:
    Answers will vary. Students may feel Rousseau's views are consistent with his idea that people in a society need to work together for the common good, recognizing that the assumption of his time was that women were by nature inferior to men.

    DIF: A   REF: 449   OBJ: C18S1-2
    TOP: Social systems, Rousseau

ESSAY

47. ANS:
    Up until the Enlightenment, governments existed to serve the needs of the ruler, not "the people." Locke felt that the people have a right to overthrow a government that fails its obligations or violates people's rights.

    DIF: D   REF: 447   OBJ: C18S4-3
    TOP: Continuity and change, John Locke

48. ANS:
King George and his advisers decided that English colonists in North America must pay the cost of their own defense, and for the troops stationed on the frontier. Britain began to enforce laws regulating colonial trade and passed new laws to increase the taxes paid by colonists.

DIF: D   REF: 459   OBJ: C18S3-3
TOP: Impact of the individual, King George III

49. ANS:
The thinkers of the time believed people could use reason to discover the natural laws that underlie a just society.

DIF: E   REF: 446   OBJ: C18S1-1
TOP: Social systems, Age of Reason

50. ANS:
Answers should include three of the following: freedom of speech, freedom of religion, the idea that all people are created equal under the law, the right of everyone to own property, liberty for all, justice for all, the will of the majority as the basis for government.

DIF: A   REF: 462-463   OBJ: C18S4-3
TOP: Continuity and change, Englightenment ideas

51. ANS:
Students who assume the role of an Enlightenment philosopher will point to the necessity of reform in order to improve an unjust world based on irrationality and the self-interest of the powerful. Students who take the role of a church official will state that the old order was the will of God and that it was intended that life on Earth be a struggle so that people could achieve a place in heaven.

DIF: D   REF: 451   OBJ: C18S2-1
TOP: Social systems, Enlightenment ideas

52. ANS:
People have a natural right to life, liberty, and property, and a government should exist to support those rights. If it fails, or violates people's natural rights, it can be overthrown.

DIF: A   REF: 461-463   OBJ: C18S4-3
TOP: Impact of the individual, John Locke

CHAPTER 19—THE FRENCH REVOLUTION AND NAPOLEON (1789–1815)

Matching

Match each term with the correct statement below.
  a. abdicate
  b. deficit spending
  c. plebiscite
  d. sans-culottes
  e. suffrage

____ 1. Spending more money than is taken in

____ 2. Working-class revolutionaries

____ 3. The right to vote

____ 4. Ballot in which voters say yes or no to an issue

____ 5. To give up power

Match each person with the correct statement below.
  a. Napoleon
  b. Jacques Louis David
  c. Maximilien Robespierre
  d. Olympe de Gouges
  e. Clemens von Metternich

____ 6. Jacobin revolutionary who led the Reign of Terror

____ 7. French journalist who demanded equal rights for women

____ 8. Leading painter during the French Revolution

____ 9. French emperor who dominated Europe in the early 1800s

____ 10. Austrian prince who wanted to restore the status quo of 1792 at the Congress of Vienna

Match each term with the correct statement below.
  a. blockade
  b. bourgeoisie
  c. émigré
  d. nationalism
  e. sans-culottes

____ 11. The wealthiest members of the Third Estate

____ 12. A person who fled revolutionary France to live in another country

____ 13. Radical working-class men and women

____ 14. A feeling of pride in, and intense devotion to, one's country

____ 15. A military tactic through which ports are shut off to keep people or supplies from moving in or out

Match each person with the correct statement below.
- a. Louis XVI
- b. Clemens von Metternich
- c. Napoleon
- d. Olympe de Gouges
- e. Robespierre

_____ 16. "Let all three estates list their grievances to me."

_____ 17. "Lives must be sacrificed for liberty."

_____ 18. "Woman's rights are the same as those of man."

_____ 19. "I love power as a musician loves his violin."

_____ 20. "Monarchy is the only way to save Europe from the ravages of nationalism."

Multiple Choice
Identify the letter of the choice that best completes the statement or answers the question.

_____ 21. The bourgeoisie belonged to which of the following groups?
- a. the First Estate
- b. the Second Estate
- c. the Third Estate
- d. the aristocracy

_____ 22. The Constitution of 1791
- a. abolished the monarchy.
- b. established a new Legislative Assembly.
- c. gave the vote to all citizens.
- d. reestablished the old provinces.

_____ 23. During the Reign of Terror, Robespierre tried to
- a. execute all French nobles.
- b. restore the Catholic Church.
- c. crush all opposition to the revolution.
- d. reinstate the monarchy.

_____ 24. Which of the following areas did Napoleon annex to France?
- a. the Netherlands
- b. Russia
- c. Poland
- d. Britain

_____ 25. Which of the following was the chief goal of the Congress of Vienna?
- a. to punish France
- b. to create a united Europe
- c. to create a lasting peace
- d. to strengthen Germany

_____ 26. Why did the Congress of Vienna redraw the boundaries of some European countries?
- a. to encircle France with strong countries
- b. to create more countries
- c. to distribute land more fairly
- d. to prevent the growth of nationalism

George G. Harrap and Company Limited

Figure 19-1

____ 27. In Figure 19-1, why are the scepter, or staff, and the globe shown falling from Napoleon's hands?
   a. to show Napoleon playing with his power
   b. to show Napoleon losing his power
   c. to show Napoleon passing on control of his empire
   d. to show Napoleon's juggling abilities

____ 28. At which of the following times was Figure 19-1 most likely drawn?
   a. after Napoleon's defeat at the Battle of Nations
   b. as he claimed victory after victory in Europe
   c. at the beginning of his military career
   d. when he was crowned emperor of the French

____ 29. In Figure 19-1 featuring Napoleon, what do the scepter, or staff, and the globe with the cross on it represent?
   a. defeat   c. toys
   b. power   d. freedom

____ 30. What is the cartoonist trying to show by including Russian buildings on the lower right in Figure 19-1?
   a. Russia has a unique architectural style.
   b. Russia is a world power.
   c. Russia is an important element in Napoleon's fall from power.
   d. Russia is a religious country.

_____ 31. Which of the following statements about France's social structure is true?
   a. The Third Estate was made up entirely of peasants.
   b. The Second Estate was content with the social structure.
   c. There was inequality among the three estates.
   d. Most people belonged to the First Estate.

_____ 32. France's economy was mainly supported by
   a. the First Estate.
   b. the Third Estate.
   c. the king.
   d. the nobles.

_____ 33. French nobles resisted Necker's financial reforms because
   a. they supported free trade.
   b. they were already taxed too heavily.
   c. they wanted to pay no taxes.
   d. they thought the answer was to create more jobs for the Third Estate.

_____ 34. The Declaration of the Rights of Man and the Citizen stated that
   a. all men were born free and equal in rights.
   b. all male citizens had the right to vote.
   c. male and female citizens were equal before the law.
   d. all citizens had to pay equal taxes.

_____ 35. How did the French respond to threats to the revolution?
   a. by using mediation to settle differences
   b. by becoming more radical
   c. by welcoming their opponents into the decision-making process
   d. by ensuring that all citizens were free to speak

_____ 36. How did the Napoleonic Code reflect Enlightenment principles?
   a. It guaranteed the equality of all citizens before the law.
   b. It guaranteed women equal rights.
   c. It valued individual rights above all else.
   d. It valued the security of the state over individual liberty.

Short Answer

37. Describe the three divisions of France's social structure before the French Revolution.

38. Identify three causes of the financial crisis France faced in the late 1780s.

39. Give two examples of how popular uprisings moved the French Revolution forward.

40. Identify the four stages of the revolution.

41. List five ways the revolution changed life in France.

42. List the main events in the rise and fall of Napoleon.

43. Describe the chief goal of the Congress of Vienna.

Read the following excerpt from the Declaration of the Rights of Man and the Citizen adopted by the National Assembly in 1789. Then answer the questions that follow.

"The representatives of the French people, organized as a national assembly, believing that the ignorance, neglect, or contempt of the rights of man are the sole causes of public misfortunes and the corruption of governments, have determined to set forth in a solemn declaration, the natural, inalienable and sacred rights of man. . . .

The aim of all political association is the preservation of the natural . . . rights of man. These rights are liberty, property, security, and resistance to oppression.

Liberty consists in the freedom to do everything which injures no one else. . . .

Law is the expression of the general will. Every citizen has a right to participate personally, or through his representative, in its formation.

No person shall be accused, arrested, or imprisoned except in the cases and according to the forms prescribed by law."

44. What does the declaration say are the natural rights of man?

45. Based on this excerpt, how do you think the monarchy viewed the French people before the revolution?

46. How does this excerpt redefine the relationship between the French people and their government?

Essay
On a separate sheet of paper, write an answer to the following questions.

47. **Comparing** In what ways was the Declaration of the Rights of Man and the Citizen similar to the Declaration of Independence?

48. **Drawing Conclusions** Do you think Napoleon did more to help or hurt the causes of the French Revolution? Use examples of his actions to support your answer.

49. **Synthesizing Information** How did the Reign of Terror contradict the ideals of the French Revolution as formulated in the Declaration of the Rights of Man and the Citizen?

50. **Identifying Main Ideas** Why is it possible to say that the "new order" established in Europe by the Congress of Vienna after Napoleon's defeat was actually an "old order"?

51. **Predicting Consequences** What do you think would be a likely consequence of the Congress of Vienna's decision to redraw Europe's boundaries without any concern for national cultures?

CHAPTER 19—THE FRENCH REVOLUTION AND NAPOLEON (1789–1815)
Answer Section

MATCHING

1. ANS: B   DIF: E   REF: 470   OBJ: C19S1-2
   TOP: Economics, Eeficit spending
2. ANS: D   DIF: E   REF: 477   OBJ: C19S2-3
   TOP: Political systems, Sans-culottes
3. ANS: E   DIF: E   REF: 478   OBJ: C19S3-1
   TOP: Political systems, Suffrage
4. ANS: C   DIF: E   REF: 485   OBJ: C19S4-1
   TOP: Political systems, Plebiscite
5. ANS: A   DIF: E   REF: 490   OBJ: C19S5-2
   TOP: Political systems, Abdicate

6. ANS: C   DIF: E   REF: 480   OBJ: C19S3-1
   TOP: Impact of the individual, Maximilien Robespierre
7. ANS: D   DIF: E   REF: 482   OBJ: C19S3-3
   TOP: Impact of the individual, Olympe de Gouges
8. ANS: B   DIF: E   REF: 483   OBJ: C19S3-3
   TOP: Impact of the individual, Jacques Louis David
9. ANS: A   DIF: E   REF: 486-487   OBJ: C19S4-3
   TOP: Impact of the individual, Napoleon
10. ANS: E   DIF: E   REF: 492   OBJ: C19S5-3
    TOP: Impact of the individual, Clemens von Metternich

11. ANS: B   DIF: E   REF: 469   OBJ: C19S1-1
    TOP: Social systems, Third Estate
12. ANS: C   DIF: E   REF: 476   OBJ: C19S2-3
    TOP: Social systems, Émigré
13. ANS: E   DIF: E   REF: 477   OBJ: C19S2-3
    TOP: Political systems, Sans-culottes
14. ANS: D   DIF: E   REF: 483   OBJ: C19S3-3
    TOP: Political systems, Nationalism
15. ANS: A   DIF: E   REF: 487   OBJ: C19S4-3
    TOP: Political systems, Blockade

16. ANS: A   DIF: E   REF: 471   OBJ: C19S1-3
    TOP: Impact of the individual, Louis XVI
17. ANS: E   DIF: E   REF: 480   OBJ: C19S3-1
    TOP: Political systems, Reign of Terror
18. ANS: D   DIF: E   REF: 482   OBJ: C19S3-3
    TOP: Social systems, Women's suffrage
19. ANS: C   DIF: E   REF: 484-485   OBJ: C19S4-3
    TOP: Impact of the individual, Napoleon

20. ANS: B   DIF: E   REF: 492   OBJ: C19S5-3
    TOP: Political systems, Clemens von Metternich

MULTIPLE CHOICE

21. ANS: C   DIF: A   REF: 469   OBJ: C19S1-1
    TOP: Social systems, Third Estate
22. ANS: B   DIF: D   REF: 475-476   OBJ: C19S2-2
    TOP: Continuity and change, Constitution of 1791
23. ANS: C   DIF: A   REF: 480   OBJ: C19S3-2
    TOP: Political systems, Reign of Terror
24. ANS: A   DIF: A   REF: 486   OBJ: C19S4-3
    TOP: Power and conflict, Napoleon
25. ANS: C   DIF: D   REF: 492   OBJ: C19S5-2
    TOP: Continuity and change, Congress of Vienna
26. ANS: A   DIF: A   REF: 493   OBJ: C19S5-3
    TOP: Geography, Congress of Vienna
27. ANS: B   DIF: E   REF: 488-490   OBJ: C19S5-1
    TOP: Continuity and change, Fall of Napoleon
28. ANS: A   DIF: A   REF: 488-490   OBJ: C19S5-1
    TOP: Continuity and change, Fall of Napoleon
29. ANS: B   DIF: A   REF: 488-490   OBJ: C19S5-1
    TOP: Continuity and change, Fall of Napoleon
30. ANS: C   DIF: A   REF: 488-490   OBJ: C19S5-1
    TOP: Continuity and change, Fall of Napoleon
31. ANS: C   DIF: A   REF: 468-470   OBJ: C19S1-1
    TOP: Social systems, Ancien regime
32. ANS: B   DIF: A   REF: 469   OBJ: C19S1-2
    TOP: Economics, Third Estate
33. ANS: C   DIF: E   REF: 470   OBJ: C19S1-3
    TOP: Economics, Failure of reform
34. ANS: A   DIF: A   REF: 474   OBJ: C19S2-2
    TOP: Political systems, Declaration of the Rights of Man
35. ANS: B   DIF: E   REF: 478-482   OBJ: C19S3-1
    TOP: Political systems, Radical phase of French Revolution
36. ANS: A   DIF: D   REF: 486   OBJ: C19S4-2
    TOP: Social systems, Napoleonic Code

SHORT ANSWER

37. ANS:
The First Estate was made up of the clergy. The Second Estate was made up of the nobility. The Third Estate was made up of the bourgeoisie (or middle class) as well as peasants and city workers.

DIF: E   REF: 468-470   OBJ: C19S1-1
TOP: Social systems, Ancien regime

38. ANS:
Answers should include three of the following: deficit spending, overspending, a declining economy, poor harvests, the failure of economic reform.

DIF: A   REF: 470-471   OBJ: C19S1-2
TOP: Economics, France faces financial crisis

39. ANS:
Answers may include two of the following: the storming of the Bastille—set the revolution in motion and pushed the National Assembly to take action; women's march on Versailles—forced the return of the king to Paris and pushed the National Assembly to turn France into a constitutional monarchy; uprisings by the sans-culottes and "September massacres"—pushed the revolution into a more radical stage.

DIF: A   REF: 473-475, 477-478   OBJ: C19S2-1
TOP: Political systems, Popular uprisings

40. ANS:
the moderate phase; the radical phase; the Directory; the Age of Napoleon

DIF: D   REF: 473   OBJ: C19S3-1
TOP: Political systems, Stages of the French Revolution

41. ANS:
Answers may include five of the following: the revolution abolished the old social order and made all French men equal citizens; it instituted a new government; it brought the Church under state control; it changed fashion; it introduced nationalism; it made public education available; it encouraged religious toleration; and it promoted France as a secular nation instead of a religious one.

DIF: A   REF: 482-483   OBJ: C19S3-3
TOP: Social systems, Changes in daily life

42. ANS:
Main events in the rise of Napoleon: He won several victories against the Austrians and captured most of northern Italy; he helped overthrow the Directory and set himself up as First Consul; he declared himself emperor of the French; he defeated all the major powers, except for Britain. Main events in the fall of Napoleon: He lost his campaign against Russia, which led to his defeat by Russia, Britain, and Prussia; he abdicated.

DIF: A   REF: 484-490   OBJ: C19S4-1
TOP: Impact of the individual, Napoleon

43. ANS:
    to create a lasting European peace by establishing strong nations surrounding France and a balance of power and by protecting the system of monarchy

    DIF: A   REF: 492-493   OBJ: C19S5-2
    TOP: Political systems, Congress of Vienna

44. ANS:
    liberty, property, security, and resistance to oppression

    DIF: E   REF: 474   OBJ: C19S2-2
    TOP: Political systems, Declaration of the Rights of Man

45. ANS:
    Answers should point to the idea that the monarchy most likely viewed the French people as resources to be used as the monarchy saw fit and worth little consideration as entities by themselves.

    DIF: A   REF: 474   OBJ: C19S2-2
    TOP: Political systems, Declaration of the Rights of Man

46. ANS:
    The government exists for the benefit of the people, rather than the people existing for the benefit of those governing them.

    DIF: D   REF: 474   OBJ: C19S2-2
    TOP: Political systems, Declaration of the Rights of Man

ESSAY

47. ANS:
    It was similar in that it stated that all men are born equal; that they are born with certain natural rights, including liberty, property, security, and resistance to oppression; and that the government exists to protect these natural rights.

    DIF: A   REF: 474   OBJ: C19S2-2
    TOP: Political systems, Declaration of the Rights of Man

48. ANS:
    Students who think that Napoleon hurt the revolution may point to the facts that he took away many of the liberties the French people gained during the revolution, including women's rights, and that his defeat restored the monarchy. Students who believe Napoleon helped the French Revolution may point to the facts that he codified many of the changes brought about by the revolution into law (the Napoleonic Code); and that more people had the right to vote, own property, and be educated than under the old regime.

    DIF: D   REF: 485-486   OBJ: C19S4-2
    TOP: Impact of the individual, Napoleon

49. ANS:
It denied people their rights to liberty, property, security, and resistance to oppression.

DIF: D   REF: 474, 480   OBJ: C19S3-2
TOP: Political systems, Reign of Terror

50. ANS:
Part of the aim of the "new order" was to restore political conditions to what they had been in 1792. To do this, the monarchy was reinstated in France and in the other European countries that Napoleon had conquered.

DIF: A   REF: 493   OBJ: C19S5-3
TOP: Continuity and change, Congress of Vienna

51. ANS:
Most students will probably say that this would inflame feelings of nationalism and eventually lead to war.

DIF: A   REF: 492-493   OBJ: C19S5-3
TOP: Diversity, Congress of Vienna

CHAPTER 20—THE INDUSTRIAL REVOLUTION BEGINS (1750–1850)

Matching

Match each term with the correct statement below.
a.   urbanization
b.   enclosure
c.   socialism
d.   factories
e.   utilitarianism

_____   1.   The movement that increased farm production was called ____.

_____   2.   New inventions in the textile industry made it necessary to change from the "putting out system" to producing cloth in ____.

_____   3.   The movement of people from the country to cities is called ____.

_____   4.   ____ is the idea that the goal of society should be "the greatest happiness for the greatest number" of its citizens.

_____   5.   According to ____, society as a group rather than individuals should own and operate farms and businesses.

Match each person with the correct statement below.
a.   John Stuart Mill
b.   John Wesley
c.   Karl Marx
d.   Jethro Tull
e.   Thomas Malthus

_____   6.   Inventor of the seed drill

_____   7.   Founder of the Methodist Church

_____   8.   Economist who predicted that the population would outpace the food supply

_____   9.   Thinker who argued that actions are right if they promote happiness and wrong if they cause pain

_____ 10.   Philosopher who thought that history was a struggle between classes

Match each term with the correct statement below.
a.   communism
b.   proletariat
c.   socialism
d.   turnpike
e.   urbanization

_____ 11.   A privately built road that charged travelers a fee

_____ 12.   The movement of people from the country to cities

_____ 13.   An economic system in which society owns large farms and businesses

_____ 14.   A form of socialism that focuses on ending class struggle

_____ 15.   The working class

Match each person with the correct statement below.

a. Robert Owen   d. James Watt
b. David Ricardo   e. Jeremy Bentham
c. Abraham Darby

_____ 16. Inventor who improved the steam engine

_____ 17. A leader in developing Britain's iron industry

_____ 18. Economist who believed that when wages were high, the poor had more children

_____ 19. Thinker who promoted the idea of the "greatest happiness for the greatest number"

_____ 20. Mill owner who worked for child labor laws

Multiple Choice

Identify the letter of the choice that best completes the statement or answers the question.

Population (in millions)				
∘	1700	1750	1800	1850
Belgium	1.75	2.25	3.25	4.50
Britain	5.75	6.00	9.25	18.00
France	22.00	24.00	29.00	36.00
Germany	13.00	15.00	18.00	27.00
Italy	13.00	15.00	19.00	25.00

Figure 20-1

_____ 21. According to Figure 20-1, which country had the largest population in 1750?
a. Britain   c. Germany
b. France   d. Italy

_____ 22. According to Figure 20-1, which country's population nearly doubled between 1800 and 1850?
a. Belgium   c. France
b. Britain   d. Germany

_____ 23. According to Figure 20-1, what was Britain's population in 1750?
a. 18 million   c. 2.25 million
b. 6 million   d. 5.75 million

_____ 24. Which of the following statements is supported by Figure 20-1?
a. In 1750, Germany and France had about the same number of people.
b. The biggest increase in population for France and Germany was between 1750 and 1800.
c. Belgium had the greatest population by 1850.
d. The populations of all the countries increased steadily.

_____ 25. Which of the following helped British farmers increase food production in the 1700s?
  a. reducing the size of their farms
  b. improved farm machinery
  c. new kinds of crops
  d. the availability of more farmworkers

_____ 26. Which of the following became an important source of power for the Industrial Revolution?
  a. the steam engine   c. the windmill
  b. animals   d. the dynamo

_____ 27. Why was coal important to the Industrial Revolution?
  a. Mining it gave jobs to unemployed farm laborers.
  b. It provided the fuel to produce iron.
  c. Trading it with other countries brought wealth to invest in industry.
  d. It provided fuel to heat workers' homes.

_____ 28. Early in the Industrial Revolution, working-class women
  a. received the same pay as men.
  b. worked only part time.
  c. were not allowed to work in coal mines.
  d. worked 12 or more hours a day outside the home.

_____ 29. Who was most likely to support the idea that society should be based on cooperation instead of competition?
  a. Adam Smith   c. Robert Owen
  b. David Ricardo   d. Jeremy Bentham

_____ 30. Which of the following conditions during the Industrial Revolution supported Karl Marx's ideas?
  a. There were a few wealthy business people while the majority of people were poor.
  b. More material goods were available.
  c. People were no longer threatened by famine.
  d. People left the countryside and moved to the cities.

_____ 31. During the agricultural revolution in the 1700s, wealthy landowners increased food production by
  a. practicing enclosure.
  b. leaving part of the land unplanted every year.
  c. hiring more farmworkers.
  d. giving peasants bonuses.

_____ 32. Which of the following is a reason explaining why Britain took the lead in the Industrial Revolution?
  a. British workers were well paid.
  b. The government owned the factories.
  c. The British business class had large profits to invest.
  d. The British people were the most well educated in the world.

_____ 33. Industrialization in the textile industry resulted in
  a. better-paying jobs.
  b. the establishment of factories.
  c. improved working conditions.
  d. slower production times.

_____ 34. Which of the following statements regarding workers in mines and factories during the early Industrial Revolution is true?
  a. They were allowed to form unions.
  b. Their working conditions were dangerous and inhumane.
  c. Although working conditions were harsh, they were paid well.
  d. The British government was interested in improving their lives.

_____ 35. Which group benefited the most from the Industrial Revolution?
  a. the working class
  b. farmers
  c. the middle class
  d. the nobility

_____ 36. The idea that the goal of society should be "the greatest happiness for the greatest number" of its citizens was a philosophy held by
  a. utilitarians.
  b. Marxists.
  c. Utopians.
  d. capitalists.

Short Answer

37. List three factors that played a role in the agricultural revolution in Britain in the 1700s.

38. Explain how the agricultural revolution contributed to population growth in Britain.

39. Identify three energy sources that helped power the Industrial Revolution.

40. List five factors that helped Britain take the lead in industrialization.

41. Describe how the factory system changed the nature of work.

42. List three reasons why factory owners often preferred women workers to men.

43. Describe the significance of the ideas of each of the following in relation to the Industrial Revolution: Thomas Malthus, Jeremy Bentham, Karl Marx.

Read the following excerpt from Fanny Kemble's account of her ride on one of the first trips of the Liverpool & Manchester Railroad. Then answer the questions that follow.

> "He [Stephenson, one of the developers of the railroad] explained to me the whole construction of the steam-engine. . . . We then rejoined the rest of the party, and the engine having received its supply of water, the carriage was placed behind it, for it cannot turn, and was set off at its utmost speed, thirty-five miles an hour, swifter than a bird flies. . . . You cannot conceive what that sensation of cutting air was. . . . The wind, which was strong, or perhaps the force of our own thrusting against it, absolutely weighed my eyelids down. . . . When I closed my eyes this sensation of flying was quite delightful, and strange beyond description; yet, strange as it was, I had a perfect sense of security, and not the slightest fear."

44. Based on this excerpt, how would you characterize Fanny Kemble's reaction to her experience?

45. Assume you are a factory worker hearing this account read to you. Explain your reaction.

46. Based on Fanny Kemble's reaction, how do you think this new form of transportation was received in Britain?

Essay
On a separate sheet of paper, write an answer to the following questions.

47. **Recognizing Causes and Effects** How did Britain's agricultural revolution help it industrialize early?

48. **Defending a Position** Do you think the material benefits of industrialization outweighed the suffering it caused? Defend your position with examples from the text.

49. **Applying Information** What do you think were two of the hardest adjustments that a person who gave up farming to move to a city and work in a factory during the Industrial Revolution had to make?

50. **Identifying Main Ideas** How was Karl Marx's Communist Manifesto a reflection of the times he lived in?

51. **Linking Past and Present** Do you think that industrialization has improved the quality of life for most people today? Explain.

52. **Identifying Alternatives** Taking into consideration the theories of thinkers like Jeremy Bentham, John Stuart Mill, and Karl Marx and reformers like Robert Owen, imagine a scenario that would have allowed Britain to industrialize in a more humane fashion than happened. Describe it briefly.

CHAPTER 20—THE INDUSTRIAL REVOLUTION BEGINS (1750–1850)
Answer Section

MATCHING

1. ANS: B   DIF: E   REF: 499   OBJ: C20S1-2
    TOP: Economics, Enclosure
2. ANS: D   DIF: E   REF: 502   OBJ: C20S2-2
    TOP: Technology, Factory system
3. ANS: A   DIF: E   REF: 505   OBJ: C20S3-1
    TOP: Social systems, Urbanization
4. ANS: E   DIF: E   REF: 511   OBJ: C20S4-2
    TOP: Social systems, Utilitarianism
5. ANS: C   DIF: E   REF: 511-512   OBJ: C20S4-2
    TOP: Political systems, Socialism

6. ANS: D   DIF: E   REF: 499   OBJ: C20S1-2
    TOP: Impact of the individual, Jethro Tull
7. ANS: B   DIF: E   REF: 508   OBJ: C20S3-3
    TOP: Impact of the individual, John Wesley
8. ANS: E   DIF: E   REF: 510   OBJ: C20S4-1
    TOP: Impact of the individual, Thomas Malthus
9. ANS: A   DIF: E   REF: 511   OBJ: C20S4-2
    TOP: Impact of the individual, John Stuart Mill
10. ANS: C   DIF: E   REF: 512-513   OBJ: C20S4-3
    TOP: Impact of the individual, Karl Marx

11. ANS: D   DIF: E   REF: 514   OBJ: C20S2-3
    TOP: Technology, Turnpike
12. ANS: E   DIF: E   REF: 515   OBJ: C20S3-1
    TOP: Social systems, Urbanization
13. ANS: C   DIF: E   REF: 511-512   OBJ: C20S4-2
    TOP: Political systems, Socialism
14. ANS: A   DIF: E   REF: 512-513   OBJ: C20S4-3
    TOP: Political systems, Communism
15. ANS: B   DIF: E   REF: 512-513   OBJ: C20S4-3
    TOP: Political systems, Proletariat

16. ANS: D   DIF: E   REF: 500   OBJ: C20S1-3
    TOP: Impact of the individual, James Watt
17. ANS: C   DIF: E   REF: 500   OBJ: C20S1-3
    TOP: Impact of the individual, Abraham Darby
18. ANS: B   DIF: E   REF: 510   OBJ: C20S4-1
    TOP: Impact of the individual, David Ricardo
19. ANS: E   DIF: E   REF: 511   OBJ: C20S4-2
    TOP: Impact of the individual, Jeremy Bentham

20. ANS: A   DIF: E   REF: 512   OBJ: C20S4-2
     TOP: Impact of the individual, Robert Owen

MULTIPLE CHOICE

21. ANS: B   DIF: E   REF: 500   OBJ: C20S1-2
     TOP: Continuity and change, Population explosion
22. ANS: B   DIF: A   REF: 500   OBJ: C20S1-2
     TOP: Continuity and change, Population explosion
23. ANS: B   DIF: E   REF: 500   OBJ: C20S1-2
     TOP: Continuity and change, Population explosion
24. ANS: D   DIF: A   REF: 500   OBJ: C20S1-2
     TOP: Continuity and change, Population explosion
25. ANS: B   DIF: A   REF: 499   OBJ: C20S1-1
     TOP: Technology, Second agricultural revolution
26. ANS: A   DIF: A   REF: 500   OBJ: C20S1-3
     TOP: Technology, Steam engine
27. ANS: B   DIF: A   REF: 501   OBJ: C20S2-2
     TOP: Technology, Iron production
28. ANS: D   DIF: A   REF: 506   OBJ: C20S3-2
     TOP: Technology, Women workers
29. ANS: C   DIF: D   REF: 512   OBJ: C20S4-2
     TOP: Social systems, Utopians
30. ANS: A   DIF: E   REF: 512-513   OBJ: C20S4-3
     TOP: Political systems, Scientific socialism
31. ANS: A   DIF: A   REF: 499   OBJ: C20S1-1
     TOP: Technology, Enclosure
32. ANS: C   DIF: A   REF: 501-502   OBJ: C20S2-1
     TOP: Economics, Britain leads the Industrial Revolution
33. ANS: B   DIF: A   REF: 502   OBJ: C20S2-3
     TOP: Technology, First factories
34. ANS: B   DIF: E   REF: 506   OBJ: C20S3-2
     TOP: Technology, Working conditions
35. ANS: C   DIF: A   REF: 508-509   OBJ: C20S3-3
     TOP: Social systems, New middle class
36. ANS: A   DIF: A   REF: 511   OBJ: C20S4-1
     TOP: Social systems, Utilitarians

SHORT ANSWER

37. ANS:
     Answers should include three of the following: enclosure, the use of fertilizer and other methods to renew the soil, new methods of crop rotation, and new mechanical devices.

     DIF: E   REF: 499   OBJ: C20S1-1
     TOP: Technology, Second agricultural revolution

38. ANS:
The agricultural revolution lowered the death rate by reducing famine and allowing people to eat better, which improved their health and made them more resistant to disease.

DIF: A   REF: 500   OBJ: C20S1-2
TOP: Technology, Second agricultural revolution

39. ANS:
steam, coal, and water

DIF: A   REF: 500   OBJ: C20S1-3
TOP: Technology, Energy revolution

40. ANS:
an abundance of coal (natural resources), an abundance of workers (human resources), technological know-how, capital and a market for goods (good economic conditions), a stable government and an entrepreneurial outlook (good political and social conditions)

DIF: D   REF: 501-502   OBJ: C20S2-1
TOP: Economics, Britain leads the Industrial Revolution

41. ANS:
It made it rigid and took it out of the context of nature and away from the family. Also, workers in factories were no longer toiling for their own consumption, but working for someone else's profit.

DIF: D   REF: 506   OBJ: C20S3-1
TOP: Continuity and change, Factory system

42. ANS:
They thought women could adapt more easily to machines. They thought women were easier to manage than men. They were able to pay women less than men.

DIF: A   REF: 506   OBJ: C20S3-2
TOP: Economics, Women workers

43. ANS:
Thomas Malthus—tried to explain the relationship of population growth and family size to widespread poverty during the Industrial Revolution. Jeremy Bentham—tried to justify some government intervention on behalf of the poor during the Industrial Revolution with his theory of utilitarianism. Karl Marx—tried to show that capitalism, the foundation of the Industrial Revolution, was evil because it exploited the workers.

DIF: D   REF: 510-513   OBJ: C20S4-1
TOP: Impact of the individual, New ways of thinking

44. ANS:
Kembel's reaction was one of wonder and delight.

DIF: A   REF: 503-504   OBJ: C20S2-1
TOP: Technology, Revolution in transportation

45. ANS:
Most students will probably answer that they would be amazed, excited, and a little overwhelmed. Some might react with skepticism.

DIF: A   REF: 503-504   OBJ: C20S3-1
TOP: Technology, Revolution in transportation

46. ANS:
Most students will probably think that the British were excited about the railroad and welcomed it.

DIF: A   REF: 503-504   OBJ: C20S3-1
TOP: Technology, Revolution in transportation

ESSAY

47. ANS:
The agricultural revolution freed many people from farm labor and allowed them to work in the factories. Also, an increase in the food supply supported a growing population, which increased the demand for goods and fueled the growth of factories.

DIF: A   REF: 499,501   OBJ: C20S2-1
TOP: Technology, Britain leads the Industrial Revolution

48. ANS:
Answers should be supported by examples.

DIF: D   REF: 509   OBJ: C20S3-3
TOP: Continuity and change, Industrialization

49. ANS:
Answers might include two of the following: the switch from work that was varied and performed out in nature to monotonous work performed in ugly, unhealthy surroundings; the loss of community; the loss of control over one's work; the loss of independence.

DIF: A   REF: 505-506   OBJ: C20S3-1
TOP: Continuity and change, Urbanization

50. ANS:
Answers should draw the connection between Marx's focus on history as the story of the struggle between the "haves" and "have-nots" and the development of capitalism with its small group of wealthy and its mass of impoverished workers under industrialization.

DIF: D   REF: 512-513   OBJ: C20S4-3
TOP: Political systems, Communist Manifesto

51. ANS:
Answers should be supported by a sound explanation.

DIF: A   REF: 509   OBJ: C20S3-3
TOP: Continuity and change, Industrialization

52. ANS:
Students' answers should reflect some degree of understanding of these men's philosophies and attempt to apply them.

DIF: D   REF: 511-513   OBJ: C20S4-2
TOP: Social systems, Industrialization

CHAPTER 21—REVOLUTIONS IN EUROPE AND LATIN AMERICA (1790–1848)

Matching

Match each term with the correct statement below.

a. autonomy   d. Frankfurt Assembly
b. el Grito de Dolores   e. ideology
c. February Days

____ 1. System of thought and belief

____ 2. Self-rule

____ 3. Uprisings in Paris that protested government attempts to silence critics in 1848

____ 4. Meeting of delegates from German states to create a constitution

____ 5. Speech that called the people of Mexico to fight for independence

Match each person with the correct statement below.

a. Louis Kossuth   d. Toussaint L'Ouverture
b. Louis XVIII   e. Tupac Amaru
c. Adam Smith

____ 6. Laissez-faire economist supported by early 1800 liberals

____ 7. King of France who issued the Charter of French Liberties

____ 8. Leader of Hungarian nationalists

____ 9. Leader of revolution in Haiti

____ 10. Leader of Native American revolt against Spanish system of forced labor

Match each person with the correct statement below.

a. Simón Bolívar   e. Louis Philippe
b. Miguel Hidalgo   f. Clemens von Metternich
c. Louis XVIII   g. Pedro
d. Louis Napoleon   h. Toussaint L'Ouverture

____ 11. Leader who dominated Austrian politics for more than 30 years

____ 12. King of France who was restored to the throne by the Congress of Vienna

____ 13. Ruler of France known as the "citizen king"

____ 14. President of the Second Republic who proclaimed himself emperor of France

____ 15. General who led Haitians to independence

____ 16. Creole priest who led the fight for Mexican independence

_____ 17. Leader of the fight for independence in Venezuela

_____ 18. Emperor of an independent Brazil

Multiple Choice
Identify the letter of the choice that best completes the statement or answers the question.

_____ 19. Which of the following goals represents the ideology of nationalists?
   a. establishment of a homeland for people with a common heritage
   b. restoration of power to royal families
   c. acceptance of an established church
   d. tolerance for ethnic minorities

_____ 20. Which of the following terms best reflects conditions in Europe after 1815?
   a. stability
   b. peace
   c. rebellion
   d. democracy

_____ 21. Which of the following nations gained independence from Holland?
   a. Poland
   b. Belgium
   c. Italy
   d. Hungary

_____ 22. Which of the following results was caused by revolts in the Austrian empire?
   a. Universal manhood suffrage was granted.
   b. Hungary gained independence.
   c. Austria became a republic.
   d. Metternich resigned.

_____ 23. Which group dominated Latin American social and political life in the early 1800s?
   a. creoles
   b. peninsulares
   c. mestizos
   d. mulattoes

_____ 24. Which of the following events was the spark that finally set off a widespread revolt in Latin America in the early 1800s?
   a. Napoleon's invasion of Spain
   b. the American Revolution
   c. the French Revolution
   d. uprisings in the Balkans

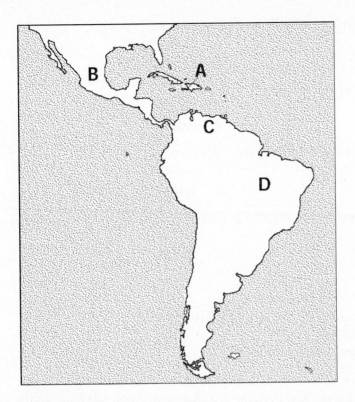

Figure 21-1

_____ 25. The letter A in Figure 21-1 marks the nation led to independence by
a. Simón Bolívar.
b. Miguel Hidalgo.
c. Toussaint L'Ouverture.
d. José de San Martín.

_____ 26. Which letter in Figure 21-1 marks the nation in which Augustín de Iturbide overthrew Spanish rule?
a. A
b. B
c. C
d. D

_____ 27. The letter A in Figure 21-1 marks the nation in which
a. Toussaint L'Ouverture led a revolt against French rule.
b. Augustín de Iturbide overthrew Spanish rule.
c. Simón Bolívar established a republic.
d. Dom Pedro made himself emperor.

_____ 28. Which letter in Figure 21-1 marks the nation in which Miguel Hidalgo urged the people to fight for independence?
a. A
b. B
c. C
d. D

_____ 29. Which of the following goals represents conservative ideology in Europe in the early 1800s?
a. restoration of power to royal families
b. establishment of a homeland for each national group
c. support for freedom of the press
d. tolerance for religious differences

_____ 30. Which of the following groups generally supported nationalist goals?
    a. monarchs   c. church leaders
    b. noble landowner   d. ethnic groups

_____ 31. In the early 1800s, Serbs gained autonomy within
    a. Greece.   c. Spain.
    b. the Ottoman empire.   d. Austria.

_____ 32. The period of unrest in Europe after 1815 was caused by
    a. opposing ideologies.   c. competition for colonies.
    b. religious conflicts.   d. demand for resources.

_____ 33. Which of the following countries succeeded in gaining independence as a result of revolutions in 1830?
    a. Belgium   c. Hungary
    b. Poland   d. Italy

_____ 34. What happened as a result of the Frankfurt Assembly?
    a. Germany was united under Frederick William IV.
    b. Germany became a republic.
    c. Conservatives accepted workers' demands.
    d. Liberals were defeated.

_____ 35. Discontent in Latin America resulted from the domination of social and political life by
    a. mulattoes.   c. peninsulares.
    b. mestizos.   d. creoles.

_____ 36. Which of the following places won independence from France and became the only nonslave nation in the Western Hemisphere?
    a. Haiti   c. Venezuela
    b. Mexico   d. Brazil

Short Answer

37. List three differences between conservative and liberal ideologies in Europe in the early 1800s.

38. Explain how liberals and nationalists contributed to unrest in Europe after 1815.

39. Describe the social and economic problems in France that led to revolts in 1830 and 1848.

40. Identify European countries that, like France, experienced revolutions in 1830 or in 1848.

41. Explain two reasons why the revolts of 1830 and 1848 generally failed.

42. Explain why Haiti's struggle for freedom was long and complex.

43. Explain how the way that Brazil achieved independence differed from independence movements in other Latin American countries.

Read the following excerpt from a speech Louis Napoleon gave in October 1852. Then answer the questions that follow.

"Indeed, . . . never has a people testified in a manner more direct, spontaneous, and unanimous, the longing to be freed from anxiety as to the future by concentrating in a single person an authority which shall accord [agree] with their desires. They realize now both the false hopes with which they have been deluded [deceived] and the dangers which threaten them. . . .

I concede, nevertheless, that, like the emperor [Napoleon Bonaparte], I have many conquests to make. . . . I would conquer, for the sake of religion, morality, and material ease, that portion of the population, still very numerous, which, in the midst of a country of faith and belief, hardly knows the precepts [teachings] of Christ; which, in the midst of the most fertile country of the world, is hardly able to enjoy the primary necessities of life. We have immense uncultivated districts to bring under cultivation, roads to open, harbors to construct, rivers to render navigable, canals to finish, and our network of railroads to bring to completion. . . .

This is what I understand by the empire, if the empire is to be reestablished. These are the conquests which I contemplate, and all of you who surround me, who, like myself, wish the good of our common country, you are my soldiers."

44. According to Louis Napoleon, what form of government did the French people want?

45. According to the excerpt, what conquests did Louis Napoleon believe he had to make?

46. What improvements did Louis Napoleon propose to make?

Essay
On a separate sheet of paper, write an answer to the following questions.

47. **Recognizing Causes and Effects** How did opposing ideologies affect conditions in Europe after 1815?

48. **Analyzing Information** What social and political conditions that emerged under Spanish rule led to revolutions in Latin America?

49. **Recognizing Causes and Effects** How did differences between conservative and liberal goals lead to conflict in Europe?

50. **Drawing Conclusions** Were the revolutions of 1830 and 1848 a victory for conservatives or liberals? Why?

51. **Analyzing Information** Describe the positive and negative effects of nationalism in Europe after 1815.

52. **Recognizing Causes and Effects** Explain how events in Europe influenced revolutions in Latin America.

CHAPTER 21—REVOLUTIONS IN EUROPE AND LATIN AMERICA (1790–1848)
Answer Section

MATCHING

1. ANS: E   DIF: E   REF: 518   OBJ: C21S1-1
   TOP: Political systems, Ideology
2. ANS: A   DIF: E   REF: 520   OBJ: C21S1-3
   TOP: Political systems, Autonomy
3. ANS: C   DIF: E   REF: 522   OBJ: C21S2-1
   TOP: Political systems, February Days
4. ANS: D   DIF: E   REF: 526   OBJ: C21S2-3
   TOP: Political systems, Frankfurt Assembly
5. ANS: B   DIF: E   REF: 530-531   OBJ: C21S3-2
   TOP: Political systems, Independence for Mexico

6. ANS: C   DIF: E   REF: 519   OBJ: C21S1-2
   TOP: Impact of the individual, Adam Smith
7. ANS: B   DIF: E   REF: 521   OBJ: C21S2-1
   TOP: Impact of the individual, Louis XVIII
8. ANS: A   DIF: E   REF: 525   OBJ: C21S2-3
   TOP: Impact of the individual, Louis Kossuth
9. ANS: D   DIF: E   REF: 528-530   OBJ: C21S3-2
   TOP: Impact of the individual, Toussaint L'Ouverture
10. ANS: E   DIF: E   REF: 531   OBJ: C21S3-3
    TOP: Impact of the individual, Tupac Amaru

11. ANS: F   DIF: E   REF: 525   OBJ: C21S2-3
    TOP: Impact of the individual, Clemens von Metternich
12. ANS: C   DIF: E   REF: 521   OBJ: C21S2-1
    TOP: Impact of the individual, Louis XVIII
13. ANS: E   DIF: E   REF: 522   OBJ: C21S2-1
    TOP: Impact of the individual, Louis Philippe
14. ANS: D   DIF: E   REF: 522-524   OBJ: C21S2-1
    TOP: Impact of the individual, Louis Napoleon
15. ANS: H   DIF: E   REF: 528-530   OBJ: C21S3-2
    TOP: Impact of the individual, Toussaint L'Ouverture
16. ANS: B   DIF: E   REF: 530-531   OBJ: C21S3-2
    TOP: Impact of the individual, Miguel Hidalgo
17. ANS: A   DIF: E   REF: 527, 532   OBJ: C21S3-3
    TOP: Impact of the individual, Simón Bolívar
18. ANS: G   DIF: E   REF: 533   OBJ: C21S3-3
    TOP: Impact of the individual, Dom Pedro

MULTIPLE CHOICE

19. ANS: A   DIF: D   REF: 519   OBJ: C21S1-1
    TOP: Political systems, Nationalists
20. ANS: C   DIF: A   REF: 519-520   OBJ: C21S1-3
    TOP: Political systems, Revolts against the old order
21. ANS: B   DIF: E   REF: 524   OBJ: C21S2-2
    TOP: Continuity and change, Independence for Belgium
22. ANS: D   DIF: A   REF: 525   OBJ: C21S2-3
    TOP: Political systems, Metternich
23. ANS: B   DIF: A   REF: 527   OBJ: C21S3-1
    TOP: Social systems, Peninsulares
24. ANS: A   DIF: A   REF: 528   OBJ: C21S3-1
    TOP: Global interaction, Revolts in Latin America
25. ANS: C   DIF: A   REF: 528-530   OBJ: C21S3-2
    TOP: Impact of the individual, Toussaint L'Ouverture
26. ANS: B   DIF: A   REF: 530-531   OBJ: C21S3-3
    TOP: Continuity and change, Independence for Mexico
27. ANS: A   DIF: A   REF: 528-530   OBJ: C21S3-2
    TOP: Continuity and change, Independence for Haiti
28. ANS: B   DIF: A   REF: 530-531   OBJ: C21S3-3
    TOP: Continuity and change, Independence for Mexico
29. ANS: A   DIF: A   REF: 518   OBJ: C21S1-1
    TOP: Political systems, Conservative ideology
30. ANS: D   DIF: A   REF: 519   OBJ: C21S1-2
    TOP: Diversity, Ethnic groups support nationalism
31. ANS: B   DIF: E   REF: 520   OBJ: C21S1-2
    TOP: Continuity and change, Independence for Serbia
32. ANS: A   DIF: A   REF: 519-520   OBJ: C21S1-3
    TOP: Continuity and change, Europe after 1815
33. ANS: A   DIF: A   REF: 524   OBJ: C21S2-2
    TOP: Continuity and change, Revolutions of 1830
34. ANS: D   DIF: A   REF: 526   OBJ: C21S2-3
    TOP: Continuity and change, Turmoil in the German states
35. ANS: C   DIF: A   REF: 527-528   OBJ: C21S3-1
    TOP: Social systems, Peninsulares
36. ANS: A   DIF: A   REF: 528-530   OBJ: C21S3-2
    TOP: Continuity and change, Independence for Haiti

SHORT ANSWER

37. ANS:
Conservatives favored monarchies, established churches, and aristocracy. Liberals favored constitutional governments, freedom of religion, and individual rights.

DIF: A   REF: 518-519   OBJ: C21S1-1
TOP: Political systems, Opposing ideologies

38. ANS:
Liberals challenged conservative forces by speaking out in favor of reform. Nationalists fought to gain independence from empires and establish their own homelands.

DIF: A   REF: 519-520   OBJ: C21S1-3
TOP: Continuity and change, Revolts against the old order

39. ANS:
In 1830, middle-class citizens resented the privileges of the French aristocracy and wanted the government to extend suffrage. Working-class people demanded decent pay. Louis Philippe's policies favored the middle class over the workers. An economic slump in the 1840s caused additional unrest, and workers rioted against the upper- and middle-class interests that controlled the government.

DIF: D   REF: 521-524   OBJ: C21S2-1
TOP: Continuity and change, Revolutions in France

40. ANS:
Revolutions took place in Belgium, Poland, Austria, Italy, and Germany.

DIF: E   REF: 524-526   OBJ: C21S2-2
TOP: Continuity and change, Revolutions of 1830 and 1848

41. ANS:
The revolutions of 1830 and 1848 did not have the support of all the people. The revolutionaries lacked unity because workers wanted radical economic change while liberals wanted moderate political reforms.

DIF: A   REF: 524-526   OBJ: C21S2-3
TOP: Continuity and change, Revolutions of 1830 and 1848

42. ANS:
Haiti's struggle began as a slave revolt led by Toussaint L'Ouverture. Full independence was gained. After his death, conflict continued until 1820, when Haiti became a republic.

DIF: A   REF: 528-530   OBJ: C21S3-2
TOP: Continuity and change, Independence for Haiti

43. ANS:
The Portuguese ruler of Brazil proclaimed himself emperor of an independent nation. In other Latin American countries, independence was won through revolutionary wars.

DIF: A   REF: 528-533   OBJ: C21S3-3
TOP: Continuity and change, Independence for Brazil

44. ANS:
Louis Napoleon stated that the French wanted an empire with authority concentrated in a single person.

DIF: A   REF: 522-524   OBJ: C21S2-1
TOP: Political systems, Louis Napoleon

45. ANS:
He wanted to end conflicts, spread Christianity, and ease poverty within the empire.

DIF: D   REF: 522-524   OBJ: C21S2-1
TOP: Impact of the individual, Louis Napoleon

46. ANS:
He proposed to bring additional areas under cultivation, to open roads, to construct harbors, to make rivers navigable, and to finish canals and railroads.

DIF: D   REF: 522-524   OBJ: C21S2-1
TOP: Impact of the individual, Louis Napoleon

ESSAY

47. ANS:
The ideologies of conservatives, liberals, and nationalists often conflicted. Nationalists and liberals challenged the old order, which was supported by conservatives. Reformers demanded change, and conservative rulers used force to crush uprisings.

DIF: D   REF: 518-522   OBJ: C21S1-3
TOP: Political systems, Europe after 1815

48. ANS:
Only peninsulares could hold top jobs in government and the Church. Creoles, mestizos, and mulattoes resented their unequal status. Native Americans and African slaves protested economic hardships and lack of freedom imposed by Spanish rule.

DIF: D   REF: 527-528   OBJ: C21S3-1
TOP: Continuity and change, Revolutions in Latin America

49. ANS:
Conservatives supported monarchy, hierarchy of social classes, and an established church. Liberals opposed all these ideas. In order to achieve constitutional governments, liberals revolted against the old order.

DIF: D   REF: 518-520   OBJ: C21S1-1
TOP: Political systems, Opposing ideologies

50. ANS:
Liberals succeeded in gaining independence for Belgium. In most other places, however, revolutions failed because they did not have mass support. In 1850, conservatives remained in control of most European nations.

DIF: D   REF: 524-526   OBJ: C21S2-3
TOP: Continuity and change, Revolutions of 1830 and 1848

51. ANS:
Nationalism united people with a common heritage. It gave them a sense of identity and a common goal of establishing their own homeland. It also led to intolerance and persecution of minorities.

DIF: D   REF: 519-520   OBJ: C21S1-2
TOP: Diversity, Nationalism in Europe

52. ANS:
Latin Americans were influenced by the works of Enlightenment thinkers. Creoles, like Simón Bolívar, traveled in Europe during the French Revolution and were inspired by French ideals. Napoleon's invasion of Spain led Latin Americans to view Spain as weak and to demand independence from foreign rule.

DIF: D   REF: 528   OBJ: C21S3-1
TOP: Global interaction, Revolutions in Latin America

CHAPTER 22—LIFE IN THE INDUSTRIAL AGE (1800–1914)

Matching

Match each term with the correct statement below.
a. cartel
b. corporation
c. impressionism
d. interchangeable parts

e. social gospel
f. racism
g. realism
h. romanticism

____ 1. ____ were identical components that speeded both assembly and repair because they could be used in place of one another.

____ 2. A business owned by stockholders is called a ____.

____ 3. When a group of large businesses bands together to control a single industry, it is called a ____.

____ 4. ____ is the belief that one racial group is superior to another.

____ 5. Protestant churches in Europe and the United States urged their worshipers to become involved in a movement to help others known as the ____.

____ 6. Artists who were part of a movement called ____ aimed to excite strong emotions with their work.

____ 7. ____ was an artistic movement that attempted to represent the world as it was.

____ 8. Painters who were part of the movement known as ____ focused on capturing fleeting visual impressions.

Match each term with the correct statement below.
a. assembly line
b. corporation
c. impressionism

d. Social Darwinism
e. suffrage

____ 9. A way of organizing workers and machines in order to assemble a finished product efficiently

____ 10. A business owned by stockholders

____ 11. The right to vote

____ 12. The idea that the fittest would always beat out their competitors, whether in war or industry

____ 13. A style of painting that tries to capture the fleeting effects of light on an object

Match each person with the correct statement below.
a. Henry Bessemer
b. John Dalton
c. Charles Dickens

d. Louis Pasteur
e. Louis Sullivan

____ 14. British engineer who invented a process to produce steel

_____ 15. French doctor who proved the "germ theory"

_____ 16. American architect who designed skyscrapers

_____ 17. Quaker schoolteacher who developed modern atomic theory

_____ 18. A realist English writer who portrayed the lives of slum dwellers

Multiple Choice
Identify the letter of the choice that best completes the statement or answers the question.

_____ 19. By 1900, which of the following pairs of countries were the world's leading industrial nations?
    a.   Britain and the United States   c.   Japan and Germany
    b.   Germany and the United States   d.   Britain and Germany

_____ 20. Which of the following was a direct result of the discovery that germs caused disease?
    a.   the development of anesthesia   c.   the beginning of nursing
    b.   higher death rates   d.   improved sanitation

_____ 21. In nineteenth-century cities, the poor lived
    a.   in planned residential neighborhoods.
    b.   on the outskirts of the city.
    c.   in skyscrapers.
    d.   in tenements near the factories.

_____ 22. Which of the following is the most closely linked to labor reform?
    a.   ministers   c.   unions
    b.   Social Darwinists   d.   city planners

_____ 23. Which of the following groups grew the fastest during the 1800s?
    a.   the middle class   c.   the nobility
    b.   peasants   d.   the upper class

_____ 24. Which of the following was the most highly regarded by the middle class during the 1800s?
    a.   honesty   c.   generosity
    b.   respectability   d.   individuality

_____ 25. Why does Darwin's theory of evolution cause controversy?
    a.   It disagrees with the biblical account of creation.
    b.   It states that religion is a way for the state to control the masses.
    c.   It denies the existence of God.
    d.   It challenges the moral authority of the church.

_____ 26. An example of a romantic painting might be a
    a.   landscape showing a violent storm.
    b.   portrait of a middle-class family.
    c.   scene of a modern city.
    d.   scene of workers in a factory.

Figure 22-1

_____ 27. What is "the ballot" in Figure 22-1 meant to bring to the viewer's mind?
    a. a rolled-up piece of paper
    b. a baby
    c. the fight to equal rights
    d. the right for women to stay at home

_____ 28. According to Figure 22-1, how would the vote affect women?
    a. It would change their life greatly.
    b. It would make them happier.
    c. It would change their life hardly at all.
    d. It would allow them to stay at home with their children.

_____ 29. Figure 22-1 was drawn from the point of view of
    a. suffragist.
    b. a liberal male.
    c. an anti-suffragist.
    d. a socialist.

_____ 30. According to Figure 22-1, American women were
    a. not ready to have the vote.
    b. fooling themselves if they thought the vote would lead to fulfillment.
    c. hoping the vote would free them from their domestic responsibilities.
    d. not working hard enough to get the vote.

_____ 31. Which of the following countries were the world's industrial leaders in 1900?
a. Britain and France
b. Germany and the United States
c. Russia and Germany
d. Belgium and Germany

_____ 32. One scientist whose work contributed directly to increased life expectancy in the late 1800s was
a. Dmitri Mendeleyev.
b. Charles Lyell.
c. Alfred Nobel.
d. Joseph Lister.

_____ 33. Which of the following new features of city life in the late 1800s had the greatest impact on the poor?
a. sewage systems
b. skyscrapers
c. multistory apartment buildings
d. paved streets

_____ 34. The saying "a woman's place is in the home" reflected the values of which of the following groups in 1850?
a. the working class
b. the middle class
c. miners
d. farmworkers

_____ 35. Darwin challenged traditional beliefs by asserting that
a. Earth was older than formerly thought.
b. women were equal to men.
c. all forms of life evolved over millions of years.
d. the sun was the center of the universe.

_____ 36. The romantic movement in art and literature was a reaction against
a. socialism.
b. nationalism.
c. the Enlightenment.
d. the French Revolution.

Short Answer

37. List three technological advances that helped industry grow.

38. Define the term corporation and explain the connection between technology and the growth of these new ways of doing business.

39. Identify the contributions of Louis Pasteur, Robert Koch, Florence Nightingale, and Joseph Lister, and explain their significance.

40. Describe three ways the lives of workers who lived in cities changed during the later Industrial Revolution.

41. Identify three middle-class values during the 1800s.

42. Explain how Darwin's theory of natural selection challenged traditional Christian beliefs.

43. Compare the responses of realist and romantic artists to the industrial world.

Read the following poem, "To a Skylark," by Percy Bysshe Shelley. Then answer the questions that follow.

"Hail to thee, blithe spirit!
Bird thou never wert,
That from heaven, or near it,
Pourest thy full heart
In profuse strains of unpremeditated art,

• • •

Better than all measures
Of delightful sound,
Better than all treasures
That in books are found,
Thy skill to poet were, thou scorner of the ground!

Teach me half the gladness
That thy brain must know,
Such harmonious madness
From my lips would flow,
The world should listen then, as I am listening now."

44. What does Shelley mean by "unpremeditated art"?

45. How does Shelley express his view that nature is more rewarding than intellect and reason?

46. Using the poem, identify three characteristics of romantic art.

Essay
On a separate sheet of paper, write an answer to the following questions.

47. **Recognizing Causes and Effects** Explain how Social Darwinism encouraged racism.

48. **Comparing** Compare the responses of realist and romantic artists to the industrial world.

49. **Predicting Consequences** How do you think politics changed when workers received the right to vote?

50. **Understanding Main Ideas** During the period of industrialization the economy shifted from agricultural to industrial. How did this change affect the social order?

51. **Recognizing Causes and Effects** What problem associated with life in the city did skyscrapers address?

52. **Making Inferences** Why do you suppose it took Western European women longer to gain their full rights than it did women who lived in frontier lands like Australia and New Zealand?

CHAPTER 22—LIFE IN THE INDUSTRIAL AGE (1800–1914)
Answer Section

MATCHING

1. ANS: D   DIF: E   REF: 546   OBJ: C22S1-2
   TOP: Technology, Interchangeable parts

2. ANS: B   DIF: E   REF: 549   OBJ: C22S1-3
   TOP: Economics, Corporation

3. ANS: A   DIF: E   REF: 550   OBJ: C22S1-3
   TOP: Economics, Cartel

4. ANS: F   DIF: E   REF: 561   OBJ: C22S3-3
   TOP: Diversity, Social Darwinism

5. ANS: E   DIF: E   REF: 561   OBJ: C22S3-4
   TOP: Religion, Social gospel

6. ANS: H   DIF: E   REF: 562-563   OBJ: C22S4-1
   TOP: Art and literature, Romanticism

7. ANS: G   DIF: E   REF: 563-565   OBJ: C22S4-2
   TOP: Art and literature, Realism

8. ANS: C   DIF: E   REF: 565   OBJ: C22S4-2
   TOP: Art and literature, Impressionism

9. ANS: A   DIF: E   REF: 546   OBJ: C22S1-2
   TOP: Technology, New methods of production

10. ANS: B   DIF: E   REF: 549   OBJ: C22S1-3
    TOP: Economics, Corporation

11. ANS: E   DIF: E   REF: 558   OBJ: C22S3-2
    TOP: Political systems, Suffrage

12. ANS: D   DIF: E   REF: 561   OBJ: C22S3-3
    TOP: Social systems, Social Darwinism

13. ANS: C   DIF: E   REF: 565   OBJ: C22S4-2
    TOP: Art and literature, Impressionism

14. ANS: A   DIF: E   REF: 546   OBJ: C22S1-2
    TOP: Impact of the individual, Henry Bessemer

15. ANS: D   DIF: E   REF: 551   OBJ: C22S2-1
    TOP: Impact of the individual, Louis Pasteur

16. ANS: E   DIF: E   REF: 552   OBJ: C22S2-2
    TOP: Impact of the individual, Louis Sullivan

17. ANS: B   DIF: E   REF: 559   OBJ: C22S3-3
    TOP: Impact of the individual, John Dalton

18. ANS: C   DIF: E   REF: 564   OBJ: C22S4-2
    TOP: Impact of the individual, Charles Dickens

MULTIPLE CHOICE

19. ANS: B   DIF: A   REF: 544   OBJ: C22S1-1
    TOP: Continuity and change, Industrial nations
20. ANS: D   DIF: A   REF: 551   OBJ: C22S2-1
    TOP: Technology, Germ theory
21. ANS: D   DIF: E   REF: 552   OBJ: C22S2-2
    TOP: Social systems, Slums
22. ANS: C   DIF: A   REF: 553-554   OBJ: C22S2-3
    TOP: Economics, Labor reform
23. ANS: A   DIF: D   REF: 555-556   OBJ: C22S3-1
    TOP: Social systems, New social order
24. ANS: B   DIF: A   REF: 555-556   OBJ: C22S3-2
    TOP: Social systems, Middle class values
25. ANS: A   DIF: A   REF: 560-561   OBJ: C22S3-4
    TOP: Science, Theory of natural selection
26. ANS: A   DIF: A   REF: 563   OBJ: C22S4-1
    TOP: Art and literature, Romanticism
27. ANS: B   DIF: E   REF: 558   OBJ: C22S3-3
    TOP: Political and social systems, Suffrage
28. ANS: C   DIF: D   REF: 558   OBJ: C22S3-3
    TOP: Political and social systems, Suffrage
29. ANS: C   DIF: A   REF: 558   OBJ: C22S3-3
    TOP: Political and social systems, Suffrage
30. ANS: B   DIF: D   REF: 558   OBJ: C22S3-3
    TOP: Political and social systems, Suffrage
31. ANS: B   DIF: A   REF: 544   OBJ: C22S1-1
    TOP: Economics, Industrial leaders
32. ANS: D   DIF: D   REF: 552   OBJ: C22S2-1
    TOP: Impact of the individual, Joseph Lister
33. ANS: A   DIF: A   REF: 552   OBJ: C22S2-2
    TOP: Technology, Sewer systems
34. ANS: B   DIF: E   REF: 556   OBJ: C22S3-2
    TOP: Social systems, Middle class values
35. ANS: C   DIF: A   REF: 560-561   OBJ: C22S3-4
    TOP: Science, Theory of evolution
36. ANS: C   DIF: E   REF: 562-563   OBJ: C22S4-1
    TOP: Art and literature, Romanticism

SHORT ANSWER

37. ANS:
Answers could include three of the following: development of steel; new methods of production (including the assembly line); electricity; or new forms of transportation, including railroads.

DIF: A   REF: 546-548   OBJ: C22S1-2
TOP: Technology, Growth of industry

38. ANS:
A corporation is a business owned by many investors who buy shares of stock. New technologies required the investment of large amounts of money. As a result, it required more capital to start a new business than a single businessperson could provide.

DIF: A   REF: 549   OBJ: C22S1-3
TOP: Economics, Corporation

39. ANS:
Louis Pasteur proved that germs and certain diseases were linked, which led to the development of vaccines and improved sanitation and an eventual decrease in the death rate. Robert Koch identified the bacteria that caused tuberculosis, and eventually a cure was found. Florence Nightingale founded the world's first nursing school and introduced hygiene in British hospitals. Joseph Lister's discovery that antiseptics prevented infection led to their use, which drastically reduced deaths from infection.

DIF: D   REF: 551-552   OBJ: C22S2-1
TOP: Technology, Advances in medicine

40. ANS:
Answers should point to three of the following: paved streets made cities more livable; lighting made streets safer at night; sewer systems cut death rates; some could afford better clothing; people lived longer and enjoyed healthier lives; educational opportunities were available; people had access to entertainment.

DIF: E   REF: 552-553   OBJ: C22S2-3
TOP: Social systems, City life

41. ANS:
Answers may include three of the following: comfort (luxury), respectability, propriety, responsibility, or success.

DIF: A   REF: 556   OBJ: C22S3-2
TOP: Social systems, Middle class values

42. ANS:
Darwin's argument that all forms of life, including humans, had evolved over millions of years challenged the Christian belief that God created the world and all its forms of life in six days. Not only did this argument directly contradict the biblical account of creation, it reduced people to the level of animals and, many Christians felt, undermined belief in God.

DIF: A   REF: 560-561   OBJ: C22S3-4
TOP: Religion, Theory of natural selection

43. ANS:
Realists confronted the harshness of the industrial world directly and hoped to improve the lives of the poor; romantics turned away from it to focus on nature and the emotional life of humanity.

DIF: A   REF: 562-565   OBJ: C22S4-2
TOP: Art and literature, Art and the industrial world

44. ANS:
Shelley uses "unpremeditated art" in reference to the skylark's song because it is unstudied and natural.

DIF: A   REF: 562-563   OBJ: C22S4-1
TOP: Art and literature, Romanticism

45. ANS:
He says the skylark's song is "better than all treasures that in books are found."

DIF: A   REF: 562-563   OBJ: C22S4-1
TOP: Art and literature, Romanticism

46. ANS:
love of nature, use of emotional language, revolt against reason and the intellect

DIF: D   REF: 562-563   OBJ: C22S4-1
TOP: Art and literature, Romanticism

ESSAY

47. ANS:
It promoted the belief that the fittest were the most successful. Therefore, it argued, since western civilization was so successful, the white race must be superior.

DIF: D   REF: 561   OBJ: C22S3-4
TOP: Social systems, Social Darwinism

48. ANS:
Realists confronted the harshness of the industrial world directly and hoped to improve the lives of the poor; romantics turned away from it to focus on nature and the emotional life of humanity.

DIF: A   REF: 562-565   OBJ: C22S4-2
TOP: Art and literature, Art and the industrial world

49. ANS:
Politicians began to change their platforms in order to attract workers' votes. Answers might also point out that a split developed between politicians who favored upper-class interests and those who promoted the interests of the working class. This split eventually led to distinct party identities.

DIF: A   REF: 553-554   OBJ: C22S2-3
TOP: Political systems, Suffrage

50. ANS:
Answers should point to the fact that under the old social order, landowners (the aristocracy) held the highest rank because they controlled the source of food production and the means of survival. The only other social distinction of significance encompassed the peasants who worked the land. As the western world changed from an agricultural economy to an industrial one, the focus switched from land to the manufacturing of material goods as the source of wealth. Those who controlled production became the new elite, and a much more subtle and complex class system emerged based on the types of services people performed in the new industrial society.

DIF: D   REF: 555-556   OBJ: C22S3-1
TOP: Continuity and change, Industrialization

51. ANS:
overcrowding

DIF: A   REF: 552   OBJ: C22S2-2
TOP: Social systems, City life

52. ANS:
Women in frontier lands worked alongside men building their lives from scratch; whereas women in Western Europe were part of an inherited tradition of female subservience.

DIF: D   REF: 558   OBJ: C22S3-3
TOP: Social systems, Suffrage

CHAPTER 23—NATIONALISM TRIUMPHS IN EUROPE (1800–1914)

Matching

Match each person with the correct statement below.
a. Alexander II
b. an anarchist
c. Francis Joseph
d. Giuseppe Garibaldi
e. Otto von Bismarck
f. a refugee
g. William II
h. Camillo Cavour

_____ 1. "Germany must be unified at any price."

_____ 2. "There is only one master in the Reich, and that is I."

_____ 3. "We will expel the Austrians from Italy."

_____ 4. "Follow me, you glorious Red Shirts, and together we will create an Italian republic."

_____ 5. "Government should not exist."

_____ 6. "I am emperor of Austria, and the king of Hungary."

_____ 7. "It is better to abolish serfdom from above than to wait until it is abolished from below."

_____ 8. "We fled from our village when a mob attacked and tried to kill us."

Match each term with the correct statement below.
a. anarchist
b. pogrom
c. *Realpolitik*
d. refugee
e. zemstvo

_____ 9. Otto von Bismarck's political philosophy

_____ 10. A person who wants to abolish all government

_____ 11. Elected local assemblies in Russia

_____ 12. An organized massacre of helpless people

_____ 13. People who flee their homeland for safety in another place

Match each person with the correct statement below.
a. Alexander II
b. Otto von Bismarck
c. Francis Joseph
d. Giuseppe Garibaldi
e. William II

_____ 14. Prussian leader who engineered German unity

_____ 15. German ruler whose foreign policy was aimed at acquiring an overseas empire

_____ 16. Italian nationalist who helped to unify Italy

_____ 17. The emperor of Austria and king of Hungary

_____ 18. Russian czar who freed the serfs

Multiple Choice
Identify the letter of the choice that best completes the statement or answers the question.

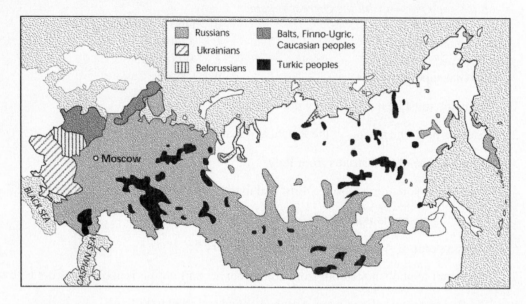

Figure 23-1

_____ 19. What does Figure 23-1 show about Russia in the 1800s?
   a. the growth of its empire
   b. its population density
   c. the distribution of its ethnic groups
   d. the location of nationalist movements

_____ 20. Which of the following can be most accurately inferred from Figure 23-1?
   a. Most of Russia's population was made up of Ukrainians.
   b. The most active nationalist movements were among non-Slavic peoples.
   c. Many different national groups made up Russia's population.
   d. The Belorussians were in the strongest position to have their demand for independence from Russia granted.

_____ 21. Which of the following would be the best title for the map of Russia in 1800 (Figure 23-1)?
   a. Population Density in Russia   c. Nationalities of Russia
   b. The Growth of the Russian Empire   d. Russian Expansion

_____ 22. According to Figure 23-1, which of the following statements is the most reasonable?
   a. Turkic peoples had the strongest argument in favor of independence.
   b. The Ukrainians were treated the most harshly of any national group.
   c. Most of Moscow's population in 1800 were Russians.
   d. Most nationalist revolts occurred in or around Moscow.

_____ 23. Otto von Bismarck was responsible for the
  a. creation of the *Zollverein*.
  b. unification of Germany.
  c. loss of the Franco-Prussian War.
  d. rise of Napoleon III.

_____ 24. Which of the following was a result of the Franco-Prussian War?
  a. Prussia defeated France.
  b. France defeated Prussia.
  c. Austria defeated Prussia.
  d. France defeated Austria.

_____ 25. Which of the following contributed to Germany's growth as an industrial power under Bismarck?
  a. tight state control over industry
  b. a large overseas empire
  c. substantial iron and coal reserves
  d. Prussia's victory over the French in the Franco-Prussian War

_____ 26. The *Kulturkampf* refers to Bismarck's attempt to
  a. encourage appreciation for the arts.
  b. destroy nationalist movements.
  c. discourage socialism.
  d. weaken the influence of the Catholic Church.

_____ 27. William II of Germany pursued a foreign policy aimed at
  a. destroying the French navy.
  b. preventing foreigners from coming to Germany.
  c. winning overseas colonies for Germany.
  d. encouraging socialist revolutions in Africa and Asia.

_____ 28. Which of the following made Italy hard to unite into a single country?
  a. lack of a common language
  b. regional differences
  c. lack of natural resources
  d. ethnic differences

_____ 29. A major threat to the Hapsburg empire came from
  a. nationalist demands.
  b. the Ottoman empire.
  c. socialist reformers.
  d. the French.

_____ 30. The revolution of 1905 broke out as a result of
  a. persecution of the Jews.
  b. the killing of demonstrators on Bloody Sunday.
  c. the freeing of the serfs.
  d. Napoleon's invasion of Russia.

_____ 31. Which of the following happened LAST?
  a. Prussia gained control of Schleswig.
  b. Prussia defeated France.
  c. Prussia went to war with Austria.
  d. Prussia created the *Zollverein*.

_____ 32. How did the German government encourage economic development?
  a. It protected its industries from foreign competition.
  b. It subsidized industry.
  c. It owned and managed Germany's industry.
  d. It prohibited the sale of foreign goods in Germany.

____ 33. Under Bismarck, Germany took a pioneering role in
a. social and economic reform.
b. political reform.
c. socialist reform.
d. judicial reform.

____ 34. Nationalism posed the biggest threat to which of the following?
a. Prussia
b. Italy
c. Germany
d. the Austrian empire

____ 35. Which of the following contributed most to the growth of nationalist movements in the Balkans in the mid-1800s?
a. the decline of the Ottoman empire
b. the spread of democracy
c. competition between Britain and France for the Balkans
d. Germany's growing power

____ 36. The revolution of 1905 led to
a. democracy in Russia.
b. minor changes in Russia.
c. the freeing of Russian serfs.
d. equal voting rights for all citizens.

Short Answer

37. Explain how each of the following wars helped Prussia to unite Germany: war with Denmark, the Austro-Prussian War, and the Franco-Prussian War.

38. List five factors that helped German industry grow in the late 1800s.

39. In one sentence, explain the objective of Bismarck's domestic policy regarding Catholics and socialists.

40. Describe the tension between regionalism and nationalism in Italy.

41. Explain how the weakening of the Ottoman empire led to conflict in the Balkans.

42. Describe Russia's social structure and explain how the social structure made it difficult to achieve economic and social progress.

43. List three reforms that resulted from the revolution of 1905.

Read the following excerpt from Otto von Bismarck's memoirs. Then answer the questions that follow.

"Late in September, after being named prime minister, I gave a speech that created some excitement. I had said that we will not get nearer the goal of German unification by speeches, associations, and decisions of majorities. Only blood and iron, I stated, would settle the issue.

I insisted that parliament must place the greatest possible weight of blood and iron in the hands of the king of Prussia.

The king feared the consequences of this speech, predicting that my policies would result in our execution. I responded by saying to him that 'we must all die sooner or later, and can we perish more honorably? I fighting for my king's cause, and Your Majesty sealing with your own blood your rights as king by the grace of God.'"

44. Based on this excerpt, how does Bismarck feel about representative government? How do you know?

45. What does Bismarck mean by "I insisted that parliament must place the greatest possible weight of blood and iron in the hands of the king of Prussia"?

46. Based on this excerpt, how does Bismarck view his relationship to William I?

Essay
On a separate sheet of paper, write an answer to the following questions.

47. **Comparing** Compare the role of nationalism in Germany and in the Austrian empire. How was nationalism both a unifying and a divisive force?

48. **Applying Information** Why was the Balkan region referred to as the "Balkan powder keg"?

49. **Making Inferences** How did early German nationalism help smooth the transition to a single German state?

50. **Defending a Position** What evidence supports Metternich's belief that Italy was a "geographical expression," not a nation?

51. **Comparing** Compare the role of Cavour and Bismarck in the unification of their countries.

CHAPTER 23—NATIONALISM TRIUMPHS IN EUROPE (1800–1914)
Answer Section

MATCHING

1. ANS: E   DIF: E   REF: 571-573   OBJ: C23S1-2
   TOP: Political systems, Bismarck
2. ANS: G   DIF: E   REF: 576   OBJ: C23S2-3
   TOP: Impact of the individual, William II
3. ANS: H   DIF: E   REF: 578-579   OBJ: C23S3-2
   TOP: Power and conflict, Italian unity
4. ANS: D   DIF: E   REF: 579   OBJ: C23S3-2
   TOP: Impact of the individual, Giuseppe Garibaldi
5. ANS: B   DIF: E   REF: 580   OBJ: C23S3-3
   TOP: Political systems, Anarchy
6. ANS: C   DIF: E   REF: 582-583   OBJ: C23S4-2
   TOP: Political systems, Dual Monarchy
7. ANS: A   DIF: E   REF: 585-586   OBJ: C23S5-2
   TOP: Social systems, Emancipation of serfs
8. ANS: F   DIF: E   REF: 588   OBJ: C23S5-2
   TOP: Political systems, Refugee

9. ANS: C   DIF: E   REF: 571   OBJ: C23S1-2
   TOP: Political systems, Realpolitik
10. ANS: A   DIF: E   REF: 580   OBJ: C23S3-3
    TOP: Political systems, Anarchist
11. ANS: E   DIF: E   REF: 586   OBJ: C23S5-2
    TOP: Political systems, Zemstvo
12. ANS: B   DIF: E   REF: 588   OBJ: C23S5-2
    TOP: Religion, Pogrom
13. ANS: D   DIF: E   REF: 588   OBJ: C23S5-2
    TOP: Political systems, Refugee

14. ANS: B   DIF: E   REF: 571-573   OBJ: C23S1-2
    TOP: Impact of the individual, Otto von Bismarck
15. ANS: E   DIF: E   REF: 576   OBJ: C23S2-3
    TOP: Impact of the individual, William II
16. ANS: D   DIF: E   REF: 597   OBJ: C23S3-2
    TOP: Impact of the individual, Giuseppe Garibaldi
17. ANS: C   DIF: E   REF: 582-583   OBJ: C23S4-2
    TOP: Impact of the individual, Francis Joseph
18. ANS: A   DIF: E   REF: 585-586   OBJ: C23S5-2
    TOP: Impact of the individual, Alexander II

MULTIPLE CHOICE

19. ANS: C   DIF: A   REF: 584   OBJ: C23S5-1
    TOP: Diversity, Population of Russia
20. ANS: C   DIF: D   REF: 584   OBJ: C23S5-1
    TOP: Diversity, Population of Russia
21. ANS: C   DIF: E   REF: 584   OBJ: C23S5-1
    TOP: Diversity, Population of Russia
22. ANS: C   DIF: E   REF: 584   OBJ: C23S5-1
    TOP: Diversity, Population of Russia
23. ANS: B   DIF: E   REF: 571-573   OBJ: C23S1-2
    TOP: Impact of the individual, Otto von Bismarck
24. ANS: A   DIF: A   REF: 573   OBJ: C23S1-3
    TOP: Power and conflict, Franco-Prussian War
25. ANS: C   DIF: A   REF: 574   OBJ: C23S2-1
    TOP: Economics, German industry
26. ANS: D   DIF: A   REF: 575   OBJ: C23S2-2
    TOP: Religion, Kulturkampf
27. ANS: C   DIF: A   REF: 576   OBJ: C23S2-3
    TOP: Power and conflict, German imperialism
28. ANS: B   DIF: A   REF: 577-578   OBJ: C23S2-1
    TOP: Political systems, Italian unity
29. ANS: A   DIF: A   REF: 581-583   OBJ: C23S4-1
    TOP: Political systems, Hapsburg empire
30. ANS: B   DIF: A   REF: 588-589   OBJ: C23S5-3
    TOP: Political systems, Russian revolution of 1905
31. ANS: B   DIF: D   REF: 571-573   OBJ: C23S1-3
    TOP: Power and conflict, Germany unity
32. ANS: A   DIF: A   REF: 575   OBJ: C23S2-1
    TOP: Economics, German industry
33. ANS: A   DIF: A   REF: 575-576   OBJ: C23S2-2
    TOP: Impact of the individual, Otto von Bismarck
34. ANS: D   DIF: A   REF: 581-583   OBJ: C23S4-1
    TOP: Political systems, Austrian empire
35. ANS: A   DIF: D   REF: 583   OBJ: C23S4-3
    TOP: Continuity and change, Balkan nationalism
36. ANS: B   DIF: A   REF: 589   OBJ: C23S5-3
    TOP: Continuity and change, Russian revolution of 1905

SHORT ANSWER

37. ANS:
War with Denmark—Prussia and Austria divided Schleswig and Holstein between themselves; Austro-Prussian War—Prussia gained control of several other German states; and Franco-Prussian War—victory finally convinced the German princes to unite into a single empire under William I.

DIF: D   REF: 573   OBJ: C23S1-3
TOP: Political systems, Unification of Germany

38. ANS:
Answers should include five of the following: large deposits of coal and iron; a disciplined and educated work force; a huge home market; earlier progress in industries that had been established in the mid-1800s; scientific research and development; government support including organized banking, the development of a transportation infrastructure, and tariffs to protect home trade from foreign competition.

DIF: A   REF: 574-575   OBJ: C23S2-1
TOP: Economics, German industry

39. ANS:
He wanted to ensure that citizens' primary allegiance was to the state.

DIF: A   REF: 575   OBJ: C23S2-2
TOP: Social systems, Bismarck

40. ANS:
Most Italians felt stronger ties to their regions than they did to Italy as a nation. Therefore, it was often hard for them to move beyond regional loyalties to solve critical national issues.

DIF: A   REF: 579-580   OBJ: C23S3-3
TOP: Political systems, Italian unity

41. ANS:
As Ottoman control over the Balkans weakened, nationalist groups grew bolder in making their demands for independent nations. At the same time, European countries began to assert their ambitions in the area. The interests of these various groups often clashed.

DIF: A   REF: 583   OBJ: C23S4-3
TOP: Global interaction, Balkans

42. ANS:
Landowning nobles dominated society. Although the czar was at the top of the social structure, his power was dependent on support from the nobles. The middle class was too small to have much influence. The majority of the people were serfs. The czar could not make any reforms that affected the power of the nobles or he would lose their support. Landowning nobles had no reason to improve agriculture and took little interest in industry.

DIF: A   REF: 584-585   OBJ: C23S5-1
TOP: Continuity and change, Social structure in Russia

43. ANS:
The czar promised personal freedoms, including freedom of person, speech, and assembly, and the establishment of an elected national legislature. The prime minister enacted moderate land reforms. In the end, however, there was relatively little positive change for the peasants and the workers. Russia was still an autocracy.

DIF: A   REF: 589   OBJ: C23S5-3
TOP: Continuity and change, Russian revolution of 1905

44. ANS:
Bismarck dislikes representative government. He indicates this when he states that German unification cannot be reached "by speeches, associations, and decisions of majorities." Also, from the second paragraph it is obvious that he is a staunch supporter of the king.

DIF: A   REF: 570-571   OBJ: C23S1-2
TOP: Political systems, Otto von Bismarck

45. ANS:
He means that the parliament must place the greatest amount of power, including military power, in the hands of the king.

DIF: A   REF: 570-571   OBJ: C23S1-2
TOP: Political systems, Blood and iron

46. ANS:
Bismarck seems to view himself as bolder than the king but at the same time protective of the king's rights.

DIF: A   REF: 570-571   OBJ: C23S1-2
TOP: Impact of the individual, Otto von Bismarck

ESSAY

47. ANS:
In Germany, nationalism worked to unify the Germans into a single nation; whereas in Austria, the demands of competing national groups divided the empire and helped to tear it apart.

DIF: A   REF: 570-573, 581-583   OBJ: C23S1-1
TOP: Political systems, Nationalism

48. ANS:
Tensions among nationalist groups and foreign powers competing for control of the region had reached such a pitch by the early 1900s that the region threatened to explode at any time.

DIF: D   REF: 583   OBJ: C23S4-3
TOP: Power and conflict, Balkans

49. ANS:
Early nationalism in Germany bound Germans together even before the arrival of a formal nation.

DIF: E   REF: 570-571   OBJ: C23S1-1
TOP: Political systems, German nationalism

50. ANS:
Culturally, Italians identified themselves according to the region they were from. Also, Italy's shape sets it off from the rest of Europe and gives it a distinct physical identity.

DIF: A   REF: 577, 579-580   OBJ: C23S3-1
TOP: Geography, Italy

51. ANS:
Both Cavour and Bismarck were instrumental in achieving national unity in their countries. Both used the philosophy of *Realpolitik* and the idea that "the ends justify the means" to achieve their goals. Each military move they made was with an eye to furthering the unity of their countries. Neither was a proponent of democracy, preferring instead the monarchy as the most expedient way to achieve their ends.

DIF: D   REF: 570-571, 578-579   OBJ: C23S3-2
TOP: Impact of the individual, Cavour and Bismarck

CHAPTER 24—GROWTH OF WESTERN DEMOCRACIES (1815–1914)

Matching

Match each term with the correct statement below.
a. coalition
b. Chartism
c. home rule
d. isolationism
e. segregation

_____ 1. Movement that demanded universal male suffrage in Britain

_____ 2. Local self-government in Ireland

_____ 3. An alliance of political parties

_____ 4. Legal separation of races

_____ 5. Limited involvement in world affairs

Match each person with the correct statement below.
a. Benjamin Disraeli
b. Frederick Douglass
c. Alfred Dreyfus
d. William Gladstone
e. Emmeline Pankhurst

_____ 6. Leader of the Conservative party and prime minister in Britain who fought for social reforms

_____ 7. British suffragist leader who supported the use of violence

_____ 8. Leader of the Liberal party and prime minister in Britain who pushed for reforms in Ireland

_____ 9. French army officer unjustly convicted of spying

_____ 10. Former slave who spoke out against slavery

Match each term with the correct statement below.
a. coalition
b. Fabians
c. home rule
d. isolationism
e. segregation

_____ 11. _____ were members of a socialist organization that worked for social reform.

_____ 12. In the 1870s, Irish nationalists began to demand self-government, or _____.

_____ 13. A _____ is made up of an alliance of political parties.

_____ 14. The legal separation of the races in restaurants, hospitals, schools, and other public places is known as _____.

_____ 15. In the early 1900s, many Americans wanted to follow a foreign policy known as _____, which favored limited involvement in world affairs.

Match each person with the correct statement below.

a. Benjamin Disraeli   d. Napoleon III
b. Frederick Douglass   e. Charles Stewart Parnell
c. Theodor Herzl

_____ 16. Leader of the Conservative party and British Prime Minister

_____ 17. Irish nationalist leader

_____ 18. Ruler of the Second Empire

_____ 19. Founder of modern Zionism

_____ 20. African American who campaigned to end slavery

Multiple Choice
Identify the letter of the choice that best completes the statement or answers the question.

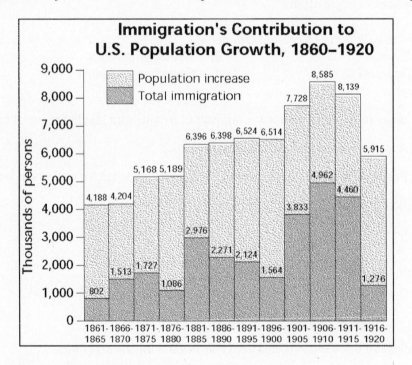

Figure 24-1

_____ 21. According to Figure 24-1, between which years was population growth in the United States the greatest?
a. 1881–1885   c. 1911–1915
b. 1906–1910   d. 1871–1875

_____ 22. According to Figure 24-1, between which years was the number of immigrants to the United States the greatest?
a. 1911–1915   c. 1901–1905
b. 1881–1885   d. 1906–1910

_____ 23. According to Figure 24-1, between what years was immigration into the United States the highest?

a. 1881–1885   c. 1876–1880

b. 1911–1915   d. 1906–1910

_____ 24. Which of the following generalizations about immigration and population growth in the United States is supported by Figure 24-1?

a. Immigration contributed little to population growth.

b. Immigration's contribution to population growth increased steadily between 1861 and 1920.

c. Immigration contributed greatly to population growth.

d. Immigration contributed most to population growth before the 1900s.

_____ 25. Which of the following groups held the most power in Parliament in the early 1800s?

a. middle-class men   c. working-class men

b. wealthy, landowning nobles   d. wealthy industrialists

_____ 26. During the 1800s, the Liberal and Conservative parties in Britain both worked to

a. extend the right to vote to more people.

b. extend home rule to Ireland.

c. repeal the reform bills.

d. abolish the office of prime minister.

_____ 27. Social reforms passed in Britain in the late 1800s helped which of the following groups most?

a. women   c. middle-class men

b. industrial workers   d. farmers

_____ 28. The aim of Napoleon III's foreign policy was to

a. reestablish the French as a European power.

b. keep France isolated.

c. establish French neutrality.

d. establish a balance of power with Britain.

_____ 29. Which of the following was true of the Third Republic's government?

a. The president was elected by universal male suffrage.

b. The prime minister was elected by the legislature.

c. The voter-elected Chamber of Deputies had great power.

d. It was based on a two-party system.

_____ 30. In 1920, the Nineteenth Amendment gave

a. African American men the right to vote.

b. citizenship to Native Americans.

c. women the right to vote.

d. slaves their freedom.

_____ 31. In the early 1800s, Parliament represented primarily the interests of

a. everyone in Britain.   c. wealthy landowners.

b. mainly the middle class.   d. the working-class majority.

____ 32. The Reform Bill of 1867 granted suffrage to
    a. working-class men.
    c. middle-class men.
    b. women.
    d. everyone over 30 years old.

____ 33. Which of the following would have most likely supported the Corn Laws in Britain?
    a. a wealthy industrialist
    c. a factory worker
    b. a farmer
    d. a lawyer

____ 34. Napoleon III appealed to the lower classes mainly because he
    a. made France a major industrial power.
    b. opposed Prussia.
    c. promised to end poverty.
    d. extended French influence to Mexico.

____ 35. Which of the following was an effect of the Dreyfus affair?
    a. increased sympathy for Jews
    c. reforms in the court system
    b. harsh laws against antisemitism
    d. demands for a Jewish state

____ 36. Before the Civil War, one of the major issues between the North and the South was
    a. free trade.
    b. the extension of slavery into new states.
    c. voting rights for women.
    d. the election of Abraham Lincoln as president.

Short Answer

37. How did the Liberal party in the House of Commons restrict the power of the Lords? Why was it necessary to do so?

38. List five economic and/or social reforms passed by the British Parliament in the 1800s and identify which group they helped.

39. Explain what the Irish nationalist leader Daniel O'Connell meant when he said "My first object is to get Ireland for the Irish."

40. Summarize the failures of Napoleon III's domestic and foreign policies in one sentence each.

41. Describe the effect of the Dreyfus affair on French society.

42. Identify two ways in which reformers worked to make the United States more democratic in the mid-1800s.

43. Compare the lives of African Americans before and after the Civil War.

Read the following excerpts from the official record of a debate in the House of Commons over extending the right to vote to working men. Then answer the questions that follow.

Robert Lowe

"Mr. Lowe delivered a powerful speech against the bill. He pointed out the danger arising from the power of the working classes to unite for the purpose of winning their objectives. He warned of the ease with which labor unions might be converted into political organizations. What tremendous power that labor unions would have if workers had the right to vote. Adopt this bill, and there was no saying where they would stop in the downward direction of democracy. Democracy would threaten our institutions, even the monarchy itself."

William Gladstone

"Mr. Gladstone praised the qualities of English factory workers who have nobly endured suffering. The qualities exhibited were the qualities, not of select men . . . but of the majority. He said that he could not see what argument could be found against giving the right to vote to such people. Is there or is there not a steady movement of the laboring classes, and is or is not that movement onwards and upwards?"

44. In this excerpt, what argument does Lowe make against passage of the bill?

45. According to the excerpt, why does Gladstone think workers should have the right to vote?

46. What does Lowe's argument against passage of the bill imply about his view of the working class? How does this differ from Gladstone's view?

Essay
On a separate sheet of paper, write an answer to the following questions.

47. **Identifying Alternatives** What alternative policy could the British have adopted toward Ireland in the 1800s?

48. **Predicting Consequences** How do you think the South's defeat in the Civil War affected its economy?

49. **Making Inferences** How do you suppose Victorian ideals clashed with the suffragist movement?

50. **Recognizing Causes and Effects** How did territorial expansion help the United States to grow economically?

51. **Making Inferences** Why do you think Queen Victoria opposed the women's suffrage movement?

CHAPTER 24—GROWTH OF WESTERN DEMOCRACIES (1815–1914)
Answer Section

MATCHING

1. ANS: B   DIF: E   REF: 595   OBJ: C24S1-3
   TOP: Political systems, Chartism
2. ANS: C   DIF: E   REF: 602   OBJ: C24S2-3
   TOP: Political systems, Home rule
3. ANS: A   DIF: E   REF: 605   OBJ: C24S3-2
   TOP: Political systems, Coalition
4. ANS: E   DIF: E   REF: 611   OBJ: C24S4-2
   TOP: Social systems, Segregation
5. ANS: D   DIF: E   REF: 613   OBJ: C24S4-3
   TOP: Global interaction, Isolationism

6. ANS: A   DIF: E   REF: 596   OBJ: C24S1-3
   TOP: Impact of the individual, Benjamin Disraeli
7. ANS: E   DIF: E   REF: 600   OBJ: C24S2-2
   TOP: Impact of the individual, Emmeline Pankhurst
8. ANS: D   DIF: E   REF: 602   OBJ: C24S2-3
   TOP: Impact of the individual, William Gladstone
9. ANS: C   DIF: E   REF: 606-607   OBJ: C24S3-2
   TOP: Impact of the individual, Alfred Dreyfus
10. ANS: B   DIF: E   REF: 609   OBJ: C24S4-2
    TOP: Impact of the individual, Frederick Douglass

11. ANS: B   DIF: E   REF: 599   OBJ: C24S2-1
    TOP: Social systems, Fabians
12. ANS: C   DIF: E   REF: 602   OBJ: C24S2-3
    TOP: Political systems, Home rule
13. ANS: A   DIF: E   REF: 605   OBJ: C24S3-2
    TOP: Political systems, Coalition
14. ANS: E   DIF: E   REF: 611   OBJ: C24S4-2
    TOP: Social systems, Segregation
15. ANS: D   DIF: E   REF: 613   OBJ: C24S4-3
    TOP: Global interaction, Isolationism

16. ANS: A   DIF: E   REF: 596   OBJ: C24S1-3
    TOP: Impact of the individual, Benjamin Disraeli
17. ANS: E   DIF: E   REF: 602   OBJ: C24S2-3
    TOP: Impact of the individual, Charles Stewart Parnell
18. ANS: D   DIF: E   REF: 603-605   OBJ: C24S3-1
    TOP: Impact of the individual, Napoleon III
19. ANS: C   DIF: E   REF: 606-607   OBJ: C24S3-2
    TOP: Impact of the individual, Theodor Herzl

20. ANS: B   DIF: E   REF: 609   OBJ: C24S4-2
    TOP: Impact of the individual, Frederick Douglass

MULTIPLE CHOICE

21. ANS: B   DIF: E   REF: 612   OBJ: C24S4-1
    TOP: Continuity and change, United States population growth
22. ANS: D   DIF: A   REF: 612   OBJ: C24S4-1
    TOP: Continuity and change, United States immigration
23. ANS: D   DIF: E   REF: 612   OBJ: C24S4-1
    TOP: Continuity and change, United States immigration
24. ANS: C   DIF: A   REF: 612   OBJ: C24S4-1
    TOP: Continuity and change, United States immigration
25. ANS: B   DIF: A   REF: 594   OBJ: C24S1-1
    TOP: Political systems, Parliament
26. ANS: A   DIF: A   REF: 596   OBJ: C24S1-2
    TOP: Political systems, Suffrage in Britain
27. ANS: B   DIF: A   REF: 599   OBJ: C24S2-1
    TOP: Social systems, British social reform
28. ANS: A   DIF: A   REF: 604-605   OBJ: C24S3-1
    TOP: Power and conflict, Napoleon III
29. ANS: C   DIF: D   REF: 605-606   OBJ: C24S3-2
    TOP: Political systems, Third Republic
30. ANS: C   DIF: A   REF: 610   OBJ: C24S4-2
    TOP: Continuity and change, Suffrage
31. ANS: C   DIF: A   REF: 594   OBJ: C24S1-1
    TOP: Political systems, Parliament
32. ANS: A   DIF: D   REF: 596   OBJ: C24S1-3
    TOP: Continuity and change, Suffrage
33. ANS: B   DIF: A   REF: 597-598   OBJ: C24S2-1
    TOP: Economics, Corn Laws
34. ANS: C   DIF: A   REF: 603   OBJ: C24S3-1
    TOP: Social systems, Napoleon III
35. ANS: D   DIF: A   REF: 606-607   OBJ: C24S3-3
    TOP: Religion, Dreyfus affair
36. ANS: B   DIF: A   REF: 611   OBJ: C24S4-3
    TOP: Continuity and change, American slavery

SHORT ANSWER

37. ANS:
    The Liberal government restricted the power of the Lords to veto tax bills, so the Lords could
    not veto the Liberals' social reforms.

    DIF: A   REF: 596   OBJ: C24S1-3
    TOP: Political systems, Parliament

38. ANS:
    Answers should include five of the following: repeal of the Corn Laws—middle and working
    class; abolition of slavery—slaves in Britain and its colonies; judicial reforms (more humane
    criminal and penal codes)—criminals; laws regulating working hours, wages, and safety
    conditions in industry—working class; laws regulating child labor—child workers;
    legalization of trade unions—workers; social welfare laws (including laws to improve public
    health and housing and to provide unemployment, accident, and health insurance)—working
    and middle class; or provisions for free elementary education for all children—society in
    general.

    DIF: A   REF: 597-599   OBJ: C24S2-1
    TOP: Economic and social systems, Reform in Britain

39. ANS:
    He meant freedom from British rule and all that it entailed, including loss of Irish land.

    DIF: E   REF: 602   OBJ: C24S2-3
    TOP: Political systems, Irish home rule

40. ANS:
    Despite economic growth, poverty continued. In foreign affairs, Napoleon suffered defeat in
    Mexico and a humiliating loss to Prussia.

    DIF: D   REF: 603-605   OBJ: C24S3-1
    TOP: Political systems, Napoleon III

41. ANS:
    The Dreyfus affair tore French society into two heated camps—the nationalists, royalists, and
    the Church, who wanted Dreyfus punished, and the liberals and republicans who thought he
    was wrongly accused.

    DIF: A   REF: 606-607   OBJ: C24S3-3
    TOP: Social systems, Dreyfus affair

42. ANS:
    Answers should include women's suffrage and abolition.

    DIF: A   REF: 609-611   OBJ: C24S4-2
    TOP: Continuity and change, American democratic reform

43. ANS:
    Before the Civil War, most African Americans were enslaved and had no political rights.
    After the war they were free people with very restricted political rights. In some ways, life
    was harder for African Americans after the war because they had to survive on their own with
    very few political and economic resources.

    DIF: A   REF: 611   OBJ: C24S4-3
    TOP: Continuity and change, Lives of African Americans

44. ANS:
Lowe argues that labor unions will become too powerful if workers have the right to vote and could turn democracy into a threat to British institutions.

DIF:　A　　　　REF: 596　　　OBJ: C24S1-2
TOP:　Political systems, Suffrage

45. ANS:
Gladstone argues that the good character of the workers makes them deserving of the vote.

DIF:　A　　　　REF: 596　　　OBJ: C24S1-3
TOP:　Political systems, Suffrage

46. ANS:
Lowe seems to view the working class as having an inferior character and thinks they will drag democracy in a "downward direction"; whereas Gladstone seems to view them in a much nobler light.

DIF:　D　　　　REF: 596　　　OBJ: C24S1-2
TOP:　Political systems, Suffrage

ESSAY

47. ANS:
Some may suggest a limited form of self-rule; others may indicate a complete withdrawal of the British from Ireland. Still others may point to more lenient ways Britain could have managed Ireland.

DIF:　A　　　　REF: 602　　　OBJ: C24S2-3
TOP:　Political systems, Ireland

48. ANS:
Answers will probably suggest that the fighting and the abolition of slavery virtually destroyed the South's economy.

DIF:　D　　　　REF: 611-612　　OBJ: C24S4-3
TOP:　Economics, Civil War

49. ANS:
Answers will vary but some may suggest that the women's suffrage movement violated the Victorian ideal of respectability, which implies an adherence to tradition and good manners. Answers may also point out that the women's suffrage movement challenged traditional family and gender roles.

DIF:　D　　　　REF: 599-600　　OBJ: C24S2-2
TOP:　Social systems, Victorian ideals

50. ANS:
It gave the United States access to more resources, including valuable minerals and land.

DIF:　A　　　　REF: 608-609, 611-612　　　OBJ: C24S4-1
TOP:　Geography, United States territorial expansion

51. ANS:
Answers should point to the fact that one of Victoria's most important values was respectability and that implied adhering to tradition and a strict code of manners. The women's suffrage movement violated both of these values. Answers may point to the structure of the family in Victoria's time and note that Victoria might have felt that the women's suffrage movement challenged traditional family roles.

DIF: D   REF: 599-600   OBJ: C24S2-2
TOP: Social systems, Queen Victoria

CHAPTER 25—THE NEW IMPERIALISM (1800–1914)

Matching

Match each term with the correct statement below.

a. cash crop
b. extraterritoriality
c. genocide
d. indemnity
e. protectorate

_____ 1. An imperialist system in which local rulers were left to rule

_____ 2. The destruction of an entire religious or ethnic group

_____ 3. A crop grown to sell on the world market

_____ 4. Payment for losses in a war

_____ 5. The right of foreigners to live under their own laws and to be tried in their own courts

Match each person with the correct statement below.

a. Ci Xi
b. Menelik II
c. Muhammad Ali
d. Ram Mohun Roy
e. Sun Yixian

_____ 6. Ethiopian ruler who successfully resisted the Italians

_____ 7. Egyptian leader who laid the foundation for modern Egypt

_____ 8. Founder of Indian nationalism

_____ 9. Powerful, conservative Chinese ruler

_____ 10. Leader of the Chinese Republic

Match each term with the correct statement below.

a. balance of trade
b. cash crop
c. extraterritoriality
d. deforestation
e. indemnity
f. protectorate
g. trade deficit
h. sphere of influence

_____ 11. In a(n) _____, local rulers governed but western powers were in actual control.

_____ 12. An area in which an outside power claimed exclusive investment or trading rights was called a(n) _____.

_____ 13. Cotton is considered a(n) _____ because it is sold on the world market.

_____ 14. Clearing farmlands or massive cutting of trees leads to _____.

_____ 15. China exported more than it imported, so it was said to have a favorable _____.

_____ 16. Some western countries bought more from the Chinese than they sold to them, which resulted in a(n) _____.

_____ 17. China had to pay Britain a huge _____ to compensate it for its losses during the Opium War.

_____ 18. British citizens in China were granted _____, or the right to live under their own laws.

Multiple Choice
Identify the letter of the choice that best completes the statement or answers the question.

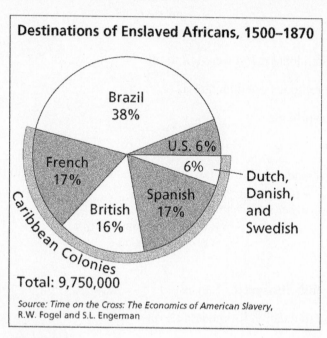

Figure 25-1

_____ 19. According to Figure 25-1, what percentage of captured Africans were sent to Brazil as slaves?
    a.   17%   c.   6%
    b.   16%   d.   38%

_____ 20. According to Figure 25-1, to which region were most of the enslaved Africans taken?
    a.   to mainland South America   c.   to the United States
    b.   to the Caribbean   d.   to Europe

_____ 21. According to Figure 25-1, what percentage of captured Africans were sent to the United States as slaves?
    a.   17%   c.   6%
    b.   38%   d.   16%

_____ 22. Which of the following statements is supported by Figure 25-1?
    a.   Slavery was rare in the Caribbean.
    b.   The Europeans were morally opposed to slavery.
    c.   Americans were less tolerant than the Europeans toward slavery.
    d.   The use of slaves was common in Brazil.

_____ 23. How did the Industrial Revolution encourage imperialism?
a. It made Europeans feel sorry for their "little brothers."
b. It created a need for land.
c. It created a need for raw materials and markets.
d. It made westerners feel obligated to improve the human species.

_____ 24. Which of the following countries gained control of much of southern Africa during the 1800s?
a. France
b. Italy
c. Spain
d. Britain

_____ 25. Why did both Britain and Russia want to control Iran?
a. to spread their political beliefs
b. to gain possession of its oil
c. to help it modernize
d. to save it from Ottoman rule

_____ 26. Which of the following was a result of the Sepoy Rebellion?
a. India gained its independence.
b. India became a protectorate of Britain.
c. Britain began to rule India directly.
d. The East India Company took over the rule of India.

_____ 27. Which of the following statements regarding China in the 1800s is true?
a. It was the center of a flourishing civilization.
b. It was in the midst of an economic revival.
c. It was a growing industrial nation.
d. Its society and economy were in decline.

_____ 28. After 1900, Chinese reformers supported
a. Confucian ideals.
b. westernization.
c. imperialism.
d. Christianity.

_____ 29. Which of the following was used as a justification for imperialism?
a. genocide
b. Social Darwinism
c. westernization
d. resistance to expansion

_____ 30. In the Boer War, the British fought descendants of which settlers?
a. Asante
b. French
c. Ottoman Turk
d. Dutch

_____ 31. Ethiopia was able to resist the Europeans because
a. its leader was educated in the West.
b. it had modern weapons and a well-trained army.
c. it formed an alliance with the Ottomans.
d. it had a favorable balance of trade.

_____ 32. Which of the following was a cause of the Ottoman empire's decline?
a. the spread of Christianity
b. the weakening of the central government
c. the growth of democracy
d. corrupting western influences

_____ 33. Why is Muhammad Ali considered the "father of modern Egypt"?
    a. He introduced industry to Egypt.
    b. He led Egypt's nationalist movement.
    c. He freed Egypt from British rule.
    d. He built the Suez Canal.

_____ 34. The Sepoy Rebellion was caused by
    a. food shortages.
    b. British insensitivity to Indian customs.
    c. a tax increase.
    d. a reduction in the sepoys' salary.

_____ 35. The Indian National Congress wanted
    a. eventual self-rule for India.   c. a tax on British goods.
    b. a revolution to end British rule.   d. control of India.

_____ 36. What caused the Taiping Rebellion?
    a. Britain's opium trade   c. a desire for self-rule
    b. peasant hardships   d. anger at western reforms

Short Answer

37. List three motives of imperialists in the late 1800s.

38. Identify three examples of African resistance to European colonization.

39. Explain why Muhammad Ali is called the "father of modern Egypt."

40. Use two examples to describe how insensitivity by the British toward Hindu and Muslim religious traditions caused the Sepoy Rebellion.

41. List three internal problems China faced in the 1800s.

42. Describe in one sentence the actions of the self-strengthening movement in China.

43. Compare the way imperial Britain exercised control over India and China.

Read the following excerpt from Facing Mount Kenya, *a study of Kikuyu tribal life by Jomo Kenyatta. Then answer the questions that follow.*

"When the Europeans first came into Kikuyuland, the Kikuyu looked upon them as wanderers…who had deserted from their homes and were lonely and in need of friends. . . .As such the Europeans were allowed to pitch their tents and to have a temporary right of occupation. . . .The Europeans were treated in this way in the belief that one day they would get tired of wandering and finally return to their own country.

These early Empire builders, knowing what they were after, played on the ignorance and sincere, hospitable nature of the people. They…soon started to build small forts or camps. . . .

Unfortunately, they [the Kikuyu] did not realize that these places were used for the preliminary preparation for taking away their land from them."

44. What are two cultural values of the Kikuyu expressed in this account?

45. Based on this account, how do you think the Europeans viewed the Kikuyu?

46. Assume you are a modern descendant of the Kikuyu and have just read this account. Explain your reaction.

Essay
On a separate sheet of paper, write an answer to the following questions.

47. **Identifying Causes and Effects** How do you think the size of the Ottoman empire contributed to its decline?

48. **Predicting Consequences** How do you suppose the improvements Britain made in communication and transportation in India affected India's transition from a British colony to an independent nation?

49. **Drawing Conclusions** Do you think British rule was a blessing or a curse for India? Support your answer with examples.

50. **Making Decisions** Do you think westernization was the most effective way to stop imperialism in China? Explain.

51. **Drawing Conclusions** Explain how British imperialism could be described as both a blessing and a curse for India.

CHAPTER 25—THE NEW IMPERIALISM (1800–1914)
Answer Section

MATCHING

1. ANS: E   DIF: E   REF: 620   OBJ: C25S1-3
   TOP: Global interaction, Protectorate
2. ANS: C   DIF: E   REF: 628-629   OBJ: C25S3-2
   TOP: Religion, Genocide
3. ANS: A   DIF: E   REF: 632-633   OBJ: C25S4-2
   TOP: Economics, Cash crop
4. ANS: D   DIF: E   REF: 636   OBJ: C25S5-1
   TOP: Economics, Indemnity
5. ANS: B   DIF: E   REF: 636   OBJ: C25S5-1
   TOP: Global interaction, Extraterritoriality
6. ANS: B   DIF: E   REF: 626   OBJ: C25S2-4
   TOP: Impact of the individual, Menilik II
7. ANS: C   DIF: E   REF: 629-630   OBJ: C25S3-2
   TOP: Impact of the individual, Muhammad Ali
8. ANS: D   DIF: E   REF: 633   OBJ: C25S4-4
   TOP: Impact of the individual, Ram Mohun Roy
9. ANS: A   DIF: E   REF: 636-639   OBJ: C25S5-2
   TOP: Impact of the individual, Ci Xi
10. ANS: E   DIF: E   REF: 639   OBJ: C25S5-3
    TOP: Impact of the individual, Sun Yixian
11. ANS: F   DIF: E   REF: 620   OBJ: C25S1-3
    TOP: Global interaction, Protectorate
12. ANS: H   DIF: E   REF: 620   OBJ: C25S1-3
    TOP: Global interaction, Sphere of influence
13. ANS: B   DIF: E   REF: 632-633   OBJ: C25S4-2
    TOP: Economics, Cash crop
14. ANS: D   DIF: E   REF: 633   OBJ: C25S4-2
    TOP: Environment, Deforestation
15. ANS: A   DIF: E   REF: 635   OBJ: C25S5-1
    TOP: Economics, Balance of trade
16. ANS: G   DIF: E   REF: 635   OBJ: C25S5-1
    TOP: Economics, Trade deficit
17. ANS: E   DIF: E   REF: 636   OBJ: C25S5-1
    TOP: Economics, Unequal treaties
18. ANS: C   DIF: E   REF: 636   OBJ: C25S5-1
    TOP: Global interaction, Extraterritoriality

MULTIPLE CHOICE

19. ANS: D   DIF: E   REF: 621-622   OBJ: C25S2-1
    TOP: Global interaction, African slave trade
20. ANS: B   DIF: D   REF: 621-622   OBJ: C25S2-1
    TOP: Global interaction, African slave trade
21. ANS: C   DIF: E   REF: 621-622   OBJ: C25S2-1
    TOP: Global interaction, African slave trade
22. ANS: D   DIF: A   REF: 621-622   OBJ: C25S2-1
    TOP: Global interaction, African slave trade
23. ANS: C   DIF: A   REF: 618   OBJ: C25S1-1
    TOP: Economics, Industrial Revolution
24. ANS: D   DIF: A   REF: 623-624   OBJ: C25S2-2
    TOP: Power and conflict, Southern Africa
25. ANS: B   DIF: A   REF: 630   OBJ: C25S3-3
    TOP: Global interaction, Iran
26. ANS: C   DIF: A   REF: 631-632   OBJ: C25S4-1
    TOP: Political systems, Sepoy Rebellion
27. ANS: D   DIF: E   REF: 636   OBJ: C25S5-2
    TOP: Continuity and change, China in decline
28. ANS: B   DIF: A   REF: 638   OBJ: C25S3-3
    TOP: Continuity and change, Westernization of China
29. ANS: B   DIF: D   REF: 618-619   OBJ: C25S1-1
    TOP: Social systems, Social Darwinism
30. ANS: D   DIF: A   REF: 624   OBJ: C25S2-2
    TOP: Power and conflict, Boer War
31. ANS: B   DIF: A   REF: 626   OBJ: C25S2-3
    TOP: Power and conflict, Ethiopia
32. ANS: B   DIF: A   REF: 627-628   OBJ: C25S3-1
    TOP: Continuity and change, Ottoman decline
33. ANS: A   DIF: A   REF: 629-630   OBJ: C25S3-2
    TOP: Impact of the individual, Muhammad Ali
34. ANS: B   DIF: E   REF: 631-632   OBJ: C25S4-1
    TOP: Religion, Sepoy Rebellion
35. ANS: A   DIF: A   REF: 634   OBJ: C25S4-3
    TOP: Political systems, Indian National Congress
36. ANS: B   DIF: D   REF: 636   OBJ: C25S5-2
    TOP: Power and conflict, Taiping Rebellion

SHORT ANSWER

37. ANS:
    Answers should include three of the following: economic motives—manufacturers needed raw materials and markets for their goods; political and military motives—bases were needed for expanding merchant and naval fleets and imperial possessions boosted the national ego; humanitarian goals—some westerners were concerned for the welfare of people living in Africa and Asia, others wanted to spread Christianity; or Social Darwinism—believers in this philosophy thought it was their natural duty to improve the human race.

    DIF: A   REF: 618-619   OBJ: C25S1-1
    TOP: Global interaction, European imperialism

38. ANS:
    Answers should include three of the following: the Algerians and West Africans battled the French, the Zulus fought the British, the Asante resisted the British, the Yao and Herero fought the Germans, and the Ethiopians successfully resisted the Italians.

    DIF: D   REF: 626   OBJ: C25S2-3
    TOP: Power and conflict, European imperialism

39. ANS:
    Muhammad Ali laid the groundwork that made modern Egypt an industrialized society and a major Middle Eastern power by introducing industry, modernizing farming, and building a well-trained army.

    DIF: A   REF: 629-630   OBJ: C25S3-2
    TOP: Impact of the individual, Muhammad Ali

40. ANS:
    Answers should use two of the following to show how British policies and laws violated religious and cultural traditions and caused the Indians to become so angry that they rebelled: Britain required Indian troops to serve overseas, and for high-caste Hindus it was a religious offense to travel overseas; a law permitting Hindu widows to remarry undermined Hindu religious beliefs; military orders that required Muslims and Hindus to bite off the tips of rifle cartridges coated with animal fat (from cows, which Hindus considered sacred or from pigs, which Muslims were forbidden to eat) violated religious sanctions.

    DIF: D   REF: 631-632   OBJ: C25S4-1
    TOP: Religion, Sepoy Rebellion

41. ANS:
    Answers should include three of the following: decaying irrigation systems and canals, which led to widescale flooding; hunger; poverty; or corruption in the royal court and civil service.

    DIF: A   REF: 636   OBJ: C25S5-2
    TOP: Continuity and change, Qing China

42. ANS:
The reformers of the self-strengthening movement imported western technology; developed shipyards, railroads, mining, and light industry; and translated western works on science, government, and the economy.

DIF: A   REF: 636-638   OBJ: C25S5-3
TOP: Continuity and change, Self-strengthening movement

43. ANS:
Britain ruled India as a colony and exercised direct and total control over it. In China, Britain controlled only trade within a designated area (sphere of influence).

DIF: A   REF: 620   OBJ: C25S1-3
TOP: Political systems, British imperialism

44. ANS:
honesty and hospitality

DIF: A   REF: 623-626   OBJ: C25S2-1   TOP: Diversity, Kikuyu

45. ANS:
They viewed them as naive, and probably even as stupid.

DIF: A   REF: 623-626   OBJ: C25S2-2   TOP: Diversity, Kikuyu

46. ANS:
Answers will likely include references to feeling angry, exploited, and possibly, hurt.

DIF: A   REF: 623-626   OBJ: C25S2-2   TOP: Diversity, Kikuyu

ESSAY

47. ANS:
The huge size of the Ottoman empire made it difficult to keep strong centralized control. As a result, rulers had a great deal of autonomy and could pursue policies not in the interest of the Ottomans.

DIF: A   REF: 627-628   OBJ: C25S3-1
TOP: Continuity and change, Ottoman decline

48. ANS:
Most answers will probably point to the fact that these improvements left India with a good infrastructure, which aided its growth after independence into a modern industrial nation.

DIF: A   REF: 631-633   OBJ: C25S4-2
TOP: Technology, Colonial India

49. ANS:
If students think it was a blessing they should support their answer with examples of the positive improvements Britain made in India, including improving its transportation and communication systems and providing it with a good system of education. If they think it was a curse, they may point out that Great Britain exploited India's human and natural resources and harmed the integrity of its culture and the identity of its people.

DIF: D   REF: 631-633   OBJ: C25S4-2
TOP: Global interaction, Colonial India

50. ANS:
Answers will vary but should be supported by explanations.

DIF: A   REF: 636-639   OBJ: C25S5-3
TOP: Political systems, Imperialism in China

51. ANS:
Answers should suggest that the British made many positive improvements in India, including improving its transportation and communication systems and providing it with a good system of education. All of this helped India prosper in the twentieth century. However, Great Britain also exploited its human and natural wealth and held India back from developing its own modern identity.

DIF: D   REF: 631-633   OBJ: C25S4-2
TOP: Global interaction, Colonial India

CHAPTER 26—NEW GLOBAL PATTERNS (1800–1914)

Matching

Match each term with the correct statement below.

a.	British North America Act	e.	Monroe Doctrine
b.	*caudillos*	f.	penal colony
c.	economic dependence	g.	regionalism
d.	indigenous	h.	zaibatsu

_____ 1. Powerful banking and industrial families in Japan

_____ 2. Original

_____ 3. Law that created the Dominion of Canada

_____ 4. Place to send people convicted of crimes

_____ 5. Loyalty to a local area

_____ 6. Local strongmen in Latin American nations

_____ 7. Relationship in which a less-developed nation's trade is controlled by a developed nation

_____ 8. Document that closed the Americas to European colonization

Match each person with the correct statement below.

a.	James Cook	d.	James Monroe
b.	Benito Juárez	e.	Matthew Perry
c.	Liliuokalani		

_____ 9. American naval officer who opened Japan to trade

_____ 10. Hawaiian queen who was overthrown by American planters

_____ 11. Captain who claimed Australia for Britain

_____ 12. Liberal leader who started La Reforma in Mexico

_____ 13. United States president who closed the Americas to European colonization

Match each place with the correct statement below.

a.	Cuba	d.	Outback
b.	French Indochina	e.	Samoa
c.	Korea		

_____ 14. Nation called the Hermit Kingdom, which came under Japanese rule in 1905

_____ 15. European empire in Southeast Asia consisting of Vietnam, Laos, and Cambodia

_____ 16. Pacific island that became a triple protectorate of the United States, Britain, and Germany

_____ 17. Rugged interior of Australia where settlers established sheep ranches and wheat farms

____ 18. Country that gained independence as a result of the Spanish-American War

Multiple Choice
Identify the letter of the choice that best completes the statement or answers the question.

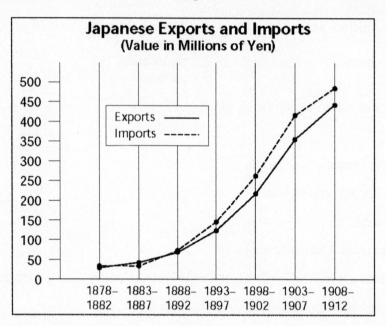

Figure 26-1

____ 19. According to Figure 26-1, the value of Japanese exports was greater than the value of imports during the period from
a. 1878–1882.   c. 1898–1902.
b. 1883–1887.   d. 1908–1912.

____ 20. According to Figure 26-1, which of the following statements best describes changes in Japanese trade from 1878 to 1912?
a. The value of imports and exports increased steadily.
b. The value of imports and exports declined steadily.
c. The value of exports increased faster than that of imports.
d. The value of imports and exports changed very little.

____ 21. According to Figure 26-1, during which of the following periods were the values of Japanese imports and exports about the same?
a. 1878–1892   c. 1898–1902
b. 1893–1897   d. 1908–1912

____ 22. Which of the following statements is accurate according to Figure 26-1?
a. Between 1878 and 1912, Japanese trade declined steadily.
b. Between 1878 and 1912, Japanese trade remained about the same.
c. After 1893, the value of Japanese imports was greater than the value of its exports.
d. After 1893, the value of Japanese exports was greater than the value of its imports.

____ 23. Which of the following results followed Perry's expedition to Japan in 1853?
    a. Japan allowed the Dutch to trade at Nagasaki.
    b. Japan opened its ports to American trade.
    c. Japan closed its ports to all foreigners.
    d. Japan defeated Perry's naval forces.

____ 24. Japan became an imperialist power by gaining control of
    a. Russia.
    c. Indochina.
    b. Thailand.
    d. Korea.

____ 25. Which of the following parts of Southeast Asia came under French rule in the 1800s?
    a. Indonesia
    c. Vietnam
    b. the Malay Peninsula
    d. Burma

____ 26. Siam remained independent by
    a. defeating invaders.
    b. becoming a buffer between British and French colonies.
    c. refusing to accept treaties with European countries.
    d. resisting modernization.

____ 27. In the late 1800s, American sugar growers overthrew Queen Liliuokalani and asked the United States to annex
    a. Cuba.
    c. Samoa.
    b. the Philippines.
    d. Hawaii.

____ 28. What did the people of Africa, Asia, and Latin America contribute to the global economy that emerged in the early 1900s?
    a. investment capital
    c. technology
    b. labor and resources
    d. manufactured goods

____ 29. Western imperialist nations tried to modernize the lands they conquered by
    a. adopting the cultural traditions of subject people.
    b. imposing western culture on subject people.
    c. encouraging subject people to keep their own traditions.
    d. showing no interest in the cultures of subject people.

____ 30. The political consequences of imperialism included
    a. increased tensions among western powers.
    b. greater cooperation among western powers.
    c. acceptance of colonial rule in Africa and Asia.
    d. strengthening of local governments in Africa and Asia.

____ 31. Which of the following places remained an independent buffer between British and French colonies in Southeast Asia?
    a. Indonesia
    c. Burma
    b. the Philippines
    d. Siam

_____ 32. As a result of the British North America Act, Canada became
   a. a self-governing nation.
   b. a British colony.
   c. divided into English-speaking and French-speaking colonies.
   d. closed to immigration.

_____ 33. Australia and New Zealand gained independence through
   a. war with Britain.
   b. nationalist movements of indigenous peoples.
   c. intervention by the United States.
   d. demands by white settlers for self-rule.

_____ 34. The United States intervened in Latin American countries in the early 1900s to
   a. spread western civilization.
   b. gain additional colonies.
   c. protect American lives and investments.
   d. grant independence.

_____ 35. Most profits from the global economy that emerged in the early 1900s went to
   a. industrialized nations of the West.
   b. local economies in Africa and Asia.
   c. European colonies in Southeast Asia.
   d. independent Latin American nations.

_____ 36. To western imperial powers, modernization meant that subject people should
   a. preserve their cultural traditions.   c. spread nonwestern cultures.
   b. accept western culture.   d. organize nationalist movements.

Short Answer

37. Explain three reasons why Japan was able to modernize rapidly.

38. Explain how Siam remained independent.

39. Describe two ways that the United States expanded its influence in the Pacific.

40. Explain two reasons why Australia and New Zealand gained independence faster than British colonies in Africa and Asia.

41. List four problems Latin American nations faced in the 1800s.

42. Explain how the Monroe Doctrine and the Roosevelt Corollary expanded United States influence in Latin America.

43. Explain how the global economy that emerged during the Age of Imperialism disrupted families in Africa, Asia, and Latin America.

Read the following excerpt from the writings of Swami Vivekananda, a Hindu teacher. Then answer the questions that follow.

"So a nation which is great in the possession of material power thinks that that is all that is to be coveted [desired], that that is all that is meant by progress, that that is all that is meant by civilization, and if there are other nations which do not care for possessions, and do not possess that power, they are not fit to live, their whole existence is useless! On the other hand, another nation may think that mere material civilization is utterly useless. . . . Each of these types has its grandeur, each has its glory. The present adjustment will be the harmonizing, the mingling of these two ideals. To the Oriental [Middle Easterners and Asians], the world of the spirit is as real as to the Occidental [Europeans and Americans] is the world of the senses. In the spiritual, the Oriental finds everything he wants or hopes for; in it he finds all that makes life real to him. . . . Machines never made mankind happy, and never will. . . . The man alone who is the lord of his mind can become happy, and none else. . . . What avails it if you have power over the whole of the world, if you have mastered every atom in the universe? That will not make you happy unless you have the power of happiness in yourself. . . . Therefore it is fitting that . . . when the Oriental wants to learn about machine-making, he should sit at the feet of the Occidental and learn from him. When the Occident wants to learn about the spirit, about God, about the soul, about the meaning and the mystery of this universe, he must sit at the feet of the Orient to learn."

44. According to Vivekananda, how did the Occidental view of life differ from the Oriental view?

45. Why did Vivekananda believe that machines could never make people happy?

46. What did Vivekananda think Orientals could learn from Occidentals? What could Orientals teach Occidentals?

Essay
On a separate sheet of paper, write an answer to the following questions.

47. **Drawing Conclusions** Why did Australia and New Zealand achieve self-rule faster than British colonies in Africa or Asia?

48. **Making Comparisons** Compare the effects of imperialism on western cultures and traditional cultures.

49. **Synthesizing Information** What factors linked Latin American nations to the world economy?

50. **Drawing Conclusions** How did imperialism increase tensions among industrial nations?

51. **Recognizing Causes and Effects** How did modernization cause Japan to become an imperialist power?

52. **Recognizing Points of View** Why did some subject people accept western culture, while others rejected it?

CHAPTER 26—NEW GLOBAL PATTERNS (1800–1914)
Answer Section

MATCHING

1. ANS: H   DIF: E   REF: 647   OBJ: C26S1-2
    TOP: Economics, Zaibatsu
2. ANS: D   DIF: E   REF: 653   OBJ: C26S3-1
    TOP: Continuity and change, Indigenous
3. ANS: A   DIF: E   REF: 654   OBJ: C26S3-1
    TOP: Political systems, Canadian self-rule
4. ANS: F   DIF: E   REF: 655-656   OBJ: C26S3-2
    TOP: Social systems, Penal colony
5. ANS: G   DIF: E   REF: 659   OBJ: C26S4-1
    TOP: Political systems, Regionalism
6. ANS: B   DIF: E   REF: 659   OBJ: C26S4-1
    TOP: Political systems, Caudillos
7. ANS: C   DIF: E   REF: 659   OBJ: C26S4-1
    TOP: Economics, Economic dependence
8. ANS: E   DIF: E   REF: 661-662   OBJ: C26S4-3
    TOP: Global interaction, Monroe Doctrine

9. ANS: E   DIF: E   REF: 645   OBJ: C26S1-1
    TOP: Impact of the individual, Matthew Perry
10. ANS: C   DIF: E   REF: 651-652   OBJ: C26S2-3
    TOP: Power and conflict, Hawaii
11. ANS: A   DIF: E   REF: 655   OBJ: C26S3-2
    TOP: Impact of the individual, James Cook
12. ANS: B   DIF: E   REF: 660   OBJ: C26S4-2
    TOP: Impact of the individual, Benito Juárez
13. ANS: D   DIF: E   REF: 661-662   OBJ: C26S4-3
    TOP: Impact of the individual, James Monroe

14. ANS: C   DIF: E   REF: 648-649   OBJ: C26S1-3
    TOP: Power and conflict, Korea
15. ANS: B   DIF: E   REF: 650-651   OBJ: C26S2-1
    TOP: Political systems, French Indochina
16. ANS: E   DIF: E   REF: 651   OBJ: C26S2-3
    TOP: Political systems, Samoa
17. ANS: D   DIF: E   REF: 656   OBJ: C26S3-2
    TOP: Geography, Australian outback
18. ANS: A   DIF: E   REF: 662   OBJ: C26S4-3
    TOP: Continuity and change, Cuba

MULTIPLE CHOICE

19. ANS: B   DIF: E   REF: 647-648   OBJ: C26S1-2
    TOP: Economics, Japanese trade

20. ANS: A   DIF: A   REF: 647-648   OBJ: C26S1-2
    TOP: Economics, Japanese trade

21. ANS: A   DIF: E   REF: 647-648   OBJ: C26S1-2
    TOP: Economics, Japanese trade

22. ANS: C   DIF: D   REF: 647-648   OBJ: C26S1-2
    TOP: Economics, Japanese trade

23. ANS: B   DIF: A   REF: 645   OBJ: C26S1-1
    TOP: Power and conflict, Opening up Japan

24. ANS: D   DIF: A   REF: 648-649   OBJ: C26S1-1
    TOP: Power and conflict, Japanese imperialism

25. ANS: C   DIF: A   REF: 650-651   OBJ: C26S2-1
    TOP: Power and conflict, Vietnam

26. ANS: B   DIF: A   REF: 651   OBJ: C26S2-2
    TOP: Political systems, Siam

27. ANS: D   DIF: E   REF: 651-652   OBJ: C26S2-3
    TOP: Power and conflict, Hawaii

28. ANS: B   DIF: A   REF: 663-664   OBJ: C26S5-1
    TOP: Economics, Global economy

29. ANS: B   DIF: A   REF: 664-667   OBJ: C26S5-2
    TOP: Global interaction, Western imperialism

30. ANS: A   DIF: A   REF: 667   OBJ: C26S5-3
    TOP: Political systems, Western imperialism

31. ANS: D   DIF: A   REF: 651   OBJ: C26S2-2
    TOP: Political systems, Siam

32. ANS: A   DIF: A   REF: 654   OBJ: C26S3-1
    TOP: Political systems, Canadian self-rule

33. ANS: D   DIF: A   REF: 655-657   OBJ: C26S3-2
    TOP: Political systems, Australia and New Zealand

34. ANS: C   DIF: A   REF: 661-662   OBJ: C26S4-3
    TOP: Global interaction, United States intervention

35. ANS: A   DIF: A   REF: 663-664   OBJ: C26S5-1
    TOP: Economics, Global economy

36. ANS: B   DIF: D   REF: 664-667   OBJ: C26S5-2
    TOP: Global interaction, Westernization

SHORT ANSWER

37. ANS:
Japan was a homogeneous society. It had a base for economic growth that started during the time of the Tokugawa. The Japanese had experience in learning from foreigners, and they were determined to resist foreign rule.

DIF: A   REF: 648   OBJ: C26S1-2
TOP: Continuity and change, Modernization of Japan

38. ANS:
Siam's rulers reformed the government, modernized the army, and hired western experts to train their people in new technology. They also abolished slavery and expanded women's rights. Britain and France guaranteed Siam's independence as a neutral zone between their colonies.

DIF: A   REF: 651   OBJ: C26S2-2
TOP: Political systems, Siam

39. ANS:
The United States secured an unequal treaty with Samoa and eventually agreed to join Germany and Britain in a triple protectorate over the island. At the request of American planters, the United States annexed Hawaii to keep Britain or Japan from doing so. Finally, the United States won control over the Philippines in the Spanish-American War.

DIF: A   REF: 651-652   OBJ: C26S2-3
TOP: Global interaction, United States in the Pacific

40. ANS:
Britain was concerned about interference from other imperial powers and wanted to counter this threat and boost development. Australia and New Zealand were sparsely populated, so white settlers quickly replaced the indigenous people. Britain felt that English-speaking whites were capable of self-rule, whereas nonwhites were not.

DIF: A   REF: 653, 655-657   OBJ: C26S3-2
TOP: Political systems, Independence movements

41. ANS:
Among the problems Latin American nations faced were feuds among leaders, geographic barriers, limited voting rights, racial prejudice, regionalism, power struggles, and economic dependence.

DIF: E   REF: 658-659   OBJ: C26S4-1
TOP: Continuity and change, Latin America

42. ANS:

By issuing the Monroe Doctrine, the United States declared the Americas closed to European colonization. Under the Roosevelt Corollary, the United States claimed international police power in the Western Hemisphere. Because of these policies, the United States intervened in several Latin American countries to protect American lives and investments.

DIF: A   REF: 661-662   OBJ: C26S4-3
TOP: Global interaction, Monroe Doctrine

43. ANS:

Families were disrupted because men left their homes to work in distant mines or cities. Women were left to grow food and support their children. In other places, daughters were sent to cities to work, while sons were kept home to farm.

DIF: A   REF: 663-664   OBJ: C26S5-1
TOP: Social systems, Global economy

44. ANS:

Occidentals believed that the possession of material power was important. Orientals believed that spiritual life was more important than material civilization.

DIF: A   REF: 664-667   OBJ: C26S5-2
TOP: Diversity, Occidental versus oriental

45. ANS:

Vivekananda believed that happiness is in the mind, not in machines. He stated that people must find the power of happiness inside themselves.

DIF: A   REF: 664-667   OBJ: C26S5-2
TOP: Diversity, Occidental versus oriental

46. ANS:

Orientals could learn about machine making from Occidentals. Orientals could teach Occidentals about God, about the soul, and about the meaning and mystery of the universe.

DIF: A   REF: 664-667   OBJ: C26S5-2
TOP: Diversity, Occidental versus oriental

ESSAY

47. ANS:

Australia and New Zealand were sparsely populated, so British settlers could take over the land. Britain felt that whites could govern themselves, whereas nonwhites in Asia and Africa were considered less capable of self-rule.

DIF: D   REF: 653, 655-657   OBJ: C26S3-2
TOP: Political systems, Independence movements

48. ANS:
Westerners gained new resources and products, knowledge of ancient civilizations, and African and Asian influences on their art and fashions. Nonwesterners benefited from western medicine and technology, but they faced pressure to abandon their traditions and accept "modern" ways. Some traditional cultures were nearly destroyed.

DIF: D   REF: 664-667   OBJ: C26S5-2
TOP: Continuity and change, Culture

49. ANS:
Foreign investments, trade, technology, and immigration helped Latin American nations move into the world economy.

DIF: D   REF: 659   OBJ: C26S4-2
TOP: Economics, World economy

50. ANS:
Competition for empire increased tensions among western powers. Rival imperial nations frequently came close to war over territories in Africa and Asia.

DIF: D   REF: 667   OBJ: C26S5-3
TOP: Power and conflict, Imperialism

51. ANS:
Japan wanted to compete with western industrial powers, but it lacked the resources needed for industrial growth. The Japanese used their modern army and navy to gain power in Korea and Manchuria.

DIF: D   REF: 648-649   OBJ: C26S1-3
TOP: Continuity and change, Japanese imperialism

52. ANS:
Some nonwesterners believed that western culture was superior to their own. They wanted to share in the material advantages of western society. Other subject people were proud of their ancient traditions. They resisted western efforts to force new ways on them.

DIF: D   REF: 664-667   OBJ: C26S5-2
TOP: Continuity and change, Culture

CHAPTER 27—WORLD WAR I AND ITS AFTERMATH (1914–1919)

Matching

Match each term with the correct statement below.
a. militarism
b. mobilize
c. propaganda

d. reparations
e. ultimatum

____ 1. The glorification of the military

____ 2. A final set of demands

____ 3. To prepare military forces for war

____ 4. Ideas that are spread in order to promote a cause or to damage an opposing cause

____ 5. Payments for war damage

Match each person with the correct statement below.
a. Edith Cavell
b. Georges Clemenceau
c. Alfred Nobel

d. Gavrilo Princip
e. Woodrow Wilson

____ 6. "It is my hope that this prize will help bring about peace in the world."

____ 7. "Death to the tyrant!"

____ 8. "I will continue to run this hospital despite the German invasion."

____ 9. "The only lasting peace will be a peace without victory."

____ 10. "Germany will be punished so that it will never again threaten France."

Match each term with the correct statement below.
a. atrocities
b. mandates
c. militarism

d. neutrality
e. total war

____ 11. ____ was one of the forces that led to the outbreak of war in Europe.

____ 12. For much of the war the United States followed a policy of ____.

____ 13. In waging a ____, a nation channels all of its resources into the war effort.

____ 14. Stories of ____ are often used in propaganda.

____ 15. After the war, Ottoman lands were divided into ____.

Match each person with the correct statement below.

a.   Georges Clemenceau   d.   Bertha von Suttner
b.   Francis Ferdinand   e.   Woodrow Wilson
c.   Kaiser William II

_____ 16. Peace activist who wrote a bestselling antiwar novel

_____ 17. Heir to the Austrian throne

_____ 18. German leader who supported Austria's war with Serbia

_____ 19. Author of the Fourteen Points

_____ 20. French representative to the Paris Peace Conference who demanded that Germany be punished

Multiple Choice
Identify the letter of the choice that best completes the statement or answers the question.

Figure 27-1

_____ 21. Propagandists used which of the following techniques in Figure 27-1?
   a.   They use half-truths.
   b.   They drew the Germans to resemble monsters.
   c.   They identified their cause with a famous person.
   d.   They used images that showed the Germans in the worst possible light.

_____ 22. Which of the following best describes how the Germans are portrayed in Figure 27-1?
   a.   as strong protectors   c.   as honorable soldiers
   b.   as cruel barbarians   d.   as compassionate invaders

_____ 23. Who issued the poster in Figure 27-1?
   a.   the German government   c.   the United States government
   b.   the Allies   d.   the neutral nations

_____ 24. What is the aim of the poster in Figure 27-1?
  a. to show the good moral character of United States soldiers
  b. to educate people about the goals of the war
  c. to stir up anger against the Germans
  d. to show the effects of war on women and children

_____ 25. Germany joined the Triple Alliance to protect itself against
  a. Russia.
  b. Britain.
  c. France.
  d. the Ottoman empire.

_____ 26. On the eve of World War I, Bosnia was ruled by
  a. Serbia.
  b. the Ottoman empire.
  c. Austria-Hungary.
  d. Germany.

_____ 27. Which of the following weapons contributed most to the stalemate on the Western Front during World War I?
  a. the tank
  b. the automatic machine gun
  c. the airplane
  d. the rifle

_____ 28. World War I was more destructive than earlier wars because
  a. the armies were more ruthless.
  b. it lasted longer.
  c. modern weapons were more deadly.
  d. airplanes could drop huge bombs.

_____ 29. Which of the following statements is true regarding the Ottoman empire in World War I?
  a. It remained neutral.
  b. It joined the Central Powers.
  c. It joined the Allies.
  d. It successfully defended its interests in the Middle East.

_____ 30. Which of the following helped the Allies to achieve the breakthrough they sought in World War I?
  a. the Russian Revolution
  b. the involvement of the United States
  c. the waging of total war
  d. the battle of Gallipoli

_____ 31. Which of the following was an effect of militarism in Europe in the late 1800s?
  a. Nations made political and military alliances.
  b. Strong governments developed.
  c. Nations made economic alliances.
  d. Political tension between nations was reduced.

_____ 32. Why was it difficult to gain an advantage over the enemy in trench warfare?
  a. Too many soldiers died of disease in the trenches.
  b. The machine gun made it nearly impossible for troops to advance.
  c. No weapons were used.
  d. Too few soldiers were willing to kill enemy soldiers.

____ 33. Which of the following helped turn World War I into a global war?
    a. the machine gun   c. the submarine
    b. the airplane   d. poison gas

____ 34. Which of the following statements is true regarding the role of women during World War I?
    a. They contributed little to the war effort.
    b. Their role differed very little from their role during peace time.
    c. They kept their nations' economies going during the war.
    d. They focused their efforts on ending the war.

____ 35. Which of the following ended Russia's involvement in World War I?
    a. the Treaty of Brest-Litovsk   c. the attack on the *Lusitania*
    b. the battle of Gallipoli   d. the battle of Caporetto

____ 36. In 1918, Europe was
    a. an economic giant.   c. in ruins.
    b. gearing up for war.   d. rebuilding itself.

Short Answer

37. Explain, using an example, how each of the following forces helped push Europe toward war: nationalism, imperialism, militarism.

38. Explain the role of the Franco-Prussian War in the rise of the alliance system in Europe.

39. Identify the Black Hand and explain why its members wanted to assassinate Archduke Francis Ferdinand.

40. Describe why the method of warfare on the Western Front during World War I led to a stalemate.

41. Explain why World War I was considered a global conflict even though most of the fighting took place in Europe.

42. List three ways total war affected ordinary citizens.

43. Describe the effect of the following on World War I: the Russian Revolution and the end of American neutrality.

Read the following excerpt from a message the Allies sent to the German delegation at Versailles. Then answer the questions that follow.

> "The conduct of Germany is almost unexampled in human history. The terrible responsibility which lies at its door can be seen in the fact that no less than seven million dead lie buried in Europe.
>
> Justice, therefore, is the only possible basis for the settlement of this terrible war. Justice is what the German delegation asks for and what Germany has been promised. Justice is what Germany shall have. But it must be justice for all. There must be justice for those who have died to free Europe from Prussian despotism. There must be justice for the people who stagger under huge war debts so that liberty might be saved. There must be justice for those millions whose homes and lands, ships and property German savagery has destroyed."

44. According to the message, why did the Allies believe they were justified in exacting such a severe peace on Germany?

45. Why would President Woodrow Wilson have disagreed with the content of this message?

46. How do the terms of the Versailles treaty reflect the ideas expressed in this message?

Essay
On a separate sheet of paper, write an answer to the following questions.

47. **Making Decisions** Do you think Germany was to blame for World War I? Explain why or why not.

48. **Predicting Consequences** List three possible negative effects of the terms of the peace reached after World War I. Be specific.

49. **Identifying Alternatives** How might Germany have prevented World War I?

50. **Identifying Central Issues** How did the machine gun change the nature of fighting?

51. **Understanding Points of View** Based on what you know about the beginnings of World War I, why do you suppose the Allies blamed Germany for the war?

52. **Making Comparisons** Compare World War I to previous wars and explain how technology changed the nature of fighting in World War I.

CHAPTER 27—WORLD WAR I AND ITS AFTERMATH (1914–1919)
Answer Section

MATCHING

1. ANS: A   DIF: E   REF: 681   OBJ: C27S1-3
    TOP: Power and conflict, Militarism
2. ANS: E   DIF: E   REF: 683   OBJ: C27S2-2
    TOP: Power and conflict, Ultimatum
3. ANS: B   DIF: E   REF: 683   OBJ: C27S2-2
    TOP: Power and conflict, Mobilization
4. ANS: C   DIF: E   REF: 690-691   OBJ: C27S4-1
    TOP: Power and conflict, Propaganda
5. ANS: D   DIF: E   REF: 694   OBJ: C27S5-1
    TOP: Power and conflict, Reparations

6. ANS: C   DIF: E   REF: 678   OBJ: C27S1-1
    TOP: Impact of the individual, Alfred Nobel
7. ANS: D   DIF: E   REF: 682   OBJ: C27S2-1
    TOP: Impact of the individual, Gavrilo Princip
8. ANS: A   DIF: E   REF: 691   OBJ: C27S4-1
    TOP: Impact of the individual, Edith Cavell
9. ANS: E   DIF: E   REF: 695-696   OBJ: C27S5-2
    TOP: Impact of the individual, Woodrow Wilson
10. ANS: B   DIF: E   REF: 695   OBJ: C27S5-2
    TOP: Impact of the individual, Georges Clemenceau

11. ANS: C   DIF: E   REF: 681   OBJ: C27S1-3
    TOP: Power and conflict, Militarism
12. ANS: D   DIF: E   REF: 692   OBJ: C27S4-3
    TOP: Power and conflict, Neutrality
13. ANS: E   DIF: E   REF: 690   OBJ: C27S4-1
    TOP: Power and conflict, Total war
14. ANS: A   DIF: E   REF: 691   OBJ: C27S4-1
    TOP: Power and conflict, Atrocities
15. ANS: B   DIF: E   REF: 696-697   OBJ: C27S5-3
    TOP: Political systems, Mandate system

16. ANS: D   DIF: E   REF: 682   OBJ: C27S2-1
    TOP: Impact of the individual, Bertha von Suttner
17. ANS: B   DIF: E   REF: 682   OBJ: C27S2-1
    TOP: Impact of the individual, Francis Ferdinand
18. ANS: C   DIF: E   REF: 683   OBJ: C27S2-2
    TOP: Impact of the individual, Kaiser William II
19. ANS: E   DIF: E   REF: 693   OBJ: C27S5-2
    TOP: Impact of the individual, Woodrow Wilson

20. ANS: A   DIF: E   REF: 695   OBJ: C27S5-2
    TOP: Impact of the individual, Georges Clemenceau

MULTIPLE CHOICE

21. ANS: D   DIF: A   REF: 690-691   OBJ: C27S4-1
    TOP: Power and conflict, Propaganda
22. ANS: B   DIF: E   REF: 690-691   OBJ: C27S4-1
    TOP: Power and conflict, Propaganda
23. ANS: C   DIF: E   REF: 690-691   OBJ: C27S4-1
    TOP: Power and conflict, Propaganda
24. ANS: C   DIF: A   REF: 690-691   OBJ: C27S4-1
    TOP: Power and conflict, Propaganda
25. ANS: C   DIF: A   REF: 681   OBJ: C27S1-3
    TOP: Political systems, Triple Alliance
26. ANS: C   DIF: A   REF: 682   OBJ: C27S2-1
    TOP: Political systems, Bosnia
27. ANS: B   DIF: A   REF: 687-688   OBJ: C27S3-1
    TOP: Technology, Machine gun
28. ANS: C   DIF: A   REF: 687-688   OBJ: C27S3-2
    TOP: Technology, Modern warfare
29. ANS: B   DIF: A   REF: 689   OBJ: C27S3-2
    TOP: Power and conflict, Ottoman empire
30. ANS: B   DIF: E   REF: 692-693   OBJ: C27S4-3
    TOP: Power and conflict, United States declares war
31. ANS: A   DIF: A   REF: 681   OBJ: C27S1-3
    TOP: Political systems, Alliances
32. ANS: B   DIF: A   REF: 685-687   OBJ: C27S3-1
    TOP: Technology, Modern warfare
33. ANS: C   DIF: A   REF: 688   OBJ: C27S3-3
    TOP: Technology, Submarine
34. ANS: C   DIF: E   REF: 691   OBJ: C27S4-2
    TOP: Economics, Women in World War I
35. ANS: A   DIF: A   REF: 691   OBJ: C27S4-2
    TOP: Power and conflict, Treaty of Brest-Litovsk
36. ANS: C   DIF: A   REF: 694   OBJ: C27S5-1
    TOP: Continuity and change, Europe in ruins

SHORT ANSWER

37. ANS:

Nationalism—National pride was a strong force in motivating several European nations, including Germany and France, to act aggressively in order to prove their country's superiority. Imperialism—Competition between countries for colonies increased tensions. For example, the Moroccan crises pitted Germany against France. Militarism—In the years before World War I, European countries focused on building up their military forces and gearing up their populations for war. For example, Britain and Germany competed with each other to build the strongest navy, which increased tension between the two countries.

DIF: A   REF: 678-681   OBJ: C27S1-2
TOP: Power and conflict, Europe moves toward war

38. ANS:

Germany signed the first alliance treaties to protect itself against France, which was eager to avenge its defeat in the Franco-Prussian War.

DIF: A   REF: 681   OBJ: C27S1-3
TOP: Political systems, Alliance system

39. ANS:

The Black Hand was a Serb terrorist group that plotted Francis Ferdinand's assassination because it viewed the Austrians as foreign oppressors. The date chosen for the archduke's visit was a special date in Serbia's history.

DIF: E   REF: 682   OBJ: C27S2-1
TOP: Political systems, Black Hand

40. ANS:

Opposing armies on the Western Front dug lines of trenches facing each other. When officers commanded them, they charged over the top toward the enemy trenches. However, because the soldiers in the trenches had machine guns, the onrushing soldiers were usually stopped before they could gain any enemy ground.

DIF: A   REF: 685-686   OBJ: C27S3-1
TOP: Technology, Modern warfare

41. ANS:

European colonies in Africa and Asia were drawn into the struggle, the Ottoman empire was involved in the fighting, and it affected parts of the Middle East. Japan seized German outposts in China and islands in the Pacific. Attacks against ships crossing the Atlantic drew the United States into the war.

DIF: A   REF: 688-689   OBJ: C27S3-3
TOP: Global interaction, World War I as global conflict

42. ANS:
Answers should include, or point to the effects of three of the following: in most countries there was universal military conscription; food, gasoline, and other commodities were rationed; citizens had to pay more taxes; certain individual freedoms were restricted (freedom of the press, freedom of expression); women took jobs outside the home.

DIF: A   REF: 690-691   OBJ: C27S4-1
TOP: Political systems, Total war

43. ANS:
The Russian Revolution resulted in Russia withdrawing from the war, which allowed Germany to concentrate its troops on the Western Front. The entry of the United States into World War I tipped the scales in favor of the Allies and brought an end to the war.

DIF: A   REF: 691-693   OBJ: C27S4-3
TOP: Power and conflict, Turning points in World War I

44. ANS:
There were millions of deaths, the Allies were left with huge war debts, and much property had been destroyed.

DIF: E   REF: 694-695   OBJ: C27S5-1
TOP: Political systems, Treaty of Versailles

45. ANS:
He did not want to treat Germany harshly. Instead, he wanted a "peace without victory."

DIF: A   REF: 695-696   OBJ: C27S5-2
TOP: Political systems, Treaty of Versailles

46. ANS:
They were severe and meant to punish Germany.

DIF: A   REF: 695-696   OBJ: C27S5-3
TOP: Political systems, Treaty of Versailles

ESSAY

47. ANS:
Some students will think Germany was to blame because it encouraged Austria to go to war against Serbia by promising support; others will side with most historians who think all participants in the war share responsibility.

DIF: A   REF: 684   OBJ: C27S2-3
TOP: Power and conflict, Germany in World War I

48. ANS:
Answers could include three of the following: Germany would be impoverished; Germany would start another war in order to seek revenge; the newly created republics would be unstable and violence would break out; colonized people would rebel; or other nations unhappy with the peace terms would start wars.

DIF: D   REF: 694-697   OBJ: C27S5-3
TOP: Political systems, Treaty of Versailles

49. ANS:
Germany could possibly have prevented World War I by refusing to support Austria against Serbia or by actively trying to dissuade Austria from going to war against Serbia.

DIF: A   REF: 683-684   OBJ: C27S2-2
TOP: Power and conflict, Germany in World War I

50. ANS:
The machine gun made combat more impersonal by enabling soldiers to kill their enemy from a distance. It also increased war casualties and was one of the technological changes that made total war necessary.

DIF: D   REF: 687-688   OBJ: C27S3-2
TOP: Technology, Modern warfare

51. ANS:
The German kaiser encouraged Austria to go to war against Serbia, which started the chain of alliances that resulted in World War I. As Austria's biggest ally, Germany was in a position to restrain Austria from going to war but chose not to.

DIF: A   REF: 683-684   OBJ: C27S2-2
TOP: Political systems, Germany in World War I

52. ANS:
World War I technology, such as the machine gun and U-boat, enabled soldiers to kill their enemies at a distance, rather than in hand-to-hand combat as in previous wars. Modern weapons also made the use of the cavalry outdated and the "charge" highly ineffective.

DIF: D   REF: 687-688   OBJ: C27S3-2
TOP: Technology, Modern warfare

CHAPTER 28—REVOLUTION IN RUSSIA (1917–1939)

Matching

Match each term with the correct statement below.
a. collective
b. kulak
c. socialist realism
d. soviet
e. totalitarian state

____ 1. A council of workers and soldiers

____ 2. A large farm owned and operated by peasants as a group

____ 3. A wealthy peasant

____ 4. A form of government in which a one-party dictatorship tries to regulate every aspect of the lives of its citizens

____ 5. A style of art glorifying Soviet life

Match each person with the correct statement below.
a. Lenin
b. Osip Mandelstam
c. Nicholas II
d. Gregory Rasputin
e. Joseph Stalin

____ 6. Russian czar who abdicated in 1917

____ 7. A "holy man" who had great influence over the czarina, Alexandra

____ 8. Marxist leader of the Russian Revolution

____ 9. Ruthless Soviet leader who industrialized the Soviet Union

____ 10. A Russian poet

Match each term with the correct statement below.
a. collective
b. command economy
c. socialist realism
d. soviets
e. totalitarian state

____ 11. After the March Revolution, socialists set up ____, or councils of workers and soldiers.

____ 12. In a ____, the government makes all the economic decisions.

____ 13. A large farm owned and operated by a group of peasants is called a ____.

____ 14. In a ____, a one-party dictatorship regulates every aspect of the lives of its citizens.

____ 15. ____ was a style of art that glorified life under communism.

Match each person with the correct statement below.

a. Anna Akhmatova

b. V. I. Lenin

c. Mikhail Sholokhov

d. Joseph Stalin

e. Leon Trotsky

_____ 16. Leader of the Bolshevik Revolution

_____ 17. Communist leader who competed with Stalin for power

_____ 18. Soviet leader who brought all economic activity under government control

_____ 19. A great Russian poet

_____ 20. Soviet writer who won the Nobel Prize

Multiple Choice

Identify the letter of the choice that best completes the statement or answers the question.

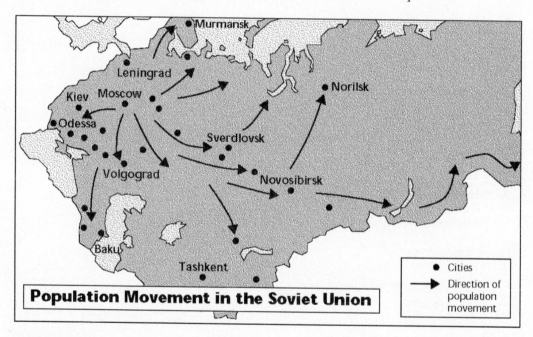

Figure 28-1

_____ 21. According to Figure 28-1, which of the following best describes the movement of the Soviet population from 1926–1939?

a. away from Leningrad and toward Moscow

b. out of the south and toward the north and west

c. away from Moscow and toward cities in the north, south, and east

d. from the east to the west

_____ 22. From Figure 28-1, it can be inferred that the population of the Soviet Union in 1926 was centered in which of the following regions?
    a.   the east
    b.   the south
    c.   the north
    d.   the west

_____ 23. Figure 28-1 gives you information about which of the following in the Soviet Union?
    a.   population growth
    b.   the location of the largest cities
    c.   the movement of people
    d.   population density

_____ 24. According to Figure 28-1, which of the following is a true statement?
    a.   People were moving away from the area around Moscow.
    b.   People were moving from the east to the west.
    c.   Most of the population was moving south.
    d.   The center of the Soviet population was shifting from the west to the north.

_____ 25. Lenin believed that a socialist revolution could succeed in Russia if
    a.   revolutions were carried out at the same time in other parts of Europe.
    b.   Russia became an industrial state.
    c.   the peasants owned the land they worked.
    d.   a small group of dedicated revolutionaries controlled the government.

_____ 26. Which of the following was a result of the Bolshevik Revolution?
    a.   civil war in Russia
    b.   World War I
    c.   war between Russia and Japan
    d.   fighting between the Bolsheviks and the Red Army

_____ 27. Lenin's New Economic Policy was designed to
    a.   end all traces of capitalism.
    b.   rebuild the Soviet economy.
    c.   make the Soviet Union into an industrial state.
    d.   end state control over farms and industry.

_____ 28. Stalin rose to power by
    a.   assassinating Lenin.
    b.   winning the confidence of the Russian people.
    c.   building a loyal following among Communist party members.
    d.   using the Red Army to defeat his enemies.

_____ 29. The main purpose of Stalin's five-year plans was to
    a.   turn the Soviet Union into a military power.
    b.   increase farm production.
    c.   produce more consumer goods.
    d.   turn the Soviet Union into a modern industrial power.

_____ 30. Which of the following is a true statement regarding Soviet society?
    a.   There were no social classes.
    b.   Farm workers made up a new elite.
    c.   Communist party members made up a privileged group.
    d.   Landowners remained at the top of the social order.

_____ 31. One cause of the March 1917 revolution in Russia was
   a.   the death of Rasputin.   c.   Lenin's return to Russia.
   b.   food shortages.   d.   the Treaty of Brest-Litovsk.

_____ 32. In the civil war that broke out after the Bolshevik Revolution, the Red Army fought against the
   a.   Bolsheviks.   c.   Communists.
   b.   Whites.   d.   Cheka.

_____ 33. Which of the following statements is true regarding the Soviet Union under Lenin?
   a.   It was a classless society.
   b.   The government was democratic.
   c.   The Communist party held absolute control over the government.
   d.   Capitalism was completely abolished.

_____ 34. Stalin became the Soviet leader as the result of
   a.   Lenin's death.   c.   a popular uprising.
   b.   Trotsky's assassination.   d.   a free election.

_____ 35. Which of the following was an effect of Stalin's five-year plans?
   a.   The Soviet standard of living increased greatly.
   b.   Agricultural output increased.
   c.   The Soviet Union became a major military power.
   d.   Heavy industry expanded.

_____ 36. Stalin mainly used propaganda to
   a.   promote militarism.   c.   wage a war against illiteracy.
   b.   increase support for communism.   d.   wage a war against smallpox.

Short Answer

37. List three immediate causes of the 1917 revolution in Russia.

38. Describe Lenin's ideal vision of Russian society under communism and the steps he took to realize that vision.

39. Identify three enemies of the Communists that emerged immediately after the Bolshevik Revolution.

40. Identify two personality traits that helped Stalin rise to power.

41. List three aims of Stalin's five-year plans.

42. Identify three techniques that the Soviet government used to control its citizens and to increase support for communism.

43. Define socialist realism and briefly describe your idea for a painting or a piece of sculpture that illustrates this art style.

Read the following excerpt from a proclamation made by the Petrograd Soviet of Workers' Deputies after the March Revolution. Then answer the questions that follow.

"The old regime has brought the country to ruin and the population to famine. . . .
. . . .The old power must be completely crushed to make way for popular government. In that lies the salvation of Russia.

In order to succeed in this struggle for democracy, the people must create their own governmental organ. Yesterday, March 12, there was formed at the capital a Soviet of Workers' Deputies, made up of representatives of factories, mills, revolted troops, and democratic and socialistic parties and groups. The Soviet. . . . has set for itself as its main task to organize the popular forces. . . .

The Soviet has appointed commissars to establish the people's authority in the wards of Petrograd. We invite the entire population of the capital to rally at once to the Soviet, to organize local committees in their wards and to take into their hands the management of local affairs.

All together, with our forces united, we will fight to wipe out completely the old government."

44. What grievances against the czar are expressed in this proclamation?

45. What goals does the proclamation support?

46. According to the proclamation, how should people reach this goal?

Essay
On a separate sheet of paper, write an answer to the following questions.

47. **Predicting Consequences** If the czars had made more reforms, do you think the socialist revolution would have been successful? Explain why or why not.

48. **Making Inferences** Why do you think the Communists discouraged religion in the Soviet Union?

49. **Applying Information** Do you think the Communists remained true to Lenin's ideals? Explain your answer.

50. **Drawing Conclusions** Did communism improve life for the average Soviet citizen? Support your answer with at least two facts.

CHAPTER 28—REVOLUTION IN RUSSIA (1917–1939)
Answer Section

MATCHING

1. ANS: D   DIF: E   REF: 703   OBJ: C28S1-3
   TOP: Political systems, Soviet

2. ANS: A   DIF: E   REF: 709-710   OBJ: C28S2-2
   TOP: Economics, Collective

3. ANS: B   DIF: E   REF: 710   OBJ: C28S2-2
   TOP: Social systems, Kulak

4. ANS: E   DIF: E   REF: 713   OBJ: C28S3-1
   TOP: Political systems, Totalitarian state

5. ANS: C   DIF: E   REF: 715   OBJ: C28S3-3
   TOP: Art and literature, Socialist realism

6. ANS: C   DIF: E   REF: 702-703   OBJ: C28S1-1
   TOP: Impact of the individual, Nicholas II

7. ANS: D   DIF: E   REF: 703   OBJ: C28S1-1
   TOP: Impact of the individual, Gregory Rasputin

8. ANS: A   DIF: E   REF: 703-704   OBJ: C28S1-2
   TOP: Impact of the individual, Lenin

9. ANS: E   DIF: E   REF: 708-710   OBJ: C28S2-2
   TOP: Impact of the individual, Joseph Stalin

10. ANS: B   DIF: E   REF: 715-716   OBJ: C28S3-3
    TOP: Art and literature, Osip Mandelstam

11. ANS: D   DIF: E   REF: 703   OBJ: C28S1-3
    TOP: Political systems, Soviet

12. ANS: B   DIF: E   REF: 708-709   OBJ: C28S2-2
    TOP: Economics, Command economy

13. ANS: A   DIF: E   REF: 709-710   OBJ: C28S2-2
    TOP: Economics, Collective

14. ANS: E   DIF: E   REF: 713   OBJ: C28S3-1
    TOP: Political systems, Totalitarian state

15. ANS: C   DIF: E   REF: 715   OBJ: C28S3-3
    TOP: Art and literature, Socialist realism

16. ANS: B   DIF: E   REF: 703-704   OBJ: C28S1-2
    TOP: Impact of the individual, V. I. Lenin

17. ANS: E   DIF: E   REF: 708   OBJ: C28S2-2
    TOP: Impact of the individual, Leon Trotsky

18. ANS: D   DIF: E   REF: 708-710   OBJ: C28S2-2
    TOP: Impact of the individual, Joseph Stalin

19. ANS: A   DIF: E   REF: 717   OBJ: C28S3-3
    TOP: Art and literature, Anna Akhmatova

20. ANS: C DIF: E REF: 717 OBJ: C28S3-3
    TOP: Impact of the individual, Mikhail Sholokhov

MULTIPLE CHOICE

21. ANS: C DIF: A REF: 708-710 OBJ: C28S2-3
    TOP: Geography, Soviet population movement
22. ANS: D DIF: A REF: 708-710 OBJ: C28S2-3
    TOP: Geography, Soviet population movement
23. ANS: C DIF: E REF: 708-710 OBJ: C28S2-3
    TOP: Geography, Soviet population movement
24. ANS: A DIF: E REF: 708-710 OBJ: C28S2-3
    TOP: Geography, Soviet population movement
25. ANS: D DIF: A REF: 703-704 OBJ: C28S1-2
    TOP: Political systems, Socialist revolution
26. ANS: A DIF: E REF: 705-706 OBJ: C28S1-3
    TOP: Political systems, Civil war in Russia
27. ANS: B DIF: A REF: 707-708 OBJ: C28S2-1
    TOP: Economics, New Economic Policy
28. ANS: C DIF: A REF: 708 OBJ: C28S2-2
    TOP: Impact of the individual, Joseph Stalin
29. ANS: D DIF: D REF: 708-710 OBJ: C28S2-3
    TOP: Economics, Five-year plans
30. ANS: C DIF: A REF: 714 OBJ: C29S3-2
    TOP: Social systems, Soviet elite
31. ANS: B DIF: A REF: 703 OBJ: C28S1-1
    TOP: Political systems, Russian revolution of 1905
32. ANS: B DIF: E REF: 705-706 OBJ: C28S1-3
    TOP: Political systems, Russian civil war
33. ANS: C DIF: A REF: 707-708 OBJ: C28S2-1
    TOP: Political systems, Lenin
34. ANS: A DIF: E REF: 708 OBJ: C28S2-2
    TOP: Continuity and change, Stalin
35. ANS: D DIF: A REF: 708-710 OBJ: C28S2-3
    TOP: Economics, Five-year plans
36. ANS: B DIF: A REF: 713 OBJ: C28S3-1
    TOP: Political systems, Propaganda

SHORT ANSWER

37. ANS:
    disasters on the World War I battlefields, food shortages, and fuel shortages

    DIF: A REF: 703 OBJ: C28S1-1
    TOP: Continuity and change, Russian revolution of 1917

38. ANS:
Lenin envisioned a classless society in which the means of production (the land and the factories) were owned by the workers. To reach this goal, Lenin ended private ownership of land and gave land to peasants. Workers gained control of factories. However, during the civil war, the Communist state took over control of factories, banks, mines, and railroads. Peasants were forced to work for the state. As a result, Lenin was not able to fully realize his goals.

DIF: A   REF: 705-706   OBJ: C28S2-1
TOP: Social systems, Communism under Lenin

39. ANS:
Answers should include three of the following: the Whites; nationalist groups in eastern European and Central Asian countries; Japan; or the Allies.

DIF: A   REF: 705   OBJ: C28S1-3
TOP: Political systems, Communism

40. ANS:
Answers might include two of the following: shrewdness; cunning; manipulativeness; or calculating.

DIF: A   REF: 708   OBJ: C28S2-2
TOP: Impact of the individual, Joseph Stalin

41. ANS:
Three aims of Stalin's five-year plans were to build up heavy industry, improve transportation, and increase farm production.

DIF: A   REF: 708-710   OBJ: C28S2-3
TOP: Economics, Five-year plans

42. ANS:
Answers should include three of the following: terror, censorship, propaganda, reward and punishment, or the promotion of atheism.

DIF: A   REF: 713-714   OBJ: C28S3-1
TOP: Political systems, Totalitarian control

43. ANS:
Socialist realism was a style of art that showed Soviet life in a positive light in order to inspire hope in Soviet citizens for a glorious future under communism. Ideas for paintings and sculpture most likely will include peasants, workers, revolutionary heroes, or Stalin.

DIF: D   REF: 715   OBJ: C28S3-3
TOP: Art and literature, Socialist realism

44. ANS:
The czar's government brought starvation and ruin to the country.

DIF: E   REF: 703   OBJ: C28S1-1
TOP: Continuity and change, March Revolution

45. ANS:
    The proclamation urges the complete destruction of the old government and its replacement with a popular government.

    DIF: A   REF: 703   OBJ: C28S1-2
    TOP: Continuity and change, March Revolution

46. ANS:
    The people should organize committees to administer local affairs.

    DIF: A   REF: 703   OBJ: C28S1-2
    TOP: Continuity and change, March Revolution

ESSAY

47. ANS:
    Answers will vary but should be supported by explanations.

    DIF: A   REF: 702-703   OBJ: C28S1-1
    TOP: Political systems, Socialist revolution

48. ANS:
    Possible answer: They wanted the Communist government to be the supreme authority.

    DIF: D   REF: 714   OBJ: C28S3-1
    TOP: Religion, War on religion

49. ANS:
    Most answers will probably say that communism did not remain true to Lenin's ideals because the state took control of the means of production, not the workers, and a classless society was never achieved. On the contrary, the Communist party became the new ruling elite.

    DIF: D   REF: 705-706, 714   OBJ: C28S1-2
    TOP: Political systems, Lenin

50. ANS:
    Most answers will probably support the idea that life for the average Soviet citizen improved under communism. Supporting facts that students may use include people had food to eat, free education, free medical care, inexpensive housing, and public transportation and recreation. Women won legal status and had access to more opportunities.

    DIF: A   REF: 714-715   OBJ: C28S3-2
    TOP: Social systems, Changes in Soviet society

CHAPTER 29—NATIONALISM AND REVOLUTION AROUND THE WORLD (1910–1939)

Matching

Match each term or person with the correct statement below.

a. apartheid
b. civil disobedience
c. Diego Rivera
d. Hirohito

e. Jiang Jieshi
f. Muhammad Ali Jinnah
g. nationalization
h. "Pancho" Villa

_____ 1. Rebel Mexican leader

_____ 2. The government takeover of natural resources, businesses, or industries

_____ 3. Muralist who portrayed the struggles of the Mexican people

_____ 4. A system of racial segregation

_____ 5. The refusal to obey unjust laws

_____ 6. Leader of the Muslims in India

_____ 7. Leader who ordered massacre of Chinese Communists

_____ 8. Emperor of Japan

Match each term or person with the correct statement below.

a. apartheid
b. civil disobedience
c. Porfirio Díaz
d. Muhammad Ali Jinnah

e. Reza Khan
f. nationalization
g. Léopold Senghor
h. Sun Yixian

_____ 9. The Mexican dictator under whom Mexican peasants suffered great hardships was _____.

_____ 10. _____ is when the government takes over control of a country's natural resources, businesses, or industries.

_____ 11. A system under which races are separated is called _____.

_____ 12. The Senegalese poet who served as his country's first president was _____.

_____ 13. The nationalist leader who modernized Iran was _____.

_____ 14. _____ is the act of refusing to obey unjust laws.

_____ 15. _____ was the leader of the Muslim League in India who supported the idea of a separate state for Muslims.

_____ 16. _____ was the leader of the first Chinese republic.

Multiple Choice
Identify the letter of the choice that best completes the statement or answers the question.

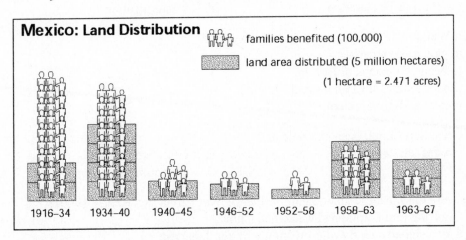

Figure 29-1

_____ 17. According to Figure 29-1, between which years did the most families benefit from land distribution?
   a.   1934 to 1940   c.   1963 to 1967
   b.   1916 to 1934   d.   1958 to 1963

_____ 18. According to Figure 29-1, between which years was the greatest amount of land area distributed?
   a.   1916 to 1934   c.   1934 to 1940
   b.   1940 to 1945   d.   1958 to 1963

_____ 19. According to Figure 29-1, about how many hectares of land were distributed to families between 1940 and 1945?
   a.   5 million   c.   1 million
   b.   .5 million   d.   20 million

_____ 20. According to Figure 29-1, between which years was the least amount of land distributed?
   a.   1916 to 1934   c.   1952 to 1958
   b.   1958 to 1963   d.   1940 to 1945

_____ 21. The main cause of revolution in Mexico in 1910 was
   a.   a repressive government.   c.   the unequal distribution of land.
   b.   food shortages.   d.   high taxes.

_____ 22. How did Pan-Africanism encourage nationalism?
   a.   It emphasized the unity of Africans everywhere.
   b.   It stressed modernization.
   c.   It supported state ownership of land.
   d.   It demanded an end to apartheid.

_____ 23. Which of the following was a result of the establishment of the mandate system in the Middle East?
    a. Zionism
    b. the Balfour Declaration
    c. Pan-Arabism
    d. westernization

_____ 24. When World War I ended, many Indians expected
    a. to gain more territory.
    b. to become citizens of Britain.
    c. separate states for Hindus and Muslims.
    d. greater self-government.

_____ 25. The Great Salt March is an example of
    a. violent resistance.
    b. a boycott.
    c. civil disobedience.
    d. economic sanctions.

_____ 26. Why were the Japanese able to gain influence over China in the early 1900s?
    a. Civil war and famine had weakened China.
    b. China signed a treaty of protection with the Japanese.
    c. The Communists asked for their help fighting the Guomindang.
    d. Yuan Shikai was related to the Japanese emperor.

_____ 27. The ultimate aim of the May Fourth Movement was to
    a. strengthen China by modernizing it.
    b. make China a military power.
    c. win equal rights for women.
    d. install a Communist government in China.

_____ 28. One effect of the Great Depression in Japan was that
    a. civil war broke out.
    b. ultranationalists demanded expansion.
    c. Japan gave up its claim on China.
    d. Japan went bankrupt.

_____ 29. How did Diego Rivera's work reflect cultural nationalism?
    a. It decorated public buildings.
    b. It celebrated the Mexican struggle for independence using native artistic traditions.
    c. It was influenced by European art.
    d. It glorified Mexico's accomplishment under Díaz.

_____ 30. The négritude movement was a movement to
    a. make "Africa for the Africans."
    b. nationalize Africa's natural resources.
    c. free Africa from foreign domination.
    d. make Africans proud of their roots.

_____ 31. Many Indians were angry at the British after World War I because
    a. Britain had failed to protect India against the Germans.
    b. Britain refused to pay reparations to India.
    c. Britain failed to fulfill its promise to grant India greater self-government.
    d. Britain failed to acknowledge India's sacrifices in the war.

_____ 32. Which of the following did Gandhi use to fight British rule?
    a. violent demonstrations   c. propaganda
    b. passive resistance   d. armed resistance

_____ 33. Mao Zedong and Jiang Jieshi disagreed over
    a. the political future of China.
    b. how to control the warlords.
    c. the role of foreign powers in China.
    d. how to fight the Japanese.

_____ 34. Which of the following is one way Japanese democracy grew stronger during the 1920s?
    a. Women won the right to vote.   c. The Diet was formed.
    b. The emperor stepped down.   d. All men were allowed to vote.

_____ 35. Which of the following was an effect of the Great Depression on Japan?
    a. Japan went bankrupt.
    b. The demands of ultranationalists grew stronger.
    c. Civil war broke out.
    d. Japan declared war against the United States.

_____ 36. Militarists wanted to
    a. get rid of the emperor.   c. adopt western ways.
    b. reform education.   d. revive traditional Japanese values.

Short Answer

37. List three causes of the Mexican Revolution.

38. Describe three social or economic reforms between 1917 and the 1930s that were a result of the Mexican Revolution.

39. Identify Pan-Africanism and the négritude movement and explain the role they played in the growth of nationalism.

40. Tell why Indians were even less willing to put up with British rule after World War I than before it.

41. Compare the goals of Jiang Jieshi and Mao Zedong.

42. Identify the link between the Great Depression and the growth of nationalism in Japan.

43. In one sentence each, summarize the domestic and foreign goals of Japanese militarists.

   Read the following excerpt from a selection of quotations by Mohandas Gandhi compiled by a friend. Then answer the questions that follow.

   > "For me the law of Satyagraha, the law of love, is an eternal principle. . . . Its [Satyagraha's] root meaning is holding on to truth. Hence truth-force. I have also called it Love-force, or Soul-force. In the application of Satyagraha I discovered in the earliest stages that pursuit of truth did not admit of violence being inflicted on one's opponent; but that he must be weaned from error by patience and sympathy. . . . And patience means self-suffering."

44. Based on this excerpt, and upon what you have read in your text, explain in your own words what Satyagraha means.

45. Based on this excerpt, why would Satyagraha have universal applicability?

46. Based on this excerpt, why might Satyagraha appeal to those with strong religious beliefs as a tool to bring about change?

Essay
On a separate sheet of paper, write an answer to the following questions.

47. **Identifying Ideologies** Why do you think Kemal took the name Atatürk, meaning "father of the Turks"?

48. **Drawing Conclusions** Why did Japanese militarists allow the emperor to remain in power in the 1930s?

49. **Defending a Position** How did the Balfour Declaration contradict earlier promises made by the Allies? How did it contribute to conflict in Palestine?

50. **Making Comparisons** How was the May Fourth Movement in China similar to nationalist reform movements in Turkey and Iran in the 1920s and 1930s?

51. **Making Comparisons** Compare the nationalist movement in China as expressed in the May Fourth Movement to the movement of ultranationalists in Japan. How were they different?

CHAPTER 29—NATIONALISM AND REVOLUTION AROUND THE WORLD (1910–1939)
Answer Section

MATCHING

1. ANS: H   DIF: E   REF: 722   OBJ: C29S1-1
    TOP: Impact of the individual, "Pancho" Villa
2. ANS: G   DIF: E   REF: 724   OBJ: C29S1-2
    TOP: Economics, Nationalization
3. ANS: C   DIF: E   REF: 725   OBJ: C29S1-3
    TOP: Impact of the individual, Diego Rivera
4. ANS: A   DIF: E   REF: 727   OBJ: C29S2-2
    TOP: Political systems, Apartheid
5. ANS: B   DIF: E   REF: 732   OBJ: C29S3-2
    TOP: Political systems, Civil disobedience
6. ANS: F   DIF: E   REF: 733   OBJ: C29S3-3
    TOP: Impact of the individual, Muhammad Ali Jinnah
7. ANS: E   DIF: E   REF: 736   OBJ: C29S4-2
    TOP: Impact of the individual, Jiang Jieshi
8. ANS: D   DIF: E   REF: 738   OBJ: C29S5-1
    TOP: Impact of the individual, Hirohito

9. ANS: C   DIF: E   REF: 722   OBJ: C29S1-1
    TOP: Impact of the individual, Porfirio Díaz
10. ANS: F   DIF: E   REF: 724   OBJ: C29S1-2
    TOP: Economics, Nationalization
11. ANS: A   DIF: E   REF: 727   OBJ: C29S2-2
    TOP: Political systems, Apartheid
12. ANS: G   DIF: E   REF: 727   OBJ: C29S2-2
    TOP: Impact of the individual, Léopold Senghor
13. ANS: E   DIF: E   REF: 729   OBJ: C29S2-3
    TOP: Impact of the individual, Reza Khan
14. ANS: B   DIF: E   REF: 732   OBJ: C29S3-2
    TOP: Political systems, Civil disobedience
15. ANS: D   DIF: E   REF: 733   OBJ: C29S3-3
    TOP: Impact of the individual, Muhammad Ali Jinnah
16. ANS: H   DIF: E   REF: 734   OBJ: C29S4-1
    TOP: Impact of the individual, Sun Yixian

MULTIPLE CHOICE

17. ANS: B   DIF: D   REF: 724   OBJ: C29S1-2
    TOP: Economics, Land distribution

18. ANS: C   DIF: E   REF: 724   OBJ: C29S1-2
    TOP: Economics, Land distribution
19. ANS: A   DIF: A   REF: 724   OBJ: C29S1-2
    TOP: Economics, Land distribution
20. ANS: C   DIF: D   REF: 724   OBJ: C29S1-2
    TOP: Economics, Land distribution
21. ANS: C   DIF: A   REF: 722   OBJ: C29S1-1
    TOP: Political systems, Mexican Revolution
22. ANS: A   DIF: A   REF: 727   OBJ: C29S2-1
    TOP: Political systems, Pan-Africanism
23. ANS: C   DIF: A   REF: 729   OBJ: C29S2-2
    TOP: Political systems, Pan-Arabism
24. ANS: D   DIF: A   REF: 731   OBJ: C29S3-1
    TOP: Continuity and change, India seeks self-rule
25. ANS: C   DIF: A   REF: 736   OBJ: C29S3-2
    TOP: Political systems, Great Salt March
26. ANS: A   DIF: A   REF: 734   OBJ: C29S4-1
    TOP: Power and conflict, Japanese imperialism
27. ANS: A   DIF: A   REF: 735   OBJ: C29S4-2
    TOP: Continuity and change, May Fourth Movement
28. ANS: B   DIF: A   REF: 739   OBJ: C29S5-2
    TOP: Political systems, Ultranationalists in Japan
29. ANS: B   DIF: A   REF: 725   OBJ: C29S1-3
    TOP: Art and literature, Cultural nationalism
30. ANS: D   DIF: A   REF: 727   OBJ: C29S2-1
    TOP: Diversity, Negritude movement
31. ANS: C   DIF: A   REF: 731   OBJ: C29S3-1
    TOP: Continuity and change, India seeks self-rule
32. ANS: B   DIF: E   REF: 732   OBJ: C29S3-2
    TOP: Political systems, Civil disobedience
33. ANS: A   DIF: A   REF: 736   OBJ: C29S4-3
    TOP: Impact of the individual, Mao and Jiang
34. ANS: D   DIF: A   REF: 738   OBJ: C29S5-1
    TOP: Political systems, Japanese democracy
35. ANS: B   DIF: A   REF: 739   OBJ: C29S5-2
    TOP: Political systems, Ultranationalists in Japan
36. ANS: D   DIF: A   REF: 741   OBJ: C29S5-3
    TOP: Political systems, Japanese militarists

SHORT ANSWER

37. ANS:
Answers should include three of the following: poverty, the unequal distribution of land, low wages, or the demand for democratic reforms.

DIF: A   REF: 722   OBJ: C29S1-1
TOP: Political systems, Mexican Revolution

38. ANS:
Answers should include three of the following: large estates were broken up, valuable natural resources were nationalized, laws protecting workers—including the right to strike and minimum wage laws—were passed, men were given the right to vote, women gained more rights, education was made available to the poor, the government helped some Indian communities regain their lands.

DIF: E   REF: 724   OBJ: C29S1-2
TOP: Continuity and change, Reform in Mexico

39. ANS:
Pan-Africanism was a movement that promoted the unity of Africans and people of African descent everywhere in the world. The négritude movement was a literary movement that celebrated the cultural heritage of Africans. Both movements helped foster a sense of pride and unity among Africans, which nourished the nationalist spirit.

DIF: A   REF: 727   OBJ: C29S2-1
TOP: Continuity and change, African nationalism

40. ANS:
After thousands of Indians sacrificed their lives fighting to preserve the British empire in World War I, British rule seemed an irony and even more of an injustice to many Indians when the war was over.

DIF: E   REF: 731   OBJ: C29S3-3
TOP: Continuity and change, India seeks self-rule

41. ANS:
Both Jiang Jieshi and Mao Zedong were nationalists who wanted to end foreign domination and unite China. Mao was deeply committed to communism and building a nation that could provide a new life for the masses.

DIF: A   REF: 736   OBJ: C29S4-3
TOP: Political systems, Mao and Jiang

42. ANS:
The Great Depression caused the price of Japanese exports to drop dramatically. As a result, unemployment soared. These economic pressures made the Japanese resent the western powers and their influence over the Japanese.

DIF: A   REF: 739   OBJ: C29S5-2
TOP: Economics, Great Depression and Japan

43. ANS:
Domestic goals: to revive traditional values and extinguish western influences. Foreign goals: to expand Japanese territory and to gain valuable raw materials.

DIF: D   REF: 741   OBJ: C29S5-3
TOP: Political systems, Japanese militarists

44. ANS:
Possible answer: It means self-sacrifice to bring about just change.

DIF: A   REF: 732   OBJ: C29S3-2
TOP: Political systems, Civil disobedience

45. ANS:
It can be used by any one person or group anywhere.

DIF: D   REF: 732   OBJ: C29S3-2
TOP: Political systems, Civil disobedience

46. ANS:
Possible answer: Many religions oppose the use of violence, see love as an effective force, and teach the existence of soul-force.

DIF: A   REF: 732   OBJ: C29S3-2
TOP: Religion, Civil disobedience

ESSAY

47. ANS:
Kemal saw himself as the creator of the modern Turkish people.

DIF: A   REF: 728-729   OBJ: C29S2-3
TOP: Impact of the individual, Atatürk

48. ANS:
The government built a cult around the emperor who was believed to be descended from the sun goddess.

DIF: D   REF: 741   OBJ: C29S5-3
TOP: Political systems, Japanese militarists

49. ANS:
In the Balfour Declaration, Britain supported the idea of setting up "a national home for the Jewish people" in Palestine. This contradicted an earlier set of promises made by the Allies promising the Arabs their own kingdoms in former Ottoman lands, including Palestine. These contradictory promises led to conflict between Arab and Jewish nationalists.

DIF: A   REF: 730   OBJ: C29S2-3
TOP: Political systems, Balfour Declaration

50. ANS:
All three nationalist movements looked to the West as a model for modernizing and strengthening their nations in order to avoid or end foreign domination.

DIF: D   REF: 728-729, 735   OBJ: C29S4-2
TOP: Political systems, Nationalist reform movements

51. ANS:
Many Chinese nationalists rejected traditional values and looked to the West for insight and knowledge about how to strengthen China; whereas in Japan, nationalists rejected western ideas and turned back to their traditional values as a way to make their country stronger.

DIF: D   REF: 735, 739   OBJ: C29S4-2
TOP: Continuity and change, Nationalists and ultranationalists

CHAPTER 30—CRISIS OF DEMOCRACY IN THE WEST (1919–1939)

Matching

Match each term or person with the correct statement below.

a. Leon Blum
b. concentration camp
c. Marie Curie
d. flapper

e. general strike
f. Franklin D. Roosevelt
g. stream of consciousness
h. Virginia Woolf

_____ 1. Strike by workers in many different industries at the same time

_____ 2. Head of the socialist French government in the mid-1930s

_____ 3. American president who introduced the New Deal

_____ 4. Polish-born scientist who experimented with radioactivity

_____ 5. A writing technique that relates a character's thoughts and feelings as they occur

_____ 6. British novelist who wrote using stream of consciousness

_____ 7. A young woman during the 1920s who rejected traditional ways

_____ 8. A detention center for civilians considered enemies of the state

Match each term or person with the correct statement below

a. concentration camp
b. Albert Einstein
c. general strike
d. James Joyce

e. Pablo Picasso
f. Benito Mussolini
g. stream of consciousness
h. Frank Lloyd Wright

_____ 9. When workers in many different industries refuse to work at the same time it is called a _____.

_____ 10. The German physicist who advanced the theory of relativity was _____.

_____ 11. _____ is a writing technique that portrays a character's thoughts and feelings as they occur.

_____ 12. _____ was an Irish author who used the stream of consciousness technique.

_____ 13. The Spanish artist who helped create cubism was _____.

_____ 14. The American architect who believed that the function of a building should determine its form was _____.

_____ 15. A _____ is a detention center for civilians considered enemies of the state.

_____ 16. _____ was the Fascist head of Italy.

Multiple Choice
Identify the letter of the choice that best completes the statement or answers the question.

_____ 17. The purpose of the Kellogg-Briand Pact was to
  a. establish military alliances.
  b. end war forever.
  c. promote economic cooperation among nations.
  d. establish Germany's borders.

_____ 18. One effect of the Great Depression was
  a. high unemployment.
  b. lower tariffs.
  c. an increase in global trade.
  d. the spread of democracy.

_____ 19. The idea that space and time are not absolute is known as
  a. psychoanalysis.
  b. the theory of relativity.
  c. Newton's Law.
  d. the theory of uncertainty.

_____ 20. An artist who uses triangles, squares, and circles to represent people and objects would be called a
  a. Bauhaus artist.
  b. Dadaist.
  c. cubist.
  d. surrealist.

_____ 21. Why were Italians attracted to fascism in the 1920s?
  a. It promised order in a time of uncertainty.
  b. It guaranteed a job for everyone.
  c. It promised to restore "rule by reason" to Italy.
  d. It restored the Church as the most important institution in Italy.

_____ 22. Which of the following describes fascism?
  a. It was democratic.
  b. It glorified blind loyalty to the state.
  c. It promoted communist ideas.
  d. It condemned warfare.

_____ 23. Which of the following statements regarding Germany under Hitler is true?
  a. Most Germans were barely affected by Nazism.
  b. The Nazis controlled all aspects of German life.
  c. The Nazis controlled the government but had little influence on other German institutions.
  d. The Nazis kept firm control over Germany but followed moderate and tolerant policies.

_____ 24. Which of the following helped Adolf Hitler gain power in Germany?
  a. promise of a new democracy
  b. big business and labor
  c. support of the Weimar government
  d. the Great Depression

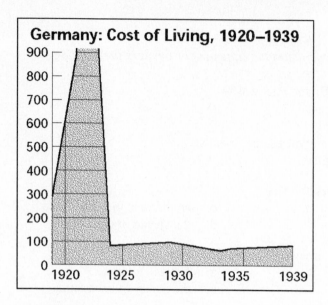

Figure 30-1

_____ 25. According to Figure 30-1, between which two years did the cost of living in Germany increase the most?
   a. 1920 and 1925
   b. 1925 and 1930
   c. 1930 and 1935
   d. 1935 and 1939

_____ 26. According to Figure 30-1, in which of the following years was the cost of living the lowest?
   a. 1924
   b. 1933
   c. 1935
   d. 1939

_____ 27. According to Figure 30-1, in which of the following years was the cost of living the highest?
   a. 1920
   b. 1923
   c. 1930
   d. 1939

_____ 28. One effect of the Kellogg-Briand Pact was
   a. the pursuit of disarmament.
   b. the establishment of the League of Nations.
   c. the formation of new alliances.
   d. the end of war.

_____ 29. The Maginot Line was created in France in order to
   a. rebuild the nation's struggling economy.
   b. end the threat of revolution.
   c. prop up the unstable government.
   d. prevent another German invasion.

_____ 30. One effect of the Great Depression in the United States was
   a. low unemployment.
   b. limits on immigration.
   c. more government involvement in people's lives.
   d. a reduction in social programs.

____ 31. After World War I, the works of many important writers expressed
a. hope in the future.
b. feelings of hopelessness and loss.
c. confidence that new technology would solve the world's problems.
d. deep spiritual joy.

____ 32. Which of the following had the greatest impact on women's lives after World War I?
a. New Deal programs
b. labor-saving devices
c. equal-opportunity laws
d. the creation of many new jobs

____ 33. Many Italians supported the Fascist party because it
a. promised a better life.
b. was the only political party.
c. pledged to unite Italy and Germany.
d. ended the influence of the Church.

____ 34. Which of the following traits was most valued in Fascist Italy?
a. individuality
b. rationality
c. loyalty
d. generosity

____ 35. One of Hitler's goals was the
a. continuation of the Weimar Republic.
b. persecution and elimination of Jews.
c. spread of communism throughout the world.
d. creation of a global state.

Short Answer

36. Identify the Kellogg-Briand Pact and explain how it reflected the "spirit of Locarno."

37. List three causes of the Great Depression and three effects it had on western nations.

38. Explain how scientific developments after the war contributed to a sense of uncertainty about the world.

39. Identify two problems Italy faced after the war and explain how they helped Mussolini rise to power.

40. Compose a one- or two-sentence personality profile of the ideal Fascist.

41. Explain how Hitler's rise to power was a response to the failures of the Weimar government.

Read the following excerpt from a 1926 speech by Adolf Hitler. Then answer the questions that follow.

"The fundamental motif [theme] through all the centuries has been the principle that force and power are the determining factors. All development is struggle. Only force rules. Force is the first law. . . . Only through struggle have states and the world become great. If one should ask whether this struggle is gruesome, then the only answer could be: For the weak, yes, for humanity as a whole, no.

World history provides that in the struggle between nations, that race has always won out whose drive for self-preservation was the more pronounced, the stronger. . . . Unfortunately, the contemporary world stresses internationalism instead of the innate values of race, democracy and the majority instead of the worth of a great leader. Instead of everlasting struggle, the world preaches cowardly pacifism, and everlasting peace. These three things, considered in the light of their ultimate consequences, are the causes of the downfall of all humanity. The practical result of conciliation [peace] among nations is the renunciation [denial] of a people's own strength and their voluntary enslavement."

42. According to this speech, what two factors determine events in history?

43. What ideas in this speech are linked to Social Darwinism?

44. What phrase indicates that Hitler believed in sacrificing some people in order that others may prosper?

Essay
On a separate sheet of paper, write an answer to the following questions.

45. **Comparing** How was the relationship of the individual and the state in Fascist Italy different from the relationship between the individual and the state in a democracy like the United States?

46. **Analyzing Primary Sources** "None but members of the nation [Volk] may be citizens of the state. None but those of German blood, whatever their creed, may be members of the nation. No Jew, therefore, may be a member of the nation." How does the denial of citizenship to Jews follow from the Nazi belief that the state derives from the Volk?

47. **Identifying Main Ideas** How did scientific developments after the war contribute to a sense of uncertainty about the world?

48. **Recognizing Causes and Effects** Why do you suppose a major goal of both the Fascists and the Nazis was educating the youth?

49. **Identifying Main Ideas** Choose one postwar writer and one artist and link their work to the spiritual state of humanity after the war.

50. **Comparing** Contrast the role of women in Fascist Italy with that of women in the United States after World War I.

CHAPTER 30—CRISIS OF DEMOCRACY IN THE WEST (1919–1939)
Answer Section

MATCHING

1. ANS: E   DIF: E   REF: 748   OBJ: C30S1-3
    TOP: Economics, General strike

2. ANS: A   DIF: E   REF: 750   OBJ: C30S1-3
    TOP: Impact of individual, Leon Blum

3. ANS: F   DIF: E   REF: 751   OBJ: C30S1-3
    TOP: Impact of individual, Franklin D. Roosevelt

4. ANS: C   DIF: E   REF: 752   OBJ: C30S2-1
    TOP: Science, Marie Curie

5. ANS: G   DIF: E   REF: 754   OBJ: C30S2-2
    TOP: Art and literature, Stream of consciousness

6. ANS: H   DIF: E   REF: 754   OBJ: C30S2-2
    TOP: Impact of individual, Virginia Woolf

7. ANS: D   DIF: E   REF: 756   OBJ: C30S2-3
    TOP: Social systems, Flapper

8. ANS: B   DIF: E   REF: 765   OBJ: C30S4-4
    TOP: Political systems, Concentration camp

9. ANS: C   DIF: E   REF: 748   OBJ: C30S1-3
    TOP: Economics, General strike

10. ANS: B   DIF: E   REF: 752   OBJ: C30S2-1
    TOP: Science, Albert Einstein

11. ANS: G   DIF: E   REF: 754   OBJ: C30S2-2
    TOP: Art and literature, Stream of consciousness

12. ANS: D   DIF: E   REF: 754   OBJ: C30S2-2
    TOP: Art and literature, James Joyce

13. ANS: E   DIF: E   REF: 753   OBJ: C30S2-2
    TOP: Art and literature, Pablo Picasso

14. ANS: H   DIF: E   REF: 754   OBJ: C30S2-2
    TOP: Art and literature, Frank Lloyd Wright

15. ANS: A   DIF: E   REF: 765   OBJ: C30S4-4
    TOP: Political systems, Concentration camp

16. ANS: F   DIF: E   REF: 757-758   OBJ: C30S3-1
    TOP: Impact of the individual, Benito Mussolini

MULTIPLE CHOICE

17. ANS: B   DIF: A   REF: 747   OBJ: C30S1-1
    TOP: Global interaction, Kellogg-Briand Pact

18. ANS: A   DIF: A   REF: 747-748   OBJ: C30S1-3
    TOP: Economics, Great Depression

19. ANS: B   DIF: A   REF: 752   OBJ: C30S2-1
    TOP: Science, Theory of relativity
20. ANS: C   DIF: D   REF: 753   OBJ: C30S2-2
    TOP: Art and literature, Cubism
21. ANS: A   DIF: A   REF: 760   OBJ: C30S3-1
    TOP: Continuity and change, Fascism
22. ANS: B   DIF: A   REF: 758-760   OBJ: C30S3-2
    TOP: Political systems, Fascism
23. ANS: B   DIF: A   REF: 763   OBJ: C30S4-2
    TOP: Political systems, Nazis
24. ANS: D   DIF: A   REF: 762-763   OBJ: C30S4-2
    TOP: Political systems, Adolph Hitler
25. ANS: A   DIF: A   REF: 760-764   OBJ: C30S4-1
    TOP: Economics, Cost of living in Germany
26. ANS: B   DIF: E   REF: 760-764   OBJ: C30S4-1
    TOP: Economics, Cost of living in Germany
27. ANS: B   DIF: D   REF: 760-764   OBJ: C30S4-1
    TOP: Economics, Cost of living in Germany
28. ANS: A   DIF: D   REF: 747   OBJ: C30S1-1
    TOP: Global interaction, Kellogg-Briand Pact
29. ANS: D   DIF: A   REF: 750   OBJ: C30S1-2
    TOP: Global interaction, Maginot Line
30. ANS: C   DIF: A   REF: 747-748   OBJ: C30S1-3
    TOP: Economics, Great Depression
31. ANS: B   DIF: A   REF: 754   OBJ: C30S2-2
    TOP: Art and literature, Postwar writers
32. ANS: B   DIF: D   REF: 756   OBJ: C30S2-3
    TOP: Social systems, Labor-saving devices
33. ANS: A   DIF: E   REF: 760   OBJ: C30S3-1
    TOP: Political systems, Fascism
34. ANS: C   DIF: A   REF: 758   OBJ: C30S3-3
    TOP: Political systems, Fascism
35. ANS: B   DIF: E   REF: 765   OBJ: C30S4-2
    TOP: Religion, "Final solution"

SHORT ANSWER

36. ANS:
    The Kellogg-Briand Pact was an agreement signed by almost all independent nations that promised to give up war as an instrument of national policy. It reflected the "spirit of Locarno" in its renunciation of war.

    DIF: A   REF: 747   OBJ: C30S1-1
    TOP: Global interaction, Kellogg-Briand Pact

37. ANS:
Causes should include: overproduction of goods; rising wages for industrial workers while farmers' earnings were falling; and the New York stock market crash. Effects should include: widespread unemployment; growth of economic nationalism (including protective tariffs); loss of faith in democracy; or increase in social programs.

DIF: D   REF: 747-748   OBJ: C30S1-3
TOP: Economics, Great Depression

38. ANS:
Scientific developments after the war pointed to a constantly changing universe. For example, investigation into radioactivity showed that atoms could change, while Einstein's work led him to believe that even space and time were not fixed.

DIF: A   REF: 752-753   OBJ: C30S2-1
TOP: Science, New views of the universe

39. ANS:
Italians were frustrated by the economic chaos and political corruption in Italy including high unemployment, rising taxes, and a decline in trade. Italians welcomed a strong leader like Mussolini who could bring Italy's problems under control.

DIF: A   REF: 757   OBJ: C30S3-1
TOP: Continuity and change, Mussolini

40. ANS:
Fascists believe the individual is less important than the State as a whole. They are blindly loyal to the state and glorify action, violence, and discipline; they are anti-democratic and emphasize emotion.

DIF: A   REF: 758   OBJ: C30S3-3
TOP: Political systems, Fascism

41. ANS:
The Weimar government was weak. Germans resented it for its inability to solve the country's economic problems, and they blamed it for the Versailles treaty. Germans saw in Hitler a strong leader who would take charge and give Germany a future.

DIF: A   REF: 761-762   OBJ: C30S4-1
TOP: Continuity and change, Hitler

42. ANS:
force and power

DIF: E   REF: 762-763   OBJ: C30S4-2
TOP: Continuity and change, Hitler

43. ANS:
The idea that the strongest will eventually win out over the weak and that this is necessary and good for humanity.

DIF: A   REF: 762-763   OBJ: C30S4-2
TOP: Continuity and change, Hitler

44. ANS:
"For the weak, yes, for humanity as a whole, no."

DIF: A   REF: 762-763   OBJ: C30S4-2
TOP: Continuity and change, Hitler

ESSAY

45. ANS:
In Fascist Italy the state was supreme and the individual only had importance in service to the state. In the United States it is the individual who is supremely important and the state only has meaning so far as it serves the needs of individuals.

DIF: D   REF: 758   OBJ: C30S3-3
TOP: Political systems, Fascism

46. ANS:
The Jews do not have German blood according to Hitler. Therefore, they cannot be part of the Volk, or nation.

DIF: A   REF: 765   OBJ: C30S4-2
TOP: Religion, "Final solution"

47. ANS:
Scientific developments after the war pointed to a constantly changing universe. For example, investigation into radioactivity showed that atoms could change, while Einstein's work led him to believe that even space and time were not fixed.

DIF: A   REF: 752-753   OBJ: C30S2-1
TOP: Science, New views of the universe

48. ANS:
Youths were impressionable and, when educated in the party ideology, were likely to be committed and loyal for life.

DIF: A   REF: 760   OBJ: C30S3-2
TOP: Social systems, Fascism

49. ANS:
T. S. Eliot's poem *The Waste Land* reflects the spiritual emptiness, hopelessness, and lack of joy many people felt after the war. The paintings of Dada show the world as a chaotic and immoral place, which reflects the lack of purpose and the unclear sense of direction that many people felt at the end of the war.

DIF: D   REF: 753-754   OBJ: C30S2-2   TOP: Art and literature

50. ANS:
In Fascist Italy, women's primary role was to bear children. Almost anything else was viewed as a selfish pursuit and discouraged. In the United States, women had won the right to vote and were beginning to be viewed in a more multifaceted way. They were finding encouragement to pursue a variety of jobs and interests.

DIF: A   REF: 756-758   OBJ: C30S3-2
TOP: Social systems, Role of women

CHAPTER 31—WORLD WAR II AND ITS AFTERMATH (1931–1955)

Matching

Match each term with the correct statement below.

a. appeasement	e. containment
b. blitzkrieg	f. genocide
c. cold war	g. kamikaze
d. collaborator	h. pacifism

_____ 1. Giving in to the demands of an aggressor in order to keep the peace

_____ 2. Opposition to all war

_____ 3. Lightning war

_____ 4. Deliberate destruction of a group of people

_____ 5. One who cooperates with an enemy force occupying a country

_____ 6. Japanese pilots who undertook suicide missions to attack American warships

_____ 7. Limiting communism to areas already under Soviet control

_____ 8. State of tension and hostility among nations without armed conflict

Match each person with the correct statement below.

a. Winston Churchill	d. Haile Selassie
b. Francisco Franco	e. Harry Truman
c. Dwight Eisenhower	

_____ 9. Ethiopian king who appealed to the League of Nations for help

_____ 10. Nationalist general who created a Fascist dictatorship in Spain

_____ 11. Prime minister who rallied Britain to fight against Nazi aggression

_____ 12. Supreme Allied commander in Europe

_____ 13. President who issued a policy stating that Americans would resist Soviet expansion in the world

Match each place with the correct statement below.

a. Dunkirk	d. Hiroshima
b. El Alamein	e. Pearl Harbor
c. Guernica	

_____ 14. Town that was brutally attacked by Germany during the Spanish Civil War

_____ 15. Beach on the English Channel where Allied troops were rescued from advancing Nazis

_____ 16. Naval base in Hawaii that was attacked by Japan in 1941

_____ 17. Site of a battle in Egypt that became a turning point in World War II

_____ 18. Japanese city destroyed by an atomic bomb dropped by the United States in 1945

Multiple Choice
Identify the letter of the choice that best completes the statement or answers the question.

_____ 19. Which of the following became a dress rehearsal for World War II by demonstrating the destructive power of modern warfare?
   a. the invasion of Ethiopia
   b. the Anschluss
   c. the Spanish Civil War
   d. the surrender of the Sudetenland

_____ 20. Which of the following cities was the target of a Nazi blitz for two months in 1941?
   a. London
   b. Dunkirk
   c. Paris
   d. Vichy

_____ 21. "Operation Barbarossa" refers to Hitler's plan to conquer
   a. Greece.
   b. North Africa.
   c. Britain.
   d. the Soviet Union.

_____ 22. The Japanese attack on Pearl Harbor, Hawaii,
   a. brought the war to an end.
   b. brought the United States into the war.
   c. ended U.S. interference in Asia and the Pacific.
   d. tested the destructive power of its bombers.

_____ 23. "D-Day" refers to the
   a. Allied invasion of France.
   b. entry of the United States into the war.
   c. end of World War II.
   d. British victory in North Africa.

_____ 24. Which of these battles was a turning point after which the United States took the offensive in the Pacific?
   a. Pearl Harbor
   b. Midway Island
   c. Iwo Jima
   d. Burma

_____ 25. The Allied forces ended the war in Europe by
   a. invading Italy.
   b. bombing Hiroshima.
   c. liberating Paris.
   d. capturing Berlin.

_____ 26. Which nation suffered the highest number of casualties in World War II?
   a. Germany
   b. the United States
   c. the Soviet Union
   d. Japan

Figure 31-1

_____ 27. According to Figure 31-1, which country was divided after World War II?
  a. Austria
  b. Poland
  c. Yugoslavia
  d. Germany

_____ 28. According to Figure 31-1, which free country shared a border with the Soviet Union?
  a. Turkey
  b. Greece
  c. Austria
  d. Italy

_____ 29. According to Figure 31-1, which of the following areas was added to the Soviet Union after World War II?
  a. Turkey
  b. Latvia
  c. Switzerland
  d. Austria

_____ 30. According to Figure 31-1, which of the following Eastern European countries remained free of Soviet control?
  a. Poland
  b. Albania
  c. Greece
  d. Hungary

_____ 31. In response to Axis aggression in the 1930s, western democracies followed a policy of
  a. containment.
  b. appeasement.
  c. aggression.
  d. genocide.

_____ 32. The term Holocaust refers to the
   a. bombing of Britain.
   b. mobilization for total war.
   c. massacre of more than six million Jews.
   d. turning point of the war in North Africa.

_____ 33. The Battle of Midway was the turning point that
   a. brought the United States into the war.
   b. allowed the United States to take the offensive in the Pacific.
   c. forced Japan to surrender.
   d. started Japan's uninterrupted series of victories.

_____ 34. The war in Europe ended with the
   a. bombing of Hiroshima.
   b. Battle of the Bulge.
   c. capture and execution of Mussolini.
   d. surrender of Germany.

_____ 35. The nation that suffered the greatest number of both civilian and military dead and wounded in World War II was
   a. the Soviet Union.   c. Japan.
   b. Britain.   d. Germany.

_____ 36. The major rivals in the Cold War were
   a. Britain and France.
   b. Germany and Italy.
   c. the United States and the Soviet Union.
   d. China and Japan.

Short Answer

37. Identify three acts of aggression by dictators in the 1930s.

38. Give three reasons why western democracies were unable to stop aggressive dictators.

39. Describe two ways that technology affected the fighting in World War II.

40. Identify three ways that mobilization for war affected Americans on the home front.

41. Explain how El Alamein and Stalingrad were turning points in World War II.

42. List three events that led to the defeat of Germany.

43. Explain two reasons why the United States used the atomic bomb on Japan.

Read the following excerpt from the diary of Anne Frank, a young Jewish girl who lived in hiding from the Nazis for two years during World War II. Then answer the questions that follow.

> "Tuesday, 6 June, 1944
> 'This is D-Day' came the announcement over the English news and quite rightly, 'this is the day.' The invasion has begun! . . . Great commotion in the 'Secret Annex' [the hiding place]! Would the long-awaited liberation that has been talked of so much, but which still seems too wonderful, too much like a fairy tale, ever come true? . . .
> Oh, Kitty, the best part of the invasion is that I have the feeling that friends are approaching. We have been oppressed by those terrible Germans for so long, they have had their knives at our throats, that the thoughts of friends and delivery fills us with confidence! . . . Margot says, I may yet be able to go back to school in September or October."

44. Why did the announcement of the D-Day invasion provide hope for Anne Frank and her family?

45. How did Anne Frank describe the invading Allies?

46. Why do you think Anne Frank looked forward to going back to school?

Essay
On a separate sheet of paper, write an answer to the following questions.

47. **Analyzing Information** Why did the western democracies fail to stop Axis aggression in the 1930s?

48. **Synthesizing Information** How did democratic governments mobilize their resources for total war?

49. **Making Comparisons** Compare the positive and negative effects of technology in World War II.

50. **Analyzing Information** How did the Allied war effort limit the rights of citizens in democratic countries?

51. **Recognizing Causes and Effects** What were the causes and effects of the Japanese attack on Pearl Harbor in December 1941?

52. **Drawing Conclusions** Explain how differences between the Soviet Union and the West led to the Cold War.

CHAPTER 31—WORLD WAR II AND ITS AFTERMATH (1931–1955)
Answer Section

MATCHING

1. ANS: A   DIF: E   REF: 771   OBJ: C31S1-2
   TOP: Global interaction, Appeasement
2. ANS: H   DIF: E   REF: 771   OBJ: C31S1-2
   TOP: Power and conflict, Pacifism
3. ANS: B   DIF: E   REF: 775   OBJ: C31S2-1
   TOP: Power and conflict, Blitzkrieg
4. ANS: F   DIF: E   REF: 781-782   OBJ: C31S3-1
   TOP: Religion, Genocide
5. ANS: D   DIF: E   REF: 782   OBJ: C31S3-1
   TOP: Religion, Collaborator
6. ANS: G   DIF: E   REF: 789   OBJ: C31S4-3
   TOP: Power and conflict, Kamikaze
7. ANS: E   DIF: E   REF: 793   OBJ: C31S5-3
   TOP: Global interaction, Containment
8. ANS: C   DIF: E   REF: 792-793   OBJ: C31S5-3
   TOP: Global interaction, Cold War

9. ANS: D   DIF: E   REF: 770   OBJ: C31S1-1
   TOP: Power and conflict, Ethiopia
10. ANS: B   DIF: E   REF: 772   OBJ: C31S1-1
    TOP: Impact of the individual, Francisco Franco
11. ANS: A   DIF: E   REF: 776-778   OBJ: C31S2-2
    TOP: Impact of the individual, Winston Churchill
12. ANS: C   DIF: E   REF: 786   OBJ: C31S3-3
    TOP: Impact of the individual, Dwight Eisenhower
13. ANS: E   DIF: E   REF: 793   OBJ: C31S5-3
    TOP: Impact of the individual, Truman Doctrine

14. ANS: C   DIF: E   REF: 772   OBJ: C31S1-2
    TOP: Power and conflict, Spanish Civil War
15. ANS: A   DIF: E   REF: 775-776   OBJ: C31S2-1
    TOP: Power and conflict, Dunkirk
16. ANS: E   DIF: E   REF: 779-780   OBJ: C31S2-3
    TOP: Global interaction, Pearl Harbor
17. ANS: B   DIF: E   REF: 784   OBJ: C31S4-2
    TOP: Power and conflict, El Alamein
18. ANS: D   DIF: E   REF: 789-790   OBJ: C31S4-3
    TOP: Global interaction, Hiroshima

MULTIPLE CHOICE

19. ANS: C   DIF: A   REF: 772   OBJ: C31S1-2
    TOP: Power and conflict, Spanish Civil War
20. ANS: A   DIF: A   REF: 778   OBJ: C31S2-2
    TOP: Power and conflict, London blitz
21. ANS: D   DIF: A   REF: 778-779   OBJ: C31S2-2
    TOP: Power and conflict, Operation Barbarossa
22. ANS: B   DIF: A   REF: 779-780   OBJ: C31S2-3
    TOP: Global interaction, Pearl Harbor
23. ANS: A   DIF: E   REF: 786   OBJ: C31S3-3
    TOP: Power and conflict, D-Day
24. ANS: B   DIF: A   REF: 788   OBJ: C31S4-1
    TOP: Global interaction, Battle of Midway
25. ANS: D   DIF: A   REF: 788   OBJ: C31S4-2
    TOP: Power and conflict, Nazis defeated
26. ANS: C   DIF: A   REF: 791-792   OBJ: C31S5-1
    TOP: Power and conflict, War casualties
27. ANS: D   DIF: E   REF: 794-795   OBJ: C31S5-2
    TOP: Continuity and change, Divided Germany
28. ANS: A   DIF: E   REF: 794   OBJ: C31S5-2
    TOP: Continuity and change, Cold War Europe
29. ANS: B   DIF: E   REF: 794   OBJ: C31S5-2
    TOP: Continuity and change, Cold War Europe
30. ANS: C   DIF: E   REF: 794   OBJ: C31S5-2
    TOP: Continuity and change, Cold War Europe
31. ANS: B   DIF: A   REF: 771-773   OBJ: C31S1-3
    TOP: Global interaction, Appeasement
32. ANS: C   DIF: A   REF: 781-783   OBJ: C31S3-1
    TOP: Religion, Holocaust
33. ANS: B   DIF: A   REF: 788   OBJ: C31S4-1
    TOP: Global interaction, Battle of Midway
34. ANS: D   DIF: A   REF: 788   OBJ: C31S4-2
    TOP: Power and conflict, Nazis defeated
35. ANS: A   DIF: A   REF: 791-792   OBJ: C31S5-1
    TOP: Power and conflict, War casualties
36. ANS: C   DIF: E   REF: 792-793   OBJ: C31S5-3
    TOP: Global interaction, Cold War

SHORT ANSWER

37. ANS:
Japan seized Manchuria; Italy invaded Ethiopia; Germany sent troops into the Rhineland.

DIF: A   REF: 770-771   OBJ: C31S1-1
TOP: Power and conflict, Dictators challenge world peace

38. ANS:
France was suffering from political divisions. Some Britons thought Hitler was justified in challenging the harsh Versailles treaty. Both Britain and France viewed Hitler as a defense against the spread of Soviet communism. Pacifism and disgust with World War I caused governments to seek peace.

DIF: A   REF: 771   OBJ: C31S1-3
TOP: Power and conflict, Appeasement and neutrality

39. ANS:
Technology made World War II a war of rapid movement through the use of armored tanks and troop carriers and improved airplanes. Technology also increased the destructiveness of war with deadly bombs and weapons.

DIF: A   REF: 776   OBJ: C31S2-1
TOP: Technology, Modern warfare

40. ANS:
The government rationed consumer goods and regulated prices and wages. The high rate of unemployment ended. Many women replaced men in the work force. Japanese Americans lost their civil rights and freedoms.

DIF: D   REF: 784   OBJ: C31S3-2
TOP: Power and conflict, Total war

41. ANS:
The Allied victory at El Alamein stopped Rommel's advance and drove back Axis forces in North Africa. It set the stage for the Allied invasion of Italy. At Stalingrad, German troops were trapped by the Russians and finally surrendered. This victory allowed the Red Army to take the offensive and drive the Germans out of the Soviet Union.

DIF: A   REF: 784, 786   OBJ: C31S3-3
TOP: Power and conflict, Turning points

42. ANS:
Allied bombings of German cities, the Allied advance from France, and the Soviet advance on Berlin led to the final surrender of Germany.

DIF: A   REF: 788   OBJ: C31S4-2
TOP: Global interaction, Defeat of Germany

43. ANS:
President Truman wanted to avoid an invasion of mainland Japan that would cost enormous loss of life on both sides. He may also have hoped to hold off a Soviet advance by impressing them with American power.

DIF: A   REF: 789-790   OBJ: C31S4-3
TOP: Global interaction, Atomic bomb

44. ANS:
The Franks felt that they would be liberated from the Germans. Anne thought she would be able to go back to school.

DIF: A   REF: 781-783, 786   OBJ: C31S3-3
TOP: Religion, Anne Frank

45. ANS:
She described them as "friends."

DIF: A   REF: 781-783, 786   OBJ: C31S3-3
TOP: Religion, Anne Frank

46. ANS:
She wanted her life to be normal again.

DIF: D   REF: 781-783, 786   OBJ: C31S3-3
TOP: Religion, Anne Frank

ESSAY

47. ANS:
Western democracies dreaded another war. They hoped that diplomacy and compromise would prevent further aggression. They were distracted by political and economic problems.

DIF: D   REF: 771   OBJ: C31S1-3
TOP: Power and conflict, Appeasement and neutrality

48. ANS:
Governments in the United States and Britain ordered factories to produce war materials. They rationed consumer goods and regulated prices and wages. They also limited freedoms.

DIF: D   REF: 784   OBJ: C31S3-2
TOP: Power and conflict, Total war

49. ANS:
Technology produced deadly bombs and increased the destructive power of warfare. Technology also improved the design and effectiveness of airplanes and submarines, produced radar and sonar, and led to medical advances and new synthetic products.

DIF: D   REF: 776   OBJ: C31S2-1
TOP: Technology, Modern warfare

50. ANS:

They censored the press. In addition, in the United States, many Japanese Americans lost their civil rights. Some were forced into internment camps. Britain took similar action against German refugees.

DIF: D   REF: 784   OBJ: C31S3-2
TOP: Power and conflict, Total war

51. ANS:

The Japanese attacked Pearl Harbor because the United States was interfering with their plans to seize lands in Asia and the Pacific. As a result of the attack, the United States entered World War II.

DIF: D   REF: 779-780   OBJ: C31S2-3
TOP: Global interaction, Pearl Harbor

52. ANS:

The Soviet Union spread communism into Eastern Europe and dominated governments there. Western democracies, led by the United States, opposed the spread of communism. Conflicting ideologies and mutual distrust brought about the state of tension known as the Cold War.

DIF: D   REF: 793   OBJ: C31S5-3
TOP: Continuity and change, Cold War

CHAPTER 32—THE WORLD SINCE 1945: AN OVERVIEW (1945–PRESENT)

Matching

Match each term with the correct statement below.

a.	acid rain	e.	multinational corporation
b.	genetic engineering	f.	nonaligned
c.	interdependence	g.	privatization
d.	liberation theology	h.	terrorism

_____ 1. Allied to neither the United States nor the Soviet Union during the Cold War

_____ 2. Dependence of countries on goods, resources, and knowledge from other parts of the world

_____ 3. Use of random violence to reach political goals

_____ 4. A business with branches in many countries

_____ 5. The selling of state-owned industries to private investors

_____ 6. A form of pollution

_____ 7. A movement in the Catholic Church to take a more active role in opposing the social conditions that contributed to poverty in Latin America

_____ 8. Altering the chemical code of living things

Match each term with the correct statement below.

a.	acid rain	e.	multinational corporations
b.	genetic engineering	f.	nonaligned
c.	interdependence	g.	privatization
d.	liberation theology	h.	terrorism

_____ 9. A(n) _____ nation was one that sided with neither the United States nor the Soviet Union during the Cold War.

_____ 10. The dependence of countries on goods, resources, and knowledge from other parts of the world is known as _____.

_____ 11. _____ is the deliberate use of random violence to achieve political goals.

_____ 12. Businesses with branches in many countries are called _____.

_____ 13. When governments sell state-owned industries to private investors it is called _____.

_____ 14. _____ is a form of pollution in which toxic chemicals in the air come back to the Earth as rain, snow, or hail.

_____ 15. _____ was a movement among the clergy of the Catholic Church to take a more active role in opposing the social conditions that contributed to poverty in Latin America.

_____ 16. Altering the chemical code in living things is called _____.

Multiple Choice
Identify the letter of the choice that best completes the statement or answers the question.

_____ 17. After World War II, the imperial powers gave up their empires because
   a. treaties forced them to.
   b. they lacked the will to fight for them.
   c. they thought it was morally right.
   d. the Soviet Union demanded it.

_____ 18. One of the biggest factors contributing to political instability in African nations immediately after independence was
   a. the lack of natural resources.   c. the lack of common ties and goals.
   b. the failure of communism.   d. huge debts.

_____ 19. Which of the following is a primary cause of global interdependence?
   a. advances in technology   c. migration
   b. World War II   d. World War I

_____ 20. Most of the nations in the global South are
   a. poor.   c. democratic.
   b. prosperous.   d. developed.

_____ 21. Developing countries that borrowed money from the West usually
   a. made rapid progress toward modernization.
   b. were able to pay back their debts.
   c. spent much of their income trying to pay back their debt.
   d. developed economic independence.

_____ 22. Which of the following is an effect of urbanization in developing countries?
   a. The nuclear family is strong.
   b. Ties to village and family are weakened.
   c. Traditional beliefs and values thrive.
   d. Cities have become better places to live.

_____ 23. Which of the following statements regarding modern technology is true?
   a. Only a few people have benefited from it.
   b. It has solved most of the world's problems.
   c. It has helped the global South the most.
   d. It has changed life all over the globe.

_____ 24. Technology has helped form a global culture by
   a. making all cultures alike.
   b. spreading ideas rapidly.
   c. mass-producing works of art.
   d. giving all people everywhere access to computers.

Country	Literacy Rate Female / Male	Public Expenditures on Education per Student
Egypt	34 / 63	$ 185
Brazil	80 / 83	$ 321
Botswana	65 / 84	$ 462
China	62 / 84	$ 52
Iraq	49 / 70	$ 322
Rwanda	37 / 64	$ 71
Switzerland	99 / 99	$ 12,630
United States	99 / 99	$ 6,580

Figure 32-1

25. According to Figure 32-1, which of the following countries has the lowest literacy rate for women?
    a. Brazil
    b. Iraq
    c. Rwanda
    d. Egypt

26. Based on Figure 32-1, which of the following generalizations is true?
    a. There is a lower literacy rate among females than among males.
    b. Females are more likely to go on to higher education than males.
    c. Public expenditures on education per student are generally high worldwide.
    d. Public expenditures on education per student are higher in developing countries than in developed countries.

27. According to Figure 32-1, which of the following countries has the lowest rate of male literacy?
    a. China
    b. Egypt
    c. Iraq
    d. United States

28. Which of the following played a role in ending European imperialism?
    a. terrorism
    b. the Cold War
    c. the Korean War
    d. global interdependence

29. One effect of the Cold War was
    a. an outbreak of civil wars.
    b. the founding of the United Nations.
    c. increased political tension worldwide.
    d. widespread fighting.

_____ 30. Democracy failed in many new nations because
   a.   the people were unprepared for self-rule.
   b.   there were too many poor people.
   c.   the people felt more comfortable with the military in charge.
   d.   too many people were homeless.

_____ 31. Most of the world's wealth is controlled by nations in
   a.   the global South.   c.   the global North.
   b.   the developing world.   d.   the Eastern Hemisphere.

_____ 32. Which of the following poses the most immediate challenge to many developing nations?
   a.   population growth   c.   migration
   b.   nuclear proliferation   d.   global warming

_____ 33. Which of the following is an effect of urbanization in the developing world?
   a.   Traditional beliefs and values are being eroded.
   b.   People are living easier lives.
   c.   Village life is ending.
   d.   Extended families are growing stronger.

_____ 34. Based on the information in your textbook, which of the following is the best generalization about modern science and technology?
   a.   It has hurt more people than it has helped.
   b.   It has brought the world one step closer to disaster.
   c.   It has improved life for most people.
   d.   It has fulfilled its potential for solving the world's problems.

_____ 35. Which of the following played the greatest role in spreading American culture around the globe?
   a.   war   c.   artists
   b.   migrations   d.   television

Short Answer

36. List three reasons why European nations lost their empires after World War II.

37. Explain how the Cold War dominated world politics after World War II.

38. Identify three problems faced by new nations trying to establish stable, democratic governments.

39. Define the global North and global South, and compare the two regions.

40. List five factors that have prevented economic growth in developing countries.

41. Describe three leading environmental problems and explain how they are related to economic development.

42. Describe some of the ways that women's lives have changed in recent decades.

    Read the following excerpt from "Trade Lessons From the World Economy," an article by Peter F. Drucker. Then answer the questions that follow.

    "Information flows in the world economy are probably growing faster than any category of transactions in history. Consisting of meetings, software, magazines, books, movies, videos, telecommunications and a host of new technologies, information flows may already exceed money flows in the fees, royalties and profits they generate. Unlike money flows, information flows have benign economic impacts. In fact, few things so stimulate economic growth as the rapid development of information, whether telecommunications, computer data, computer networks or entertainment media. In the United States, information flows—and the goods needed to carry them—have become the largest single source of foreign currency income."

43. According to this excerpt, what are "information flows"?

44. Based on this excerpt, how do you think information flows help economic growth?

45. Based on this excerpt, how do you think easy, rapid access to information worldwide has changed the world? Explain.

Essay
On a separate sheet of paper, write an answer to the following questions.

46. **Recognizing Causes and Effects** What do you think were the difficulties faced by nations like India who chose to remain nonaligned during the Cold War?

47. **Making Decisions** If you were the leader of a developing country, which would be your top priority, economic development or protecting the environment? Explain.

48. **Recognizing Causes and Effects** How have changes in the nature of war made it important for countries to work together to solve their problems?

49. **Synthesizing Information** Why do you think leaders of developing nations might be less likely than leaders of western nations to feel that protecting the environment should take priority over economic development?

50. **Predicting Consequences** Based on what you know about increasing global interdependence, do you think the world will still be organized into self-governing nation-states a century from now?

51. **Applying Information** "In the city, life is driven by the economy; but in the village, life settles around the community." Explain what this means.

CHAPTER 32—THE WORLD SINCE 1945: AN OVERVIEW (1945–PRESENT)
Answer Section

MATCHING

1. ANS: F   DIF: E   REF: 807   OBJ: C32S1-1
   TOP: Global interaction, Nonaligned nations
2. ANS: C   DIF: E   REF: 809   OBJ: C32S1-3
   TOP: Economics, Interdependence
3. ANS: H   DIF: E   REF: 811   OBJ: C32S1-4
   TOP: Global interaction, Terrorism
4. ANS: E   DIF: E   REF: 813   OBJ: C32S2-1
   TOP: Economics, Multinational corporation
5. ANS: G   DIF: E   REF: 814   OBJ: C32S2-1
   TOP: Economics, Privatization
6. ANS: A   DIF: E   REF: 817   OBJ: C32S2-3
   TOP: Environment, Acid rain
7. ANS: D   DIF: E   REF: 819   OBJ: C32S3-1
   TOP: Religion, Liberation theology
8. ANS: B   DIF: E   REF: 820   OBJ: C32S3-3
   TOP: Technology, Genetic engineering

9. ANS: F   DIF: E   REF: 807   OBJ: C32S1-1
   TOP: Global interaction, Nonaligned movement
10. ANS: C   DIF: E   REF: 809   OBJ: C32S1-3
    TOP: Economics, Interdependence
11. ANS: H   DIF: E   REF: 811   OBJ: C32S1-4
    TOP: Global interaction, Terrorism
12. ANS: E   DIF: E   REF: 813   OBJ: C32S2-1
    TOP: Economics, Multinational corporation
13. ANS: G   DIF: E   REF: 814   OBJ: C32S2-1
    TOP: Economics, Privatization
14. ANS: A   DIF: E   REF: 817   OBJ: C32S2-3
    TOP: Environment, Acid rain
15. ANS: D   DIF: E   REF: 819   OBJ: C32S3-1
    TOP: Religion, Liberation theology
16. ANS: B   DIF: E   REF: 820   OBJ: C32S3-3
    TOP: Technology, Genetic engineering

MULTIPLE CHOICE

17. ANS: B   DIF: A   REF: 806   OBJ: C32S1-1
    TOP: Continuity and change, End to colonial empires
18. ANS: C   DIF: A   REF: 808   OBJ: C32S1-3
    TOP: Continuity and change, New African nations

19. ANS: A   DIF: D   REF: 809   OBJ: C32S1-2
    TOP: Global interaction, Interdependence

20. ANS: A   DIF: E   REF: 812   OBJ: C32S2-1
    TOP: Global interaction, Global South

21. ANS: C   DIF: A   REF: 813-814   OBJ: C32S2-2
    TOP: Global interaction, Debt crisis

22. ANS: B   DIF: A   REF: 818   OBJ: C32S3-1
    TOP: Continuity and change, Urbanization

23. ANS: D   DIF: A   REF: 820-822   OBJ: C32S3-3
    TOP: Technology, Global impact

24. ANS: B   DIF: E   REF: 820-822   OBJ: C32S3-4
    TOP: Technology, Global impact

25. ANS: D   DIF: E   REF: 818   OBJ: C32S3-2
    TOP: Social systems, Literacy

26. ANS: A   DIF: A   REF: 818   OBJ: C32S3-2
    TOP: Social systems, Literacy

27. ANS: B   DIF: A   REF: 818   OBJ: C32S3-2
    TOP: Social systems, Literacy

28. ANS: B   DIF: A   REF: 806   OBJ: C32S1-1
    TOP: Continuity and change, End to colonial empires

29. ANS: C   DIF: A   REF: 807-808   OBJ: C32S1-2
    TOP: Global interaction, Cold War

30. ANS: A   DIF: A   REF: 808-809   OBJ: C32S1-3
    TOP: Political systems, New nations

31. ANS: C   DIF: E   REF: 812   OBJ: C32S2-1
    TOP: Global interaction, Global North

32. ANS: A   DIF: A   REF: 814-815   OBJ: C32S2-2
    TOP: Continuity and change, Obstacles to development

33. ANS: A   DIF: A   REF: 818   OBJ: C32S3-1
    TOP: Continuity and change, Urbanization

34. ANS: C   DIF: A   REF: 820-822   OBJ: C32S3-2
    TOP: Technology, Global impact

35. ANS: D   DIF: A   REF: 820-822   OBJ: C32S3-3
    TOP: Global interaction, Television

SHORT ANSWER

36. ANS:
    Nationalist resistance grew stronger; the superpowers supported self-determination; the war weakened the imperial powers; they lost the will to fight to hold on to those empires.

    DIF: A   REF: 806   OBJ: C32S1-1
    TOP: Continuity and change, End to colonial empires

37. ANS:
The United States and the Soviet Union competed for world domination. Nations around the world were pressured, either for financial or military reasons (or sometimes both), to support one side or the other.

DIF: E   REF: 807-808   OBJ: C32S1-2
TOP: Global interaction, Cold War

38. ANS:
Diverse ethnic and religious groups within borders had no common ties to unify them; the new nations' peoples were unprepared for self-government; nations were plagued by civil wars and revolutions.

DIF: A   REF: 808-809   OBJ: C32S1-3
TOP: Continuity and change, New nations

39. ANS:
Global North—the industrialized nations of Western Europe and North America, along with Japan and Australia. Global South—the developing world, much of which lies south of the equator on the continents of Africa, Asia, and Latin America. The nations of the global North control most of the world's resources and enjoy a much higher standard of living than do the nations of the global South, which are generally poor and undeveloped.

DIF: A   REF: 812-813   OBJ: C32S2-1
TOP: Global interaction, Global North and South

40. ANS:
Answers should include five of the following: difficult geographic conditions, including lack of natural resources, poor farmland, and uncertain rainfall; rapidly growing populations; outdated economic patterns, including economic dependence and limited exports; foreign debt; socialism; or political instability, including unstable governments and war.

DIF: D   REF: 814-815   OBJ: C32S2-2
TOP: Economics, Obstacles to development

41. ANS:
Answers should include three of the following: strip mining, use of chemical pesticides and fertilizers, oil spills, air and water pollution, acid rain, or global warming. Explanations should point out that as countries develop, they increase their use of technologies, which in turn may damage the environment.

DIF: A   REF: 817   OBJ: C32S2-3
TOP: Environment, Growing threats

42. ANS:
In many countries women have gained equal rights to education and work outside the home. They won the right to vote in many nations, and some hold public office. At the same time, however, they still are primarily responsible for the care of children and the work in the home, which puts a heavy burden on them.

DIF: A   REF: 819-820   OBJ: C32S3-2
TOP: Continuity and change, Role of women

43. ANS:
Information flows are situations, media, or advanced technologies that act as vehicles for the exchange of information.

DIF: E   REF: 820-822   OBJ: C32S3-3
TOP: Technology, Information

44. ANS:
Possible answer: Everyone wants access to all available information and is willing to make getting it an economic priority. Also, information flows create an awareness of the larger material world and put people in touch with a global market, which expands their potential for selling products and also increases the products available for them to buy.

DIF: D   REF: 820-822   OBJ: C32S3-3
TOP: Economics, Information

45. ANS:
It has played a major role in creating a global culture.

DIF: A   REF: 820-823   OBJ: C32S3-4
TOP: Global interaction, Global culture

ESSAY

46. ANS:
Nations that chose to remain nonaligned would be less likely to receive economic aid from either of the superpowers and would not receive military aid. Nonaligned nations could be more vulnerable to military attack or revolution.

DIF: A   REF: 807   OBJ: C32S2-3
TOP: Global interaction, Nonaligned movement

47. ANS:
Some answers will give economic development priority over the environment and say that environmental issues can only be addressed after people's basic needs are met. Other answers may give the environment priority over economic development and support their answer with the reasoning that if the Earth is destroyed there will be nothing left to support human existence.

DIF: A   REF: 817   OBJ: C32S2-3
TOP: Environment, Developing nations

48. ANS:
With the development and spread of nuclear weapons and the widespread use of terrorism, even local wars have taken on a global dimension. What happens in even the remotest parts of the globe has the potential to threaten all of humankind.

DIF: A   REF: 810   OBJ: C32S1-4
TOP: Global interaction, Deadly weapons

49. ANS:
Because they head nations that are generally poor with huge populations that are barely able to survive, leaders of developing nations are likely to resist environmental protection plans and laws that would hinder economic development.

DIF: D   REF: 807   OBJ: C32S2-3
TOP: Environment, Developing nations

50. ANS:
Answers should be supported by explanations.

DIF: A   REF: 809   OBJ: C32S1-4
TOP: Global interaction, Interdependence

51. ANS:
Answers should recognize that the human being and the community are the center of and give meaning to village life, while in the city the human aspects of existence are often subjugated to the economy.

DIF: A   REF: 809   OBJ: C32S3-1
TOP: Continuity and change, Interdependence

CHAPTER 33—EUROPE AND NORTH AMERICA (1945–PRESENT)

Matching

Match each term with the correct statement below.
a. détente
b. deficit
c. dissident
d. glasnost
e. welfare state

_____ 1. The relaxation of political tensions during the Cold War

_____ 2. A government with a capitalist economy that takes responsibility for the social and economic needs of its people

_____ 3. The gap between what a government spends and what it takes in through taxes and other sources

_____ 4. A person who speaks out against the government

_____ 5. Political openness

Match each person with the correct statement below.
a. Leonid Brezhnev
b. Charles de Gaulle
c. Martin Luther King, Jr.
d. Joseph McCarthy
e. Margaret Thatcher

_____ 6. Prime minister who trimmed Britain's welfare state

_____ 7. Leader who restored France's power after World War II

_____ 8. Senator who led a campaign against communists in the United States

_____ 9. Leader of the civil rights movement in the 1950s and 1960s

_____ 10. Communist leader who controlled the Soviet Union for almost twenty years

Match each term with the correct statement below.
a. deficit
b. dissident
c. perestroika
d. service industry
e. welfare state

_____ 11. A business that provides a service rather than a product is called a _____.

_____ 12. A _____ is a country that, although it has a capitalist economy, takes great responsibility for the social and economic needs of its people.

_____ 13. The difference between what a government spends and what it takes in through taxes is called a _____.

_____ 14. A person who speaks out against the government is called a _____.

_____ 15. _____ refers to the restructuring of the Soviet government and economy under Gorbachev.

Match each person with the correct statement below.

a. Mikhail Gorbachev   d. Josip Tito

b. Helmut Kohl   e. Lech Walesa

c. Nikita Khrushchev

____ 16. The architect of German unity

____ 17. Soviet leader who called for "peaceful coexistence" with the West

____ 18. Soviet leader whose reforms led to the end of the Soviet Union

____ 19. Communist leader of Yugoslavia during the Cold War

____ 20. Head of Solidarity

Multiple Choice

Identify the letter of the choice that best completes the statement or answers the question.

____ 21. Which of the following is an effect of increasing global economic competition on the West?
   a. increased exports
   b. the growth of service industries
   c. a loss of influence in the world
   d. an increase in the number of manufacturing jobs

____ 22. Germany was able to reunite because
   a. Brandt signed a treaty with the Soviet Union.
   b. students destroyed the Berlin Wall.
   c. communism in the Soviet Union collapsed.
   d. the East Germans revolted against the Soviets.

____ 23. Which of the following is the goal of separatism in Quebec?
   a. to cut ties with the United States   c. to limit immigration
   b. to become an independent nation   d. to quit NATO

____ 24. Which of the following was a result of central economic planning in the Soviet Union?
   a. an efficient bureaucracy
   b. highly motivated workers
   c. a high standard of living
   d. shortages of food and consumer goods

____ 25. Which of the following did most Eastern European nations use to achieve democracy?
   a. peaceful reforms   c. long negotiations
   b. violent revolutions   d. civil disobedience

____ 26. The civil war in Yugoslavia was fought
   a. between communists and anti-communists.
   b. between pro-democracy supporters and followers of Milosevic.
   c. among Serbs, Croats, and Muslims.
   d. between northern and southern Yugoslavia.

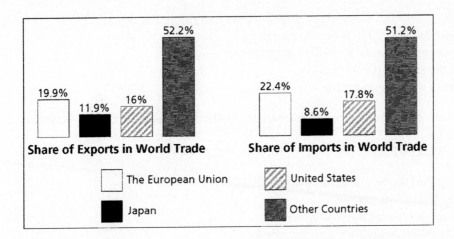

Figure 33-1

_____ 27. According to Figure 33-1, approximately how much of total world exports belonged to the European Union?
a. one-half
b. one-fifth
c. one-twentieth
d. one-tenth

_____ 28. According to Figure 33-1, how does the European Union's share of world exports compare with its share of imports?
a. Its share of exports is slightly less than its share of imports.
b. Its share of exports is four times its share of imports.
c. Its share of exports is double its share of imports.
d. Its share of exports is triple its share of imports.

_____ 29. According to Figure 33-1, what share of total world exports belonged to the European Union?
a. 11.9%
b. 19.9%
c. 16%
d. 52.2%

_____ 30. According to Figure 33-1, how do the European Union's share of total world exports compare with the share of the United States?
a. The European Union's share is twice that of the United States.
b. The European Union's share is slightly larger than that of the United States.
c. The European Union's share is smaller than that of the United States.
d. The European Union's share is three times that of the United States.

_____ 31. Which of the following was an effect of the Cold War on Europe?
a. high unemployment
b. frequent small-scale wars
c. the growth of socialism
d. its division into military alliances

_____ 32. Which of the following issues threatened to tear France apart after World War II?
a. Algerian independence
b. war in Vietnam
c. nationalization
d. the Cold War

_____ 33. During the Cold War, the primary goal of American foreign policy was to
   a. protect human rights everywhere.
   b. encourage economic growth in communist countries.
   c. stop the spread of communism.
   d. create a world without war.

_____ 34. Which of the following helped resolve trade conflicts between the United States and Canada?
   a. NAFTA   c. The United Nations
   b. The Warsaw Pact   d. NATO

_____ 35. One strength of the Soviet economy was that it
   a. could feed all its people.
   b. was almost free of unemployment.
   c. produced high-quality consumer goods.
   d. provided the Soviet people with a high standard of living.

_____ 36. Ethnic tensions in Yugoslavia resulted in
   a. "ethnic cleansing."   c. attacks against immigrants.
   b. the separatist movement.   d. a movement to increase tolerance.

Short Answer

37. Tell how each of the following affected western economies: 1973 oil crisis and global shifts in manufacturing.

38. Explain how the European Union acts as a unifying force for Europe.

39. Identify the Berlin Wall and explain how it was a symbol both of the Cold War and its end.

40. Describe three ways the civil rights movement changed life for African Americans.

41. List three challenges facing Canada.

42. Describe how the Eastern European nations were tied to the Soviet Union in each of the following ways: politically, economically, and militarily.

43. Explain the role "ethnic cleansing" played in the civil war in Bosnia.

Read the following excerpt from a speech by Mikhail Gorbachev. Then answer the questions that follow.

"Today our main job is to lift the individual spiritually, respecting his inner world and giving him moral strength. We are seeking to make the whole intellectual potential of society and all the potentialities of culture work to mold a socially active person, spiritually rich, just and conscientious. An individual must know and feel that his contribution is needed, that his dignity is not being infringed upon, that he is being treated with trust and respect. When an individual sees all this, he is capable of accomplishing much. . . .

There are quite a few people who have adapted the existing laws and practices to their own selfish interests. They give little to society, but nevertheless managed to get from it all that is possible and what even seems impossible; they have lived on unearned incomes.

The policy of restructuring puts everything in its place. We are fully restoring the principle of socialism: 'From each according to his ability, to each according to his work.'"

44. List three phrases or words in this excerpt that would lead you to believe that Gorbachev planned to take a much different position toward human rights than his predecessors.

45. According to this excerpt, what is the main goal of restructuring, or perestroika?

46. Assume that you are a Soviet citizen listening to this speech in 1985. Explain your reaction.

Essay
On a separate sheet of paper, write an answer to the following questions.

47. **Predicting Consequences** Now that the Cold War is over, what guidelines should the United States follow in dealing with other nations if it wants to remain strong in the world?

48. **Recognizing Causes and Effects** Why do you think ethnic conflicts erupted in Eastern Europe as soon as Soviet domination ended?

49. **Making Generalizations** Consider government spending on social programs in Britain and the United States since World War II. What generalization can you make regarding economic prosperity and this kind of spending?

50. **Drawing Conclusions** What do you think is the greatest challenge to Russia's democracy?

51. **Comparing** Do you think the United States is as powerful in the world as it was during the Cold War? Explain why or why not.

CHAPTER 33—EUROPE AND NORTH AMERICA (1945–PRESENT)
Answer Section

MATCHING

1. ANS: A   DIF: E   REF: 828-829   OBJ: C33S1-1
   TOP: Global interaction, Détente

2. ANS: E   DIF: E   REF: 829-830   OBJ: C33S1-2
   TOP: Political system, Welfare state

3. ANS: B   DIF: E   REF: 841   OBJ: C33S3-2
   TOP: Economics, Deficit

4. ANS: C   DIF: E   REF: 844   OBJ: C33S4-1
   TOP: Political systems, Dissident

5. ANS: D   DIF: E   REF: 846   OBJ: C33S4-2
   TOP: Political systems, Glasnost

6. ANS: E   DIF: E   REF: 834   OBJ: C33S2-1
   TOP: Impact of the individual, Margaret Thatcher

7. ANS: B   DIF: E   REF: 836   OBJ: C33S2-2
   TOP: Impact of the individual, Charles de Gaulle

8. ANS: D   DIF: E   REF: 839   OBJ: C33S3-1
   TOP: Impact of the individual, Joseph McCarthy

9. ANS: C   DIF: E   REF: 841   OBJ: C33S3-2
   TOP: Impact of the individual, Martin Luther King Jr.

10. ANS: A   DIF: E   REF: 844   OBJ: C33S4-1
    TOP: Impact of the individual, Leonid Brezhnev

11. ANS: D   DIF: E   REF: 830   OBJ: C33S1-2
    TOP: Economics, Service industry

12. ANS: E   DIF: E   REF: 829-830   OBJ: C33S1-2
    TOP: Political system, Welfare state

13. ANS: A   DIF: E   REF: 841   OBJ: C33S3-2
    TOP: Economics, Deficit

14. ANS: B   DIF: E   REF: 844   OBJ: C33S4-1
    TOP: Political systems, Dissident

15. ANS: C   DIF: E   REF: 844   OBJ: C33S4-2
    TOP: Political systems, Perestroika

16. ANS: B   DIF: E   REF: 837   OBJ: C33S2-3
    TOP: Impact of the individual, Helmut Kohl

17. ANS: C   DIF: E   REF: 843   OBJ: C33S4-1
    TOP: Impact of the individual, Nikita Khrushchev

18. ANS: A   DIF: E   REF: 846   OBJ: C33S4-2
    TOP: Impact of the individual, Mikhail Gorbachev

19. ANS: D   DIF: E   REF: 850, 852   OBJ: C33S5-1
    TOP: Impact of the individual, Josip Tito

20. ANS: E   DIF: E   REF: 850   OBJ: C33S5-1
    TOP: Impact of the individual, Lech Walesa

MULTIPLE CHOICE

21. ANS: B   DIF: D   REF: 830   OBJ: C33S1-2
    TOP: Economics, Global competition
22. ANS: C   DIF: A   REF: 837   OBJ: C33S2-3
    TOP: Political systems, Reunification of Germany
23. ANS: B   DIF: A   REF: 842   OBJ: C33S3-3
    TOP: Political systems, Quebec
24. ANS: D   DIF: A   REF: 844   OBJ: C33S4-2
    TOP: Economics, Soviet command economy
25. ANS: A   DIF: A   REF: 849-851   OBJ: C33S5-2
    TOP: Continuity and change, Democracy in Eastern Europe
26. ANS: C   DIF: E   REF: 851-853   OBJ: C33S5-3
    TOP: Power and conflict, Civil war in Yugoslavia
27. ANS: B   DIF: A   REF: 831-832   OBJ: C33S1-3
    TOP: Economics, European Union
28. ANS: A   DIF: A   REF: 831-832   OBJ: C33S1-3
    TOP: Economics, European Union
29. ANS: B   DIF: E   REF: 831-832   OBJ: C33S1-3
    TOP: Economics, European Union
30. ANS: B   DIF: A   REF: 831-832   OBJ: C33S1-3
    TOP: Economics, European Union
31. ANS: D   DIF: A   REF: 828-829   OBJ: C33S1-1
    TOP: Global interaction, Cold War
32. ANS: A   DIF: A   REF: 835   OBJ: C33S2-2
    TOP: Political systems, Algerian independence
33. ANS: C   DIF: E   REF: 839-840   OBJ: C33S3-1
    TOP: Global interaction, Cold War
34. ANS: A   DIF: A   REF: 842   OBJ: C33S3-3
    TOP: Economics, NAFTA
35. ANS: B   DIF: A   REF: 844   OBJ: C33S4-2
    TOP: Economics, Soviet unemployment
36. ANS: A   DIF: E   REF: 852   OBJ: C33S5-3
    TOP: Diversity, Ethnic cleansing

SHORT ANSWER

37. ANS:
The 1973 oil crisis slowed economic growth. The global shift in manufacturing from the West to Asia—where goods could be produced more cheaply—forced factories to close and workers to lose their jobs. It also prompted a shift in the West to service industries.

DIF: A   REF: 830   OBJ: C33S1-2
TOP: Global interaction, Economic shifts

38. ANS:
It regulates economic activity in Europe, working for regional prosperity, and promotes economic cooperation, peace, and security. To reach its goals and ensure economic prosperity for all, its members must cooperate greatly.

DIF: A   REF: 831-832   OBJ: C33S1-3
TOP: Economic and political systems, European Union

39. ANS:
The Berlin Wall was a wall that split the city of Berlin into two parts—communist-controlled East Berlin and free West Berlin. It symbolized the division of Europe during the Cold War. When the Cold War was over, the wall was torn down and Germany was reunited.

DIF: A   REF: 837   OBJ: C33S2-3
TOP: Continuity and change, Berlin Wall

40. ANS:
As a result of the civil rights movement, African Americans gained equal access to housing, jobs, and education. They also had their rights as voters protected and won elected offices.

DIF: E   REF: 841   OBJ: C33S3-2
TOP: Social systems, Civil rights movement

41. ANS:
Answers should include three of the following: defining a national identity; solving the separatist issue; redefining their relationship with the United States to be more equal; and solving environmental issues with the United States.

DIF: A   REF: 842   OBJ: C33S3-3
TOP: Continuity and change, Canada

42. ANS:
Politically—their governments were controlled from Moscow. Economically—they were forced to follow communism and use their resources to build the Soviet Union.
Militarily—they had to contribute money and troops to the Warsaw Pact and provide bases for Soviet troops.

DIF: A   REF: 849   OBJ: C33S5-1
TOP: Political systems, Soviet domination

43. ANS:
The Serbs used "ethnic cleansing" as the legitimation for removing hundreds of thousands of Croats and Muslims from the areas the Serbs controlled.

DIF: A   REF: 852   OBJ: C33S5-3
TOP: Diversity, Ethnic cleansing

44. ANS:
Possible answers could include: "respecting his inner world," "a socially active person," "moral strength," "spiritually rich," "just and conscientious," "that his dignity is not being infringed on," or "that he is treated with trust and respect."

DIF: A   REF: 846   OBJ: C33S4-1
TOP: Continuity and change, Gorbachev

45. ANS:
to mold a socially active person

DIF: D   REF: 846   OBJ: C33S4-3
TOP: Continuity and change, Perestroika

46. ANS:
Reactions may vary, but many answers will probably express great joy and anticipation because the speech promises greater personal freedom and hints at changes to the economy that will make the Soviet Union a better place to live.

DIF: E   REF: 846   OBJ: C33S4-3
TOP: Continuity and change, Perestroika

ESSAY

47. ANS:
Students' answers should be supported by good reasons.

DIF: D   REF: 839-841   OBJ: C33S3-1
TOP: Global interaction, United States as superpower

48. ANS:
The Soviets suppressed ethnic rivalries. When Soviet control ended, buried tensions quickly surfaced.

DIF: A   REF: 851-852   OBJ: C33S5-1
TOP: Continuity and change, Ethnic conflicts

49. ANS:
Answers should make the connection between flourishing economies and increased social spending and cuts in social spending when the economy is bad.

DIF: A   REF: 834, 840-841   OBJ: C33S2-1
TOP: Economics, Government spending

50. ANS:
Students' answers should include several of the following: shortages of goods, increased prices, unemployment, political turmoil, a sense of chaos among citizens, Communist politicians who want to turn the clock back, extreme nationalism, and demands by minorities within Russia.

DIF: D   REF: 846-847   OBJ: C33S4-3
TOP: Continuity and change, Russian democracy

51. ANS:
Answers will vary but should be supported by explanations.

DIF: A   REF: 839-841   OBJ: C33S3-1
TOP: Continuity and change, United States as superpower

CHAPTER 34—EAST ASIA AND SOUTHEAST ASIA (1945–PRESENT)

Matching

Match each term with the correct statement below.

a. Asian tigers
b. commune
c. Diet
d. domino theory

e. Four Modernizations
f. gross national product
g. Khmer Rouge
h. "Little Red Book"

_____ 1. Japanese parliament

_____ 2. The total value of all goods and services produced by a nation

_____ 3. A group of villages that work together to farm common land

_____ 4. Collection of Mao Zedong's writings about communism

_____ 5. Program to strengthen agriculture, industry, science, and defense in China

_____ 6. Term used to refer to the countries of Taiwan, Hong Kong, Singapore, and Korea

_____ 7. The idea that if communists took over one country, others would also fall to the communists

_____ 8. Cambodian communist guerrillas

Match each term with the correct statement below.

a. Asian tigers
b. commune
c. Diet

d. domino theory
e. gross national product

_____ 9. The Japanese parliament is called the _____.

_____ 10. _____ is the total value of all goods and services produced by a nation.

_____ 11. A(n) _____ is a group of villages that work together to farm common land.

_____ 12. Taiwan, Hong Kong, Singapore, and Korea are known as the _____.

_____ 13. The _____ is the idea that if the communists took over one country, other countries would also fall to communism.

Match each place with the correct statement below.

a. Hong Kong
b. Japan
c. Pacific Rim

d. Singapore
e. Vietnam

_____ 14. Nation that is an economic superpower

_____ 15. Tiny but prosperous island under British control until 1997

_____ 16. Island city-state located on a busy shipping route

_____ 17. Nation torn apart by a long civil war

_____ 18. Geographic region of growing global trade

Multiple Choice
Identify the letter of the choice that best completes the statement or answers the question.

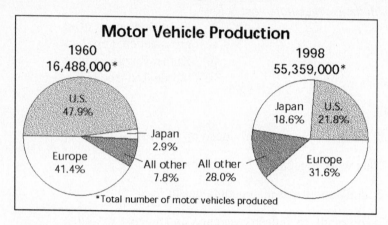

Figure 34-1

_____ 19. According to Figure 34-1, what percentage of the world's motor vehicles did Japan manufacture in 1960?
a. 47.9
b. 41.4
c. 7.8
d. 2.9

_____ 20. According to Figure 34-1, which of the following had the largest increase in the percentage of motor vehicles produced from 1960 to 1998?
a. Japan
b. United States
c. Europe
d. All other

_____ 21. According to Figure 34-1, what percentage of the world's motor vehicles did Japan manufacture in 1998?
a. 2.9
b. 21.8
c. 18.6
d. 28.0

_____ 22. According to Figure 34-1, which of the following had the largest decrease in its percentage of motor vehicle production from 1960 to 1998?
a. Japan
b. All other
c. United States
d. Europe

_____ 23. One of the goals of General MacArthur's military government was
a. to punish the Japanese people.
b. to guarantee democratic government in Japan.
c. to restore Japan to its former glory.
d. to force the Japanese to help rebuild the United States.

_____ 24. Mao Zedong was able to defeat the Nationalists because
   a. the Nationalists had no leader.
   b. he was financed by wealthy landowners.
   c. the Japanese government supported him.
   d. most of the people supported him.

_____ 25. Which of the following was true under communism in China?
   a. Peasants were moved from the countryside to the cities.
   b. The business class was glorified.
   c. Factory workers took control of the government.
   d. Land was redistributed to peasants.

_____ 26. Hong Kong and Taiwan share which of the following with China?
   a. an economic system   c. a government
   b. a similar culture   d. a democracy

_____ 27. Which of the following was most important to the economic development of Singapore?
   a. location   c. culture
   b. climate   d. natural resources

_____ 28. Which of the following was a problem faced by new nations of Southeast Asia?
   a. They were unable to feed their people.
   b. They were caught in the middle of the Cold War.
   c. They lacked the natural resources for economic development.
   d. They lacked strong leaders.

_____ 29. A long-term goal of Ho Chi Minh was
   a. to free Vietnam from foreign domination.
   b. to unite Cambodia, Laos, and Vietnam.
   c. to hold free elections in Vietnam.
   d. to make South Vietnam a free nation.

_____ 30. Why is the Pacific Rim important to the global economy?
   a. Most of the world's people live in the region.
   b. It has most of the world's resources.
   c. It has most of the world's fresh water.
   d. The volume of trade across the Pacific is greater than that across the Atlantic.

_____ 31. One effect of interdependence on Japan is that
   a. it is heavily in debt.
   b. it must work to improve international relations.
   c. it has a huge trade deficit.
   d. it has few jobs for its workers.

_____ 32. Which of the following best explains why Mao Zedong's forces triumphed in China?
   a. Mao promised to improve life for the peasants.
   b. Mao promised to defeat capitalism.
   c. Mao promised to turn China into an industrial nation.
   d. Mao promised a return to the old ways.

_____ 33. The intention of the Four Modernizations was
   a. to limit family size.   c. to get rid of noncommunists.
   b. to end the democracy movement.   d. to improve China's economy.

_____ 34. In which of the following areas is there the biggest difference between North and South Korea?
   a. culture   c. economy
   b. language   d. history

_____ 35. During the Cold War, which of the following was an American priority in Southeast Asia?
   a. to stop the spread of communism
   b. to support independence movements
   c. to establish trade alliances
   d. to establish colonies

_____ 36. Which of the following best explains why Vietnam has great economic potential?
   a. It is heavily populated.
   b. It is a communist country.
   c. It has introduced free-market reforms to attract investors.
   d. It is finally united.

Short Answer

37. Identify the two main goals of General MacArthur's military government in Japan.

38. List five reasons for Japan's economic success.

39. Describe one positive effect and one negative effect of the Four Modernizations.

40. Explain why Hong Kong's future is uncertain.

41. Describe the role of geography in Singapore's economic success.

42. List three ways the effects of the Cold War are still felt in Korea today.

43. Explain why the Pacific Rim is an important part of the global economy.

Read the following excerpts from Mao's "Little Red Book." Then answer the questions that follow.

"It is up to us to organize the people. As for the reactionaries in China, it is up to us to organize the people to overthrow them. Everything reactionary is the same; if you don't hit it, it won't fall. This is also like sweeping the floor; as a rule, where the broom does not reach, the dust will not vanish of itself. We communists are like seeds, and the people are like the soil. Wherever we go, we must unite with the people, take root and blossom among them. We should pay close attention to the well-being of the masses, from the problems of the land and labor to those of fuel, rice, cooking oil, and salt. . . . All such problems concerning the well-being of the masses should be placed on our agenda. We should discuss them, adopt and carry out decisions, and check up on the results. We should help the masses to realize that we represent their interests, that our lives are intimately bound up with theirs."

44. Based on the excerpts, to what people in China did Mao's ideas probably appeal most? Why?

45. According to the excerpts, what should the relationship be between communist leaders and the masses?

46. According to the excerpts, how would Mao legitimize the Cultural Revolution?

Essay
On a separate sheet of paper, write an answer to the following questions.

47. **Recognizing Causes and Effects** Why do you think Japan gives away so much foreign aid?

48. **Comparing** Compare the two Koreas. How do you think North Korea might benefit if the two Koreas were reunited?

49. **Making Inferences** Considering the goals of the American occupation of Japan following World War II, what do you think the United States learned from the Treaty of Versailles signed after World War I?

50. **Making Decisions** Many Americans have pressured their government to restrict trade with China until it stops violating human rights. Do you think restricted trade is a good policy? Why or why not?

51. **Linking Past and Present** Why do you think Japan's neighbors oppose its rearmament?

52. **Recognizing Points of View** Why do you think many Vietnamese saw the United States as just another imperial power?

CHAPTER 34—EAST ASIA AND SOUTHEAST ASIA (1945–PRESENT)
Answer Section

MATCHING

1. ANS: C　　　　DIF: E　　　　REF: 858　　　　OBJ: C34S1-1
   TOP: Political systems, Japanese parliament
2. ANS: F　　　　DIF: E　　　　REF: 859　　　　OBJ: C34S1-1
   TOP: Economics, Gross domestic product
3. ANS: B　　　　DIF: E　　　　REF: 863　　　　OBJ: C34S2-1
   TOP: Economics, Commune
4. ANS: H　　　　DIF: E　　　　REF: 864　　　　OBJ: C34S2-1
   TOP: Impact of the individual, Mao Zedong
5. ANS: E　　　　DIF: E　　　　REF: 864-865　　　　OBJ: C34S2-3
   TOP: Economics, Four Modernizations
6. ANS: A　　　　DIF: E　　　　REF: 868　　　　OBJ: C34S3-1
   TOP: Economics, Asian tigers
7. ANS: D　　　　DIF: E　　　　REF: 873　　　　OBJ: C34S4-1
   TOP: Political systems, Domino theory
8. ANS: G　　　　DIF: E　　　　REF: 874-875　　　　OBJ: C34S4-1
   TOP: Political systems, Khmer Rouge

9. ANS: C　　　　DIF: E　　　　REF: 858　　　　OBJ: C34S1-1
   TOP: Political systems, Japanese parliament
10. ANS: E　　　　DIF: E　　　　REF: 859　　　　OBJ: C34S1-1
    TOP: Economics, Gross domestic product
11. ANS: B　　　　DIF: E　　　　REF: 863　　　　OBJ: C34S2-1
    TOP: Economics, Commune
12. ANS: A　　　　DIF: E　　　　REF: 868　　　　OBJ: C34S3-1
    TOP: Economics, Asian tigers
13. ANS: D　　　　DIF: E　　　　REF: 873　　　　OBJ: C34S4-1
    TOP: Political systems, Domino theory

14. ANS: B　　　　DIF: E　　　　REF: 859-860　　　　OBJ: C34S1-2
    TOP: Economics, Japan as economic superpower
15. ANS: A　　　　DIF: E　　　　REF: 869　　　　OBJ: C34S3-1
    TOP: Geography, Hong Kong
16. ANS: D　　　　DIF: E　　　　REF: 869-870　　　　OBJ: C34S3-2
    TOP: Geography, Singapore
17. ANS: E　　　　DIF: E　　　　REF: 873-874　　　　OBJ: C34S4-1
    TOP: Power and conflict, Vietnam
18. ANS: C　　　　DIF: E　　　　REF: 876-877　　　　OBJ: C34S4-3
    TOP: Geography, Pacific Rim

MULTIPLE CHOICE

19. ANS: D   DIF: E   REF: 860   OBJ: C34S1-2
   TOP: Economics, Japanese motor vehicle production
20. ANS: A   DIF: A   REF: 860   OBJ: C34S1-2
   TOP: Economics, Japanese motor vehicle production
21. ANS: C   DIF: A   REF: 860   OBJ: C34S1-2
   TOP: Economics, Japanese motor vehicle production
22. ANS: C   DIF: A   REF: 860   OBJ: C34S1-2
   TOP: Economics, Japanese motor vehicle production
23. ANS: B   DIF: A   REF: 858-859   OBJ: C34S1-1
   TOP: Continuity and change, American occupation of Japan
24. ANS: D   DIF: E   REF: 862   OBJ: C34S2-1
   TOP: Impact of the individual, Mao Zedong
25. ANS: D   DIF: A   REF: 862   OBJ: C34S2-2
   TOP: Political systems, Communist China
26. ANS: B   DIF: A   REF: 868   OBJ: C34S3-1
   TOP: Culture, Links to China
27. ANS: A   DIF: D   REF: 869   OBJ: C34S3-2
   TOP: Geography, Singapore
28. ANS: B   DIF: A   REF: 875-876   OBJ: C34S4-1
   TOP: Continuity and change, New nations of Southeast Asia
29. ANS: A   DIF: D   REF: 873   OBJ: C34S4-2
   TOP: Impact of the individual, Ho Chi Minh
30. ANS: D   DIF: A   REF: 876-877   OBJ: C34S4-3
   TOP: Global interaction, Pacific Rim
31. ANS: B   DIF: A   REF: 860   OBJ: C34S1-3
   TOP: Global interaction, Japan and interdependence
32. ANS: A   DIF: D   REF: 862   OBJ: C34S2-1
   TOP: Continuity and change, Communists take over China
33. ANS: D   DIF: A   REF: 864-865   OBJ: C34S2-3
   TOP: Economics, Four Modernizations
34. ANS: C   DIF: A   REF: 870-872   OBJ: C34S3-3
   TOP: Economics, North and South Korea
35. ANS: A   DIF: E   REF: 873   OBJ: C34S4-1
   TOP: Global interaction, Cold War in Southeast Asia
36. ANS: C   DIF: A   REF: 874   OBJ: C34S4-3
   TOP: Economics, Vietnam

SHORT ANSWER

37. ANS:
to destroy militarism and to ensure democracy

DIF: E   REF: 858-859   OBJ: C34S1-1
TOP: Continuity and change, American occupation of Japan

38. ANS:
Answers should include five of the following: It had previously industrialized; its work force was well educated and highly skilled; the Japanese were brilliant at adapting western technology to meet their needs; management and labor cooperated; workers were dedicated and loyal; frugal spending habits gave the banks capital to invest in industry; it spent little on defense so that it could invest in the economy; the Japanese government supported industry, including adopting protectionist trade policies.

DIF: D   REF: 859   OBJ: C34S1-2
TOP: Economics, Japanese recovery

39. ANS:
Answers should include one of the following positive effects: the economy grew or some Chinese enjoyed a higher standard of living. Answers should also include one of the following negative effects: crime and corruption grew; economic differences between groups grew; a social gap between coastal city dwellers and farmers developed; or social unrest developed.

DIF: A   REF: 864-865   OBJ: C34S2-3
TOP: Economics, Four Modernizations

40. ANS:
Hong Kong came under Chinese rule in 1997. Its residents, along with the world, are unsure if democracy and its capitalist economic system will be allowed to survive under Chinese control.

DIF: A   REF: 869   OBJ: C34S3-1
TOP: Continuity and change, Future of Hong Kong

41. ANS:
Its location at the tip of the Malay Peninsula, on the Malacca strait halfway between China and India, made Singapore a busy and prosperous Southeast Asian seaport.

DIF: A   REF: 869   OBJ: C34S3-2
TOP: Geography, Singapore

42. ANS:
Korea is still divided into communist North Korea and democratic South Korea; North Korea and South Korea have different economic systems; they also have different political systems.

DIF: E   REF: 870-872   OBJ: C34S3-3
TOP: Political systems, Cold War and Korea

43. ANS:
The Pacific Rim is the center of global trade and has a huge potential for further growth.

    DIF: A   REF: 876-877   OBJ: C34S4-3
    TOP: Global interaction, Pacific Rim

44. ANS:
Mao's ideas appealed most to the masses, which in China were farmers, because their needs were the focus of his concern.

    DIF: E   REF: 864   OBJ: C34S2-1
    TOP: Political systems, Cultural Revolution

45. ANS:
Communist leaders are both nourished by and give nourishment to the people.

    DIF: A   REF: 864   OBJ: C34S2-2
    TOP: Political systems, Cultural Revolution

46. ANS:
Mao would say that the people in authority were reactionary because they were nonrevolutionary and everything reactionary must be overthrown.

    DIF: A   REF: 864   OBJ: C34S2-2
    TOP: Political systems, Cultural Revolution

ESSAY

47. ANS:
Answers will probably suggest that foreign aid is a way for Japan to improve international relations and to establish influence in the world.

    DIF: A   REF: 860   OBJ: C34S1-3
    TOP: Global interaction, Japan and interdependence

48. ANS:
Answers will probably point out that North Korea's economy would probably improve, along with its standard of living.

    DIF: A   REF: 870-872   OBJ: C34S3-3
    TOP: Political systems, North and South Korea

49. ANS:
Answers will likely point out that they learned that it was not in the best interests of the winners to treat the losers too harshly because the losers would feel resentful and eventually seek retribution.

    DIF: D   REF: 858-859   OBJ: C34S1-1
    TOP: Political systems, American occupation of Japan

50. ANS:
    Students who think that the United States should restrict trade might feel that it is a powerful economic weapon that the United States can use to support democratic principles in the world. Students who think that the United States should not restrict trade may point to its economic benefits and the fact that it keeps the door open for dialogue between the nations.

    DIF: A   REF: 867   OBJ: C34S2-3
    TOP: Global interaction, Human rights issues

51. ANS:
    They are afraid that Japan will resume its military aggression.

    DIF: E   REF: 861   OBJ: C34S1-1
    TOP: Political systems, Japanese rearmament

52. ANS:
    Like other imperial powers, the United States was in Vietnam for its own interests, which in this case was to fight the spread of communism.

    DIF: D   REF: 874   OBJ: C34S3-2
    TOP: Power and conflict, Vietnam

CHAPTER 35—SOUTH ASIA AND THE MIDDLE EAST (1945–PRESENT)

Matching

Match each term or person with the correct statement below.

a. Green Revolution   e. kibbutzim
b. harijan   f. Kurds
c. intifada   g. Gamal Abdel Nasser
d. Ayatollah Khomeini   h. Jawaharlal Nehru

_____ 1. The use of technological advances in agriculture to increase harvests

_____ 2. A member of the untouchable class

_____ 3. India's first prime minister

_____ 4. Farms that are run collectively

_____ 5. Ethnic group living in Turkey and Iraq

_____ 6. Leader determined to end foreign domination in Egypt

_____ 7. Leader of the Islamic revolution in Iran

_____ 8. The Palestinian uprising

Match each term with the correct statement below.

a. harijan   d. kibbutzim
b. hejab   e. ayatollah
c. intifada

_____ 9. Member of the untouchable caste

_____ 10. Farms that are run collectively

_____ 11. The covering of the body practiced by women in some Islamic countries

_____ 12. Shiite legal expert

_____ 13. The Palestinian uprising in occupied territories

Match each place with the correct statement below.

a. Bangladesh   d. Pakistan
b. Beirut   e. Palestine
c. West Bank

_____ 14. Country created because of tensions between Muslims and Hindus in India

_____ 15. Country whose geography stands in the way of its development

_____ 16. Both Arabs and Jews claim historical rights to this land

_____ 17. Area Israel won from Jordan in the 1967 war

_____ 18.   Capital of Lebanon

Multiple Choice
Identify the letter of the choice that best completes the statement or answers the question.

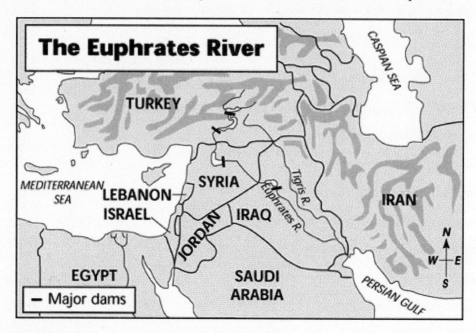

Figure 35-1

_____ 19.   According to Figure 35-1, in which of the following countries does the Euphrates River
begin?

    a.   Israel   c.   Turkey

    b.   Syria   d.   Iraq

_____ 20.   Based on Figure 35-1, which of the following is the best explanation for why Syria is
concerned about its water supply?

    a.   Turkey has built dams on the Euphrates.

    b.   The Euphrates flows through Iraq.

    c.   Many countries depend on the Euphrates for their water.

    d.   Jordan has no major rivers.

_____ 21.   According to Figure 35-1, which of the following countries are dependent on the Euphrates
River for water?

    a.   Egypt   c.   Lebanon, Israel, and Jordan

    b.   Turkey, Syria, and Iraq   d.   Saudi Arabia and Iran

_____ 22.   Based on Figure 35-1, why are water rights a vital issue in the Middle East?

    a.   Only one country has a river.

    b.   Turkey uses most of the region's water.

    c.   One country's source of water often lies in another country.

    d.   Most of the region's water lies underground.

____ 23. Tensions between which of the following two groups resulted in the partition of India?
    a. Hindus and Sikhs   c. Buddhists and Hindus
    b. Muslims and Hindus   d. Sikhs and Muslims

____ 24. One of the biggest problems facing India is
    a. growing illiteracy.   c. a failure to modernize.
    b. rapid increases in population.   d. the threat of revolution.

____ 25. Which of the following statements is true regarding India and Pakistan during the Cold War?
    a. They both remained nonaligned.
    b. Pakistan supported the Soviet Union, while India supported the United States.
    c. Pakistan allied itself with the United States, while India favored the Soviet Union.
    d. They both refused economic aid from foreign countries.

____ 26. The conflict between Palestinians and Jews in Palestine centered around
    a. differences in religion.
    b. the claim by both groups that it was their homeland.
    c. disagreements over borders.
    d. the role of the British in Palestine.

____ 27. Which of the following pairs of countries formed multiparty democratic systems?
    a. Iraq and Syria   c. Jordan and Saudi Arabia
    b. Israel and Turkey   d. Iran and Yemen

____ 28. How did Nasser challenge the West?
    a. He built the Aswan High Dam.   c. He relocated ancient temples.
    b. He gave lands to peasant farmers.   d. He nationalized the Suez Canal.

____ 29. Why did Israel become involved in the civil war in Lebanon?
    a. The United Nations was unable to keep order.
    b. The PLO was based there.
    c. They wanted to help the Palestinian refugees.
    d. They wanted to take control of Lebanon.

____ 30. The United States became involved in wars in the Persian Gulf in order
    a. to keep the region safe for democracy.
    b. to protect the lives of Americans in the region.
    c. to protect the flow of oil.
    d. to prevent environmental disasters.

____ 31. The goal of the Green Revolution was
    a. to encourage recycling.
    b. to turn India into an industrial nation.
    c. to slow India's population growth.
    d. to enable India to feed all of its people.

____ 32. Why do so many people in the Middle East support the revival of Islam?
    a. It offers alternatives to social and economic ills.
    b. It rejects modernization.
    c. It promises a single Arab state.
    d. It encourages terrorist acts.

____ 33. Which of the following groups want autonomy from Turkey?
    a. Shiites   c. Kurds
    b. Sunnis   d. Palestinians

____ 34. One effect of the revolution in Iran was that it
    a. was isolated from the international community.
    b. became a leader in the Arab world.
    c. took a stand against terrorism.
    d. became the most westernized country in the Middle East.

____ 35. Which of the following is a true statement regarding the civil war in Lebanon?
    a. The war was caused by the Palestinians.
    b. Religious differences were the main cause of the war.
    c. Economic differences between the north and the south were the real cause of the war.
    d. The war was fought among many different factions.

____ 36. Which of the following was a cause of the Persian Gulf wars and was also a result of British imperialism?
    a. border disputes   c. war debt
    b. ambitious rulers   d. political differences

Short Answer

37. List three issues South Asian nations have been struggling with since independence.

38. Why is tension between India and Pakistan of world concern?

39. Explain why there was conflict over the creation of Israel.

40. Explain why the revival of Islam is gathering so much support in the Middle East.

41. Contrast the ways Nasser and Sadat tried to modernize Egypt.

42. List three causes of the Islamic revolution in Iran.

43. Identify two geographic features of the Persian Gulf region that help explain why it was the site of two recent wars.

Read the following excerpt from a description written by Jimmy Carter of the meetings between Menachem Begin and Anwar Sadat, the leaders of Israel and Egypt, to work out a peace treaty between Israel and Egypt. Then answer the questions that follow.

> "Begin and Sadat were personally incompatible, and we decided after a few unpleasant encounters that they should not attempt to negotiate with each other. Instead, I worked with each of them separately or with their representatives. . . .
>
> It was soon obvious that he [Begin] was much more interested in discussing the Sinai than the West Bank and Gaza. After detailed negotiations began, Begin spent the best part of his energy on the minute details of each proposal, the specific language of each sentence or phrase. . . .
>
> [Sadat's] general requirements were that all Israelis leave Egyptian soil in the Sinai and that any bilateral agreement be based on a comprehensive accord involving the occupied territories, Palestinian rights, and Israel's commitment to resolve peacefully any further disputes with its neighbor."

44. According to this excerpt, why was it decided that Begin and Sadat should not negotiate directly with each other?

45. According to this excerpt, whose goals were broader, Begin's or Sadat's? Why do you think this was so?

46. Assume that you are an American and have just read this account in 1978. What would be your prediction for peace in the Middle East?

Essay
On a separate sheet of paper, write an answer to the following questions.

47. **Predicting Consequences** Why do you suppose Turkey tried to destroy its Kurdish citizens' culture?

48. **Making Decisions** Do you think the Israeli government should have allowed Jewish settlers to build houses in the occupied territories? Why or why not?

49. **Making Inferences** Why do you think tension between India and Pakistan might be of great concern to the world community?

50. **Applying Information** Why do you think Anwar Sadat risked Egypt's role as leader of the Arab world to make peace with Israel?

51. **Applying Information** Former United Nations Secretary General Boutros-Ghali warned that "The next war in the Middle East will be fought over water, not politics." Explain why you agree or disagree with this statement.

CHAPTER 35—SOUTH ASIA AND THE MIDDLE EAST (1945–PRESENT)
Answer Section

MATCHING

1. ANS: A   DIF: E   REF: 884   OBJ: C35S1-2
   TOP: Technology, Green Revolution
2. ANS: B   DIF: E   REF: 885   OBJ: C35S1-2
   TOP: Social systems, Caste system
3. ANS: H   DIF: E   REF: 883   OBJ: C35S1-2
   TOP: Impact of the individual, Jawaharlal Nehru
4. ANS: E   DIF: E   REF: 890   OBJ: C35S2-1
   TOP: Economics, Kibbutz
5. ANS: F   DIF: E   REF: 895   OBJ: C35S3-1
   TOP: Diversity, Kurds
6. ANS: G   DIF: E   REF: 895-896   OBJ: C35S3-2
   TOP: Impact of the individual, Gamal Abdel Nasser
7. ANS: D   DIF: E   REF: 898   OBJ: C35S3-3
   TOP: Impact of the individual, Ayatollah Khomeini
8. ANS: C   DIF: E   REF: 900   OBJ: C35S4-2
   TOP: Religion, Intifada

9. ANS: A   DIF: E   REF: 885   OBJ: C35S1-2
   TOP: Social systems, Caste system
10. ANS: D   DIF: E   REF: 890   OBJ: C35S2-1
    TOP: Economics, Kibbutz
11. ANS: B   DIF: E   REF: 893   OBJ: C35S2-1
    TOP: Religion, Muslim women
12. ANS: E   DIF: E   REF: 898   OBJ: C35S3-3
    TOP: Religion, Ayatollah
13. ANS: C   DIF: E   REF: 900   OBJ: C35S4-2
    TOP: Religion, Intifada

14. ANS: D   DIF: E   REF: 882-883   OBJ: C35S1-1
    TOP: Religion, Creation of Pakistan
15. ANS: A   DIF: E   REF: 886   OBJ: C35S1-3
    TOP: Geography, Bangladesh
16. ANS: E   DIF: E   REF: 900-901   OBJ: C35S4-2
    TOP: Religion, Arab-Israeli conflict
17. ANS: C   DIF: E   REF: 900   OBJ: C35S4-2
    TOP: Power and conflict, West Bank
18. ANS: B   DIF: E   REF: 901-902   OBJ: C35S4-3
    TOP: Geography, Beirut

MULTIPLE CHOICE

19.	ANS: C	DIF: E	REF: 890-891	OBJ: C35S2-2
	TOP: Geography, Water resources			
20.	ANS: A	DIF: A	REF: 890-891	OBJ: C35S2-2
	TOP: Geography, Water resources			
21.	ANS: B	DIF: E	REF: 890-891	OBJ: C35S2-2
	TOP: Geography, Water resources			
22.	ANS: B	DIF: A	REF: 890-891	OBJ: C35S2-2
	TOP: Geography, Water resources			
23.	ANS: C	DIF: E	REF: 882-883	OBJ: C35S1-1
	TOP: Religion, Creation of Pakistan			
24.	ANS: B	DIF: A	REF: 884	OBJ: C35S1-3
	TOP: Social systems, India's population explosion			
25.	ANS: B	DIF: D	REF: 886	OBJ: C35S1-4
	TOP: Global interaction, Cold War alliances			
26.	ANS: B	DIF: A	REF: 889	OBJ: C35S2-1
	TOP: Religion, Palestine			
27.	ANS: B	DIF: A	REF: 890	OBJ: C35S2-2
	TOP: Political systems, Multiparty democracies			
28.	ANS: C	DIF: A	REF: 895	OBJ: C35S3-2
	TOP: Global interaction, Nasser			
29.	ANS: B	DIF: A	REF: 901-902	OBJ: C35S4-2
	TOP: Power and conflict, Civil war in Lebanon			
30.	ANS: A	DIF: A	REF: 892	OBJ: C35S4-3
	TOP: Religion, Islamic revival			
31.	ANS: D	DIF: E	REF: 884	OBJ: C25S1-2
	TOP: Technology, Green Revolution			
32.	ANS: A	DIF: A	REF: 892	OBJ: C35S2-3
	TOP: Religion, Islamic revival			
33.	ANS: D	DIF: A	REF: 895	OBJ: C35S3-1
	TOP: Power and conflict, Kurds			
34.	ANS: A	DIF: A	REF: 898	OBJ: C35S3-3
	TOP: Global interaction, Islamic revolution in Iran			
35.	ANS: B	DIF: D	REF: 901-902	OBJ: C35S4-2
	TOP: Religion, Civil war in Lebanon			
36.	ANS: A	DIF: A	REF: 902	OBJ: C35S4-3
	TOP: Global interaction, Persian Gulf wars			

SHORT ANSWER

37. ANS:
Answers should include the following: improving agriculture to feed growing populations; limiting population growth; developing a strong industrial economy; increasing literacy; improving conditions for the poor and for women; reducing ethnic and religious tensions.

DIF: A   REF: 882-887   OBJ: C35S1-2
TOP: Continuity and change, South Asian independence

38. ANS:
India and Pakistan have tested nuclear weapons. Another war between them could have serious consequences for each side, as well as for countries surrounding them.

DIF: A   REF: 886-887   OBJ: C35S1-4
TOP: Global interaction, Nuclear technology

39. ANS:
The Jews claimed they had a historical right to the land that is now Israel, while Palestinian Arabs, who were living there, claimed it belonged to them.

DIF: E   REF: 889   OBJ: C35S2-1
TOP: Religion, Creation of Israel

40. ANS:
Many Muslims believe Islam holds hope for solving the widespread social, political, and economic problems that westernization has failed to solve and, in the view of many Muslims, has even encouraged.

DIF: A   REF: 892   OBJ: C35S2-3
TOP: Religion, Islamic revival

41. ANS:
Nasser turned to socialism and nationalization and moved to end western involvement in Egypt as ways to improve the economy and promote modernization, while Sadat encouraged private businesses and cultivated involvement with the West in hopes of improving conditions in Egypt.

DIF: D   REF: 895-896   OBJ: C35S3-2
TOP: Continuity and change, Modernization of Egypt

42. ANS:
Answers should include three of the following: political oppression; discontent and moral outrage among religious leaders; economic injustices; or resentment against the West.

DIF: A   REF: 898   OBJ: C35S3-3
TOP: Political systems, Islamic revolution in Iran

43. ANS:
The region has huge oil deposits, and the Gulf provides an outlet from which to ship the oil.

DIF: A   REF: 902-903   OBJ: C35S4-3
TOP: Global interaction, Persian Gulf wars

44. ANS:
They did not get along with each other.

DIF: E   REF: 896   OBJ: C35S2-1
TOP: Impact of the individual, Begin and Sadat

45. ANS:
Sadat's goals were broader because he had to consider the interests of other Arab countries and of the Palestinians.

DIF: A   REF: 896   OBJ: C35S4-1
TOP: Power and conflict, Arab-Israeli peace talks

46. ANS:
Answers will vary.

DIF: A   REF: 896   OBJ: C35S4-1
TOP: Power and conflict, Arab-Israeli peace talks

ESSAY

47. ANS:
Turkey tried to destroy the Kurdish citizens' culture in order to erase their unique identity and force them to integrate into Turkish society.

DIF: D   REF: 895   OBJ: C35S3-1   TOP: Diversity, Kurds

48. ANS:
Student answers will vary, but should be well reasoned and reflect an understanding of the issues.

DIF: A   REF: 900   OBJ: C35S4-1
TOP: Power and conflict, Arab-Israeli conflict

49. ANS:
Both countries have tested nuclear devices. If tension between the two should erupt into war, which it has several times in the past, then there could be a nuclear war.

DIF: D   REF: 886-887   OBJ: C35S1-4
TOP: Global interaction, Nuclear technology

50. ANS:
Students should point to the fact that Sadat felt that peace with Israel was in Egypt's best economic interests.

DIF: A   REF: 896   OBJ: C35S3-2
TOP: Political systems, Anwar Sadat

51. ANS:
Answers should be well supported and reflect the fact that water is a very valuable resource in the Middle East.

DIF: A   REF: 890-891   OBJ: C35S2-2
TOP: Geography, Water resources

CHAPTER 36—AFRICA (1945–PRESENT)

Matching

Match each term or person with the correct statement below.

a. Jomo Kenyatta
b. Nelson Mandela
c. mixed economy
d. Julius Nyerere

e. Organization of African Unity
f. Mobutu Sese Seko
g. SWAPO
h. ujamaa

_____ 1. Leader who supported nonviolent methods to gain independence for Kenya

_____ 2. Economy with both private and state-run enterprises

_____ 3. Corrupt ruler of Zaire

_____ 4. Tanzania leader who supported "African socialism"

_____ 5. Mutual cooperation

_____ 6. Leader who symbolized the struggle against apartheid

_____ 7. Guerrilla fighters in Namibia

_____ 8. Organization established to promote cooperation among African nations

Match each term or person with the correct statement below.

a. ANC
b. F. W. de Klerk
c. Mau Mau
d. Kwame Nkrumah

e. Julius Nyerere
f. mixed economy
g. Organization of African Unity
h. Mobutu Sese Seko

_____ 9. _____ used boycotts and strikes in his fight to win independence for Ghana.

_____ 10. The _____ were Kenyan guerrilla fighters.

_____ 11. A country with both private and state-run enterprises has a _____.

_____ 12. _____ destroyed the economy of Zaire.

_____ 13. In Tanzania, _____ wanted to build a classless society.

_____ 14. The South African leader who ended apartheid was _____.

_____ 15. The _____ was a South African organization that opposed white domination.

_____ 16. The _____ was established to promote cooperation among new African nations.

Multiple Choice
Identify the letter of the choice that best completes the statement or answers the question.

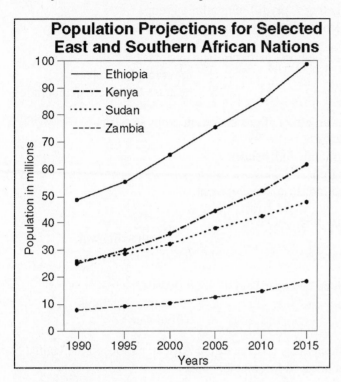

Figure 36-1

____ 17. According to Figure 36-1, which country had the greatest population in 1995?
   a.   Ethiopia   c.   Sudan
   b.   Kenya   d.   Zambia

____ 18. According to Figure 36-1, approximately what was Kenya's population in 2000?
   a.   25 million   c.   34 million
   b.   50 million   d.   100 million

____ 19. According to Figure 36-1, approximately what was Ethiopia's population in 1990?
   a.   53 million   c.   49 million
   b.   8 million   d.   100 million

____ 20. According to Figure 36-1, which country will have the smallest increase in population
        between the years 1990 and 2015?
   a.   Ethiopia   c.   Sudan
   b.   Kenya   d.   Zambia

____ 21. Which of the following countries fought a long, brutal war to gain its independence?
   a.   Algeria   c.   Zaire
   b.   Ghana   d.   South Africa

_____ 22. Why did colonial borders cause problems for new African nations?
   a.   They cut them off from important resources.
   b.   They created countries that were too small for their populations.
   c.   They forced people together from different ethnic groups.
   d.   They stopped herders from migrating with their animals.

_____ 23. Why did many new leaders adopt one-party political systems?
   a.   for efficiency   c.   to enrich themselves
   b.   to encourage unity   d.   because they were democratic

_____ 24. Which of the following was an effect of growing cash crops in Africa?
   a.   There was a food shortage.
   b.   Countries achieved economic independence.
   c.   Small farmers became rich.
   d.   Governments neglected industrial development.

_____ 25. Zimbabwe achieved majority rule
   a.   through elections.   c.   after a guerrilla war.
   b.   by using nonviolent resistance. d.   through negotiations.

_____ 26. Which of the following helped end apartheid in South Africa?
   a.   an oil embargo   c.   economic sanctions
   b.   an international vote   d.   a civil war

_____ 27. Which of the following statements is true regarding African nations in the United Nations?
   a.   African nations are not allowed full membership.
   b.   African nations are a dividing force.
   c.   African nations are an important voice for developing countries.
   d.   African nations are underrepresented.

_____ 28. Which of the following is an effect of urbanization in Africa?
   a.   lower birthrates   c.   weakened kinship ties
   b.   higher literacy rates   d.   greater equality for women

_____ 29. Which of the following generalizations regarding the way African nations won their independence is true?
   a.   Most but not all nations were able to win their independence peacefully.
   b.   All nations were forced to fight for their independence.
   c.   Economic sanctions helped many nations win their independence.
   d.   Most nations won their independence at the voting polls.

_____ 30. Why were the cash economies introduced by the Europeans unsuitable for African countries?
   a.   African countries did not favor international trade.
   b.   Most people were subsistence farmers.
   c.   Africans were not comfortable with interdependency.
   d.   Africans had no paper money.

_____ 31. Which of the following was an obstacle to unity in new African nations?
   a.   geographic barriers   c.   ethnic differences
   b.   weak economies   d.   class differences

____ 32. In Nigeria, conflict between ethnic groups led to
    a. permanent partition.   c. foreign military intervention.
    b. a new democratic constitution.   d. civil war.

____ 33. The white minority government in Rhodesia gave up power to the black majority after
    a. the British demanded that they do so.
    b. a long guerrilla war.
    c. they lost in the elections.
    d. they were forced by the OAS.

____ 34. Which of the following countries became a battleground for the Cold War in Africa?
    a. Tanzania and Zaire   c. Angola and Mozambique
    b. Kenya and Ghana   d. South Africa and Zimbabwe

____ 35. Urbanization weakened traditional cultures, but it contributed to
    a. a national identity.   c. larger families.
    b. a stronger economy.   d. stronger ethnic ties.

____ 36. Why are African Muslims attached to the Islamic revival?
    a. It calls for political reform and social justice.
    b. It encourages reliance on imports.
    c. It encourages Africans to return to their old ways.
    d. It supports western values.

Short Answer

37. Describe three ways colonial rule affected the development of new African nations.

38. Identify each of the following leaders and describe how they contributed to their nation's drive for independence: Kwame Nkrumah and Jomo Kenyatta.

39. Identify the two main challenges of newly independent African nations.

40. List five obstacles that hinder economic development in Africa.

41. Compare the goals of Mobutu in Zaire and Nyerere in Tanzania in the development of their countries.

42. List three ways urbanization and modernization have affected the lives of women in Africa.

43. Describe how Islam is a revolutionary force in Africa.

Read the following excerpt from the Freedom Charter, a document written in 1995 by South Africans. Then answer the questions that follow.

"We, the people of South Africa, black and white, together—equals, countrymen and brothers—adopt this FREEDOM CHARTER. And we pledge ourselves to strive together, sparing nothing of our strength and courage, until the democratic changes here set out have been won. . . .

Every man and woman shall have the right to vote for and stand as a candidate for all bodies which make laws. . . .

All people shall have equal rights to trade where they choose, to manufacture and to enter all trades, crafts and professions. . . .

Restriction of land ownership on a racial basis shall be ended, and all the land redivided amongst those who work it, to banish famine and land hunger. . . .

No one shall be imprisoned, deported or restricted without a fair trial. . . . All shall be free to travel without restriction from countryside to town, from province to province, and from South Africa abroad."

44. According to this excerpt, who should have the right to vote in South Africa?

45. Based on this document, how were the lives of black South Africans affected by conditions in South Africa?

46. List three demands in this document that were designed to improve the economic status of black South Africans.

Essay
On a separate sheet of paper, write an answer to the following questions.

47. **Comparing** Compare and contrast the lives of black South Africans under apartheid to the lives of black Americans in the 1950s before the passage of the major civil rights legislation. List two ways their lives were alike and two ways they were different.

48. **Synthesizing Information** How could Islam be a revolutionary force in Africa?

49. **Defending a Position** Would you agree that developing agriculture in Africa is as important as developing industry? Why or why not?

50. **Applying Information** Former South African president F. W. de Klerk once said, "One cannot build security on injustice." To what group in South Africa was he referring and why?

51. **Synthesizing Information** Why have some historians referred to Nelson Mandela as the "Father of South Africa"?

CHAPTER 36—AFRICA (1945–PRESENT)
Answer Section

MATCHING

1. ANS: A   DIF: E   REF: 911-912   OBJ: C36S1-2
    TOP: Impact of the individual, Jomo Kenyatta
2. ANS: C   DIF: E   REF: 916   OBJ: C36S2-2
    TOP: Economics, Mixed economy
3. ANS: F   DIF: E   REF: 922   OBJ: C36S3-2
    TOP: Impact of the individual, Mobutu Sese Seko
4. ANS: D   DIF: E   REF: 922-923   OBJ: C36S3-3
    TOP: Impact of the individual, Julius Nyerere
5. ANS: H   DIF: E   REF: 923   OBJ: C36S3-3
    TOP: Economics, Ujamaa
6. ANS: B   DIF: E   REF: 925-926   OBJ: C36S4-2
    TOP: Impact of the individual, Nelson Mandela
7. ANS: G   DIF: E   REF: 926-928   OBJ: C36S4-3
    TOP: Political systems, SWAPO
8. ANS: E   DIF: E   REF: 913   OBJ: C36S1-3
    TOP: Political systems, Organization of African Unity

9. ANS: D   DIF: E   REF: 911   OBJ: C36S1-2
    TOP: Impact of the individual, Kwame Nkrumah
10. ANS: C   DIF: E   REF: 911   OBJ: C36S1-2
    TOP: Power and conflict, Mau Mau
11. ANS: F   DIF: E   REF: 916   OBJ: C36S2-2
    TOP: Economics, Mixed economy
12. ANS: H   DIF: E   REF: 922   OBJ: C36S3-2
    TOP: Impact of the individual, Mobutu Sese Seko
13. ANS: E   DIF: E   REF: 922-923   OBJ: C36S3-3
    TOP: Impact of the individual, Julius Nyerere
14. ANS: B   DIF: E   REF: 929   OBJ: C36S4-2
    TOP: Impact of the individual, F. W. de Klerk
15. ANS: A   DIF: E   REF: 925-926   OBJ: C36S4-2
    TOP: Political systems, ANC
16. ANS: G   DIF: E   REF: 913   OBJ: C36S1-3
    TOP: Political systems, Organization of African Unity

MULTIPLE CHOICE

17. ANS: A   DIF: E   REF: 917   OBJ: C36S2-2
    TOP: Continuity and change, Population explosion
18. ANS: C   DIF: A   REF: 917   OBJ: C36S2-2
    TOP: Continuity and change, Population explosion

19. ANS: C DIF: E REF: 917 OBJ: C36S2-2
    TOP: Continuity and change, Population explosion
20. ANS: D DIF: D REF: 917 OBJ: C36S2-2
    TOP: Continuity and change, Population explosion
21. ANS: A DIF: A REF: 912 OBJ: C36S1-1
    TOP: Power and conflict, Algeria
22. ANS: C DIF: A REF: 909 OBJ: C36S1-2
    TOP: Diversity, National borders
23. ANS: B DIF: D REF: 915 OBJ: C36S2-1
    TOP: Political systems, One-party rule
24. ANS: A DIF: A REF: 916 OBJ: C36S2-3
    TOP: Economics, Cash crops
25. ANS: C DIF: D REF: 924 OBJ: C36S4-4
    TOP: Political systems, Zimbabwe
26. ANS: C DIF: A REF: 925-926 OBJ: C36S4-2
    TOP: Political systems, End of apartheid
27. ANS: C DIF: A REF: 913 OBJ: C36S2-3
    TOP: Global interactions, Africa and the UN
28. ANS: C DIF: A REF: 918 OBJ: C36S2-4
    TOP: Continuity and change, Urbanization
29. ANS: A DIF: A REF: 909-912 OBJ: C36S1-1
    TOP: Continuity and change, Transitions to independence
30. ANS: B DIF: A REF: 908 OBJ: C36S1-3
    TOP: Economics, Colonial legacy
31. ANS: C DIF: E REF: 915 OBJ: C36S2-1
    TOP: Political systems, Obstacles to unity
32. ANS: D DIF: A REF: 921 OBJ: C36S3-1
    TOP: Power and conflict, Civil war in Nigeria
33. ANS: B DIF: A REF: 924 OBJ: C36S3-3
    TOP: Power and conflict, Rhodesia
34. ANS: C DIF: A REF: 912 OBJ: C36S1-3
    TOP: Global interaction, Cold War and Africa
35. ANS: A DIF: A REF: 918 OBJ: C36S2-4
    TOP: Social structures, Urbanization
36. ANS: A DIF: A REF: 919 OBJ: C36S2-4
    TOP: Religion, Islamic revival

SHORT ANSWER

37. ANS:
    Answers should include three of the following: colonial rule created a pattern of economic
    dependence; undermined traditional political systems but did not educate Africans in
    democracy; often left Africans uneducated; drew artificial boundaries that forced diverse
    ethnic groups with no common identity together into a nation.

    DIF: A REF: 908-909 OBJ: C36S1-2
    TOP: Political systems, Colonial legacy

38. ANS:
Kwame Nkrumah—Ghanaian leader who advocated the use of nonviolent strikes and boycotts to win independence. Jomo Kenyatta—spokesperson and leader of the freedom movement in Kenya who became a national hero when he was jailed by the British.

DIF: A   REF: 910-912   OBJ: C36S1-3
TOP: Impact of the individual, Nkrumah and Kenyatta

39. ANS:
creating unified states with stable governments and building strong economies

DIF: A   REF: 914   OBJ: C36S2-1
TOP: Continuity and change, New African nations

40. ANS:
Answers should include five of the following: drought, deforestation; rapidly growing populations; poverty; an AIDS epidemic; economic dependence and bad economic policies; or political instability and ethnic conflict.

DIF: D   REF: 915-917   OBJ: C36S2-2
TOP: Economics, Obstacles to development

41. ANS:
Mobutu exploited Zaire for his own benefit while Nyerere strove to create a society that would benefit all people alike.

DIF: A   REF: 922-923   OBJ: C36S3-3
TOP: Impact of the individual, Mobutu and Nyerere

42. ANS:
Answers should include three of the following: improved education for a few; increased their family responsibilities; in some instances, allowed them to gain economic power; given them more legal rights (although these are usually not enforced); forced them into urban poverty.

DIF: A   REF: 918   OBJ: C36S2-4
TOP: Social structures, Women in Africa

43. ANS:
It promotes change in the status quo and calls for social justice.

DIF: A   REF: 919   OBJ: C36S2-4
TOP: Religion, Islamic revival

44. ANS:
every man and woman

DIF: E   REF: 925-926   OBJ: C36S4-2
TOP: Political systems, Blacks in South Africa

45. ANS:
They were treated as prisoners in their own country—they had no legal rights and faced economic, social, and educational restrictions.

DIF: A   REF: 925-926   OBJ: C36S4-2
TOP: Social systems, Apartheid

46. ANS:
    Answers should include three of the following: control of trade and industries for the benefit of the people; equal access to professions; prohibition of land ownership on a racial basis; redistribution of land to the people who work that land.

    DIF: A   REF: 925-926   OBJ: C36S4-1
    TOP: Economics, End of apartheid

ESSAY

47. ANS:
    Similarities could include: both groups faced restrictions on where they could live, were paid less than whites, were segregated, and faced inequalities in education, housing, etc. Differences could include: black South Africans had to carry passbooks, get permission to travel, and were assigned to homelands, and there were more restrictions on women than on men.

    DIF: A   REF: 925   OBJ: C36S4-2
    TOP: Diversity, Black South Africans and black Americans

48. ANS:
    Possible answer: Islam has potential for overturning corrupt and oppressive rulers and installing Islamic governments, and these governments might bring a new moral order and social justice to some African nations.

    DIF: D   REF: 919   OBJ: C36S2-4
    TOP: Religion, Islamic revival

49. ANS:
    Students may state that agriculture is more important in order to ensure adequate supplies of food for growing populations. Others may argue that industrialization is the key to expanding the economy, ending foreign debt, increasing exports, and raising the standard of living.

    DIF: A   REF: 916   OBJ: C36S2-3
    TOP: Economics, Agriculture versus industry

50. ANS:
    He was referring to black South Africans because they had suffered such severe discrimination and inequalities under apartheid and were threatening increasing violence if the system was not abolished.

    DIF: A   REF: 926   OBJ: C36S4-2
    TOP: Continuity and change, Apartheid

51. ANS:
    Mandela was the symbolic leader of the fight against apartheid, and when apartheid ended he became the first president of the new democratic South Africa.

    DIF: A   REF: 925-926   OBJ: C36S4-2
    TOP: Impact of the individual, Nelson Mandela

CHAPTER 37—LATIN AMERICA (1945–PRESENT)

Matching

Match each term with the correct statement below.
a. agribusiness
b. Alliance for Progress
c. Sandinistas
d. *ejidos*

e. *favelas*
f. import substitution
g. *maquiladoras*
h. Organization of American States

_____ 1. Goods produced at home to replace goods from other countries

_____ 2. Large commercial farm owned by multinational corporation

_____ 3. Group formed to promote democracy, economic cooperation, and human rights in Latin America and the United States

_____ 4. Program by which Latin American governments introduced reforms in exchange for U.S. loans and investments

_____ 5. Peasant cooperatives

_____ 6. Assembly plants

_____ 7. Reform-minded nationalists in Nicaragua

_____ 8. Slums

Match each person with the correct statement below.
a. Salvador Allende
b. Jean-Bertrand Aristide
c. Fidel Castro

d. Isabel Perón
e. Benedita da Silva

_____ 9. First black woman elected to Brazilian congress

_____ 10. Cuban dictator

_____ 11. President of Chile who was overthrown in a coup supported by the United States

_____ 12. President of Haiti who was forced into exile

_____ 13. First woman head of state in the Western Hemisphere

Match each place with the correct statement below.
a. Brazil
b. Falklands
c. El Salvador

d. Mexico
e. Nicaragua

_____ 14. Country that joined the United States and Canada in signing NAFTA

_____ 15. Country the Sandinistas set out to reform

_____ 16. Homeland of Oscar Romero, who worked for human rights

_____ 17. Country that numbered among the top 10 world economies

_____ 18. British-ruled islands seized by Argentina in 1982

Multiple Choice
Identify the letter of the choice that best completes the statement or answers the question.

_____ 19. Which of the following groups in Latin American countries generally supported conservative interests?
    a. students
    b. labor leaders
    c. business middle class
    d. peasant organizers

_____ 20. One group in Latin America that became an effective force for social reform was
    a. women.
    b. military rulers.
    c. Marxists.
    d. the middle class.

_____ 21. The United States and the Soviet Union came to the brink of nuclear war in 1962 over Soviet missile bases in
    a. Brazil.
    b. Colombia.
    c. Cuba.
    d. Haiti.

_____ 22. Which Latin American country joined Arab nations in OPEC?
    a. Argentina
    b. Venezuela
    c. Paraguay
    d. Peru

_____ 23. Which of the following issues in Brazil provoked conflict between economic development and environmental protection?
    a. destruction of the rain forest
    b. illegal immigration
    c. war on drugs
    d. free trade zone

_____ 24. Which of the following terms best describes conditions in Central American countries in the 1980s?
    a. democracy
    b. civil war
    c. prosperity
    d. peace

_____ 25. The "dirty war" refers to the kidnapping, torturing, and murdering of thousands of citizens by military leaders in
    a. Argentina.
    b. Brazil.
    c. Mexico.
    d. Nicaragua.

Figure 37-1

26. The Latin American country that is part of NAFTA is indicated in Figure 37-1 by the letter
    a. A.   c. C.
    b. B.   d. D.

27. Which letter in Figure 37-1 indicates Haiti?
    a. A   c. C
    b. B   d. D

28. Which letter in Figure 37-1 indicates the country that was ruled by Isabel Perón?
    a. A   c. C
    b. B   d. D

29. The letter A in Figure 37-1 indicates
    a. Brazil.   c. Guatemala.
    b. Colombia.   d. Mexico.

30. Which letter in Figure 37-1 indicates the poorest country in the Western Hemisphere?
    a. A   c. C
    b. B   d. D

31. The letter B in Figure 37-1 indicates
    a. Argentina.   c. El Salvador.
    b. Brazil.   d. Guatemala.

32. In the Latin American social structure, which of the following groups made up the upper class?
    a. Native Americans   c. African Americans
    b. mestizos   d. descendants of Europeans

_____ 33. The purpose of import substitution was to
   a. increase dependence on imports.
   b. encourage local manufacturing.
   c. promote exports.
   d. provide a greater variety of imports.

_____ 34. The Bay of Pigs disaster refers to a plot, supported by the United States, to invade
   a. El Salvador.   c. Cuba.
   b. Mexico.   d. Chile.

_____ 35. Which of the following is an organization formed in 1948 to promote democracy, economic cooperation, and human rights?
   a. Organization of American States
   b. Alliance for Progress
   c. Organization of Petroleum Exporting Countries
   d. North American Free Trade Agreement

_____ 36. Which of the following groups supported Juan Perón's government?
   a. the military   c. foreign investors
   b. working classes   d. educated people

Short Answer

37. Identify four conditions that contributed to unrest in Latin America.

38. Explain two ways that Latin American governments promoted economic development.

39. Describe three ways that the Cuban Revolution affected the United States.

40. Explain one advantage and one disadvantage of the *maquiladoras* system in Mexico.

41. Describe the problems that Haiti faces.

42. Summarize why Juan Perón was a popular dictator.

43. Explain three reasons for Brazil's economic miracle.

Read the following excerpt from a description of Mexico City, written by a correspondent from the New York Times. *Then answer the questions that follow.*

"For the world's largest urban center, Mexico City is in the most impractical of settings. Situated 7,400 feet above sea level, it is ringed by mountains and volcanoes, set in an earthquake zone, gradually sinking into its soft subsoil, far from water, food, and energy supplies, and literally, short of oxygen. Yet so strong has been the traditional domination of the country by its central highlands—from . . . Tenochtitlán to Mexico City itself—that the capital has continued to grow beyond its ability to function. . . .

People flocked to Mexico City because the country's economic strategy since the 1940s obliged them to do so. Resources were poured into industry, commerce, and urban construction, while agriculture was neglected. Problems were then compounded by poor planning in every area—from industrial location to water supplies—as well as by the prohibitive cost of keeping up with the population. Yet people kept coming . . . because the city still resolved many of their problems. Jobs could be found, schools were nearby and health services were accessible. . . .

But chaotic growth has not obliterated [wiped out] Mexico City's character and charm. Its very growth reflects its hospitality, always allowing one more person through the door to find a niche and make a living. Its energy and spirit somehow isolate the pleasure of living there from the pain of its noise, traffic, and pollution."

44. According to the author, why is Mexico City an impractical setting for the world's largest city?

45. Why have people flocked to Mexico City since the 1940s?

46. To which positive aspects of Mexico City does the author refer?

Essay
On a separate sheet of paper, write an answer to the following questions.

47. **Recognizing Causes and Effects** How did uneven distribution of wealth contribute to unrest in Latin American countries?

48. **Drawing Conclusions** How did Juan Perón gain the support of the urban poor?

49. **Identifying Main Ideas** How did competing ideologies influence political developments in Latin America?

50. **Analyzing Information** Why does the control of the illegal drug trade require cooperation among the United States and Latin American governments?

51. **Drawing Conclusions** How did women become an effective force for change in Latin America?

52. **Analyzing Information** Why is destruction of the Amazon rain forest a global issue?

CHAPTER 37—LATIN AMERICA (1945–PRESENT)
Answer Section

MATCHING

1. ANS: F   DIF: E   REF: 937   OBJ: C37S1-3
   TOP: Economics, Import substitution
2. ANS: A   DIF: E   REF: 938   OBJ: C37S1-3
   TOP: Economics, Agribusiness
3. ANS: H   DIF: E   REF: 942   OBJ: C37S2-2
   TOP: Political systems, Organization of American States
4. ANS: B   DIF: E   REF: 942   OBJ: C37S2-2
   TOP: Political systems, Alliance for Progress
5. ANS: D   DIF: E   REF: 944   OBJ: C37S3-1
   TOP: Economics, Peasant cooperatives
6. ANS: G   DIF: E   REF: 945   OBJ: C37S3-1
   TOP: Economics, Maquiladoras
7. ANS: C   DIF: E   REF: 946   OBJ: C37S3-2
   TOP: Political systems, Sandinistas
8. ANS: E   DIF: E   REF: 952   OBJ: C37S4-2
   TOP: Social systems, Slums

9. ANS: E   DIF: E   REF: 939   OBJ: C37S4-2
   TOP: Impact of the individual, Benedita da Silva
10. ANS: C   DIF: E   REF: 940-941   OBJ: C37S2-1
    TOP: Impact of the individual, Fidel Castro
11. ANS: A   DIF: E   REF: 941   OBJ: C37S2-2
    TOP: Impact of the individual, Salvador Allende
12. ANS: B   DIF: E   REF: 949   OBJ: C37S3-3
    TOP: Impact of the individual, Jean-Bertrande Aristide
13. ANS: D   DIF: E   REF: 951   OBJ: C37S4-1
    TOP: Impact of the individual, Isabel Perón

14. ANS: D   DIF: E   REF: 942   OBJ: C37S2-2
    TOP: Economics, NAFTA
15. ANS: E   DIF: E   REF: 946   OBJ: C37S3-2
    TOP: Political systems, Nicaragua
16. ANS: C   DIF: E   REF: 948   OBJ: C37S3-2
    TOP: Impact of the individual, Oscar Romero
17. ANS: A   DIF: E   REF: 953-955   OBJ: C37S4-3
    TOP: Economics, Brazil's economic miracle
18. ANS: B   DIF: E   REF: 951   OBJ: C37S4-3
    TOP: Power and conflict, Falklands

MULTIPLE CHOICE

19. ANS: C   DIF: A   REF: 936   OBJ: C37S1-2
    TOP: Political systems, Competing ideologies
20. ANS: A   DIF: A   REF: 938-939   OBJ: C37S1-3
    TOP: Social systems, Women and reform
21. ANS: C   DIF: A   REF: 940-941   OBJ: C37S2-1
    TOP: Power and conflict, Cuban Missile Crisis
22. ANS: B   DIF: A   REF: 942   OBJ: C37S2-3
    TOP: Global interaction, OPEC
23. ANS: A   DIF: A   REF: 943   OBJ: C37S2-3
    TOP: Environment, Amazon rain forest
24. ANS: B   DIF: A   REF: 946-948   OBJ: C37S3-2
    TOP: Continuity and change, Civil war in Central America
25. ANS: A   DIF: A   REF: 951   OBJ: C37S4-3
    TOP: Political systems, "Dirty war"
26. ANS: A   DIF: A   REF: 944   OBJ: C37S3-1
    TOP: Geography, Mexico
27. ANS: C   DIF: A   REF: 949   OBJ: C37S3-3
    TOP: Geography, Haiti
28. ANS: B   DIF: D   REF: 951   OBJ: C37S4-2
    TOP: Geography, Argentina
29. ANS: D   DIF: E   REF: 944   OBJ: C37S3-1
    TOP: Geography, Mexico
30. ANS: C   DIF: D   REF: 949   OBJ: C37S3-3
    TOP: Geography, Haiti
31. ANS: A   DIF: E   REF: 951   OBJ: C37S4-2
    TOP: Geography, Argentina
32. ANS: D   DIF: A   REF: 935   OBJ: C37S1-1
    TOP: Social systems, Latin American class system
33. ANS: B   DIF: A   REF: 937   OBJ: C37S1-3
    TOP: Economics, Import substitution
34. ANS: C   DIF: A   REF: 940   OBJ: C37S2-1
    TOP: Power and conflict, Bay of Pigs
35. ANS: A   DIF: A   REF: 942   OBJ: C37S2-2
    TOP: Political systems, Organization of American States
36. ANS: B   DIF: A   REF: 950-951   OBJ: C37S4-1
    TOP: Political systems, Juan Perón

SHORT ANSWER

37. ANS:
Uneven distribution of wealth, poverty linked to social class, rapid population growth, and rapid urbanization led to social unrest.

DIF: A   REF: 935-936   OBJ: C37S1-1
TOP: Continuity and change, Sources of unrest

38. ANS:
Latin American governments encouraged their own industries through a policy of import substitution. They expanded agriculture by opening more land for farming and promoting agriculture.

DIF: A   REF: 937-938   OBJ: C37S1-3
TOP: Economics, Economic development

39. ANS:
Many Cubans fled to the United States to escape Castro's rule. The Bay of Pigs disaster hurt the reputation of the United States. The United States and the Soviet Union came to the brink of nuclear war over Soviet missile bases in Cuba.

DIF: A   REF: 940-941   OBJ: C37S2-1
TOP: Global interaction, Cuban Revolution

40. ANS:
The *maquiladoras* system provided jobs for many Mexicans. The plants have caused environmental problems.

DIF: A   REF: 942   OBJ: C37S3-1
TOP: Global interaction, Drug wars

41. ANS:
poverty; lack of roads, electricity, and other basic services; inability to attract foreign investment; party rivalries and mounting protests; rising crime

DIF: A   REF: 949   OBJ: C37S3-3
TOP: Political systems, Haiti

42. ANS:
Juan Perón improved conditions for the working classes by boosting wages, strengthening labor unions, and promoting social reforms. His wife Eva also added to his popularity by giving money to the poor and helping women gain the right to vote.

DIF: A   REF: 950-951   OBJ: C37S4-1
TOP: Impact of the individual, Juan Perón

43. ANS:
Brazil has a large territory, many resources, and technology. It has a diversified economy. Under military rule, experts ran the economy.

DIF: A   REF: 953-955   OBJ: C37S4-2
TOP: Economics, Brazil's economic miracle

44. ANS:
It is 7,400 feet above sea level; ringed by mountains and volcanoes, in an earthquake zone; far from supplies of food, water, and energy; and short of oxygen.

DIF: A   REF: 944   OBJ: C37S3-1
TOP: Geography, Mexico City

45. ANS:
The Mexican government neglected agriculture and poured resources into industry. People moved to Mexico City because it provided jobs, schools, and health services.

DIF: A   REF: 944   OBJ: C37S3-1
TOP: Geography, Mexico City

46. ANS:
The writer refers to the city's character, charm, hospitality, energy, and spirit.

DIF: A   REF: 944   OBJ: C37S3-1
TOP: Geography, Mexico City

ESSAY

47. ANS:
A wealthy few controlled land, mines, businesses, and factories. They opposed reforms that threatened their power. Most of the population lived in poverty.

DIF: D   REF: 943   OBJ: C37S1-1
TOP: Global interaction, Amazon rain forest

48. ANS:
Juan Perón raised wages, strengthened labor unions, and promoted social reforms. Eva Perón helped by using her position to help the poor.

DIF: D   REF: 950-951   OBJ: C37S4-1
TOP: Political systems, Juan Perón

49. ANS:
Reformers and conservatives differed over how to achieve the goal of improving conditions for the poor. Military governments imposed harsh regimes. Revolutionaries overthrew governments.

DIF: D   REF: 936   OBJ: C37S1-2
TOP: Political systems, Competing ideologies

50. ANS:
Latin American governments must stop the supply of drugs being produced in their countries. The United States government must try to end the demand for drugs in its country.

DIF: D   REF: 942   OBJ: C37S2-3
TOP: Global interaction, Drug wars

51. ANS:
Women organized to campaign for schools and health care. They protested human rights violations by military governments. Women also organized mutual aid networks to provide help for the poor.

DIF: D   REF: 938-939   OBJ: C37S1-3
TOP: Social systems, Role of women

52. ANS:
The Amazon rain forest absorbs carbon dioxide and releases oxygen. It is home to many species of animals and plants that might provide cures for some diseases. Destruction of the rain forest also threatens indigenous peoples.

DIF: D   REF: 943   OBJ: C37S2-3
TOP: Environment, Amazon rain forest

UNIT 1—EARLY CIVILIZATIONS

Multiple Choice
Identify the letter of the choice that best completes the statement or answers the question.

_____ 1. How do archaeologists, anthropologists, and historians reconstruct life during the period of time called prehistory?
    a. They study the calendars from that time period.
    b. They study the artifacts of cultures from that time period.
    c. They study written records from that time period.
    d. They study the cities that were organized during that time period.

_____ 2. During early civilizations, why did most cities rise in river valleys?
    a. River valleys provided work to men who built dikes and canals.
    b. People built cities on riverbanks for easy access to travel and trade.
    c. City-state government centers were located in river valleys.
    d. These fertile areas favored farms that would support large populations.

_____ 3. The history of ancient Egypt is divided into three main periods: the Old Kingdom, the Middle Kingdom, and the New Kingdom. Which of the following events is associated with the Old Kingdom?
    a. A woman became monarch and exercised all the rights of a pharaoh.
    b. Egyptians and Hittites signed a peace treaty, the first to have survived in history.
    c. Rulers organized a large drainage project to create vast new stretches of arable land.
    d. The pyramids were built to protect the bodies of dead rulers.

_____ 4. What civilization probably produced the painting shown?

    a. Incan   c. Minoan

    b. Egyptian   d. Sumerian

_____ 5. How did geographic location influence the civilization that existed 4,000 years ago between the Tigris and Euphrates rivers?
   a. People there built tunnels to escape the flooding rivers and mummified their rulers to prepare them for the afterlife.
   b. People there performed complex surgical operations, which they described on papyrus scrolls.
   c. Stories of catastrophic floods entered their literature, and the fertile land produced surplus food that supported growing populations.
   d. People there worshiped thunder and lightning and traveled on the rivers in hollowed-out logs.

_____ 6. What important advancement did the Sumerians introduce by 3200 B.C. that would later allow historians to study their culture?
   a. The Sumerians introduced cuneiform, the earliest known form of writing.
   b. The Sumerians made the first books, using thin strips of wood and bamboo.
   c. The Sumerians created the Rosetta Stone, a black stone with a message in three scripts.
   d. The Sumerians established trade outposts in the Fertile Crescent.

_____ 7. The emperor Darius, who ruled from 522 B.C. to 486 B.C., unified the Persian empire. How did he unite this large empire, which would become a model for later rulers?
  a.   He divided the empire into provinces, each headed by a satrap, or governor, and developed a single code of laws.
  b.   He made members of his family regional governors, but he acted as the main ruler of the region.
  c.   He gave the Persians the power to elect their own officials and develop their own legal system.
  d.   He united the divided territory and placed one ruler in command of the entire empire.

_____ 8. What made the Israelites' religious beliefs unique?
  a.   The Israelites worshiped two gods, Osiris and Isis, instead of one god.
  b.   The Israelites feared God and believed that he would punish them.
  c.   The Israelites believed in one true God and that each event reflected God's plan.
  d.   The Israelites believed that gods were tied to certain places and people.

_____ 9. What have archaeologists concluded about cities in the Indus Valley from studying their careful planning and modern plumbing?
  a.   The cities had a well-organized government.
  b.   The cities flourished and then vanished without a trace.
  c.   The cities were actually less than 1,000 years old.
  d.   The cities had a single, powerful leader.

_____ 10. "We are superior to the Dravidians, a weak people whom we will conquer by following our rajahs. Our priests, one of the three basic groups in our society, memorize and recite the Vedas. We are a polytheistic people who worship Fierce Indra, the god of war. Who are we?"
  a.   Brahmans   c.   Aryans
  b.   Mystics   d.   Vedamans

_____ 11. The Zhou rulers used the Mandate of Heaven to justify their overthrow of the Shang in 1027 B.C. Which statement below correctly describes the Mandate of Heaven?
  a.   It is an order from the gods that local lords must govern their own lands.
  b.   It is the divine right to rule as long as a dynasty provides good government.
  c.   It is the sacred calligraphy symbol that stands for peace.
  d.   It is a sacred law stating that the Zhou people should rule China.

UNIT 1—EARLY CIVILIZATIONS
Answer Section

MULTIPLE CHOICE

1. ANS: B   DIF: A   REF: 8   OBJ: C1S1-2, C1S1-3
   TOP: Studying prehistory

2. ANS: D   DIF: A   REF: 15   OBJ: C1S3-1
   TOP: Rise of cities near rivers

3. ANS: D   DIF: A   REF: 26   OBJ: C2S2-2
   TOP: Old Kingdom of Egypt

4. ANS: B   DIF: A   REF: 28   OBJ: C2S2-1
   TOP: Egyptian art

5. ANS: C   DIF: A   REF: 34   OBJ: C2S3-2
   TOP: Civilization of the Fertile Crescent

6. ANS: A   DIF: A   REF: 36-37   OBJ: C2S3-3
   TOP: Cuneiform

7. ANS: A   DIF: A   REF: 42   OBJ: C2S4-3
   TOP: Unification of Persian empire

8. ANS: C   DIF: A   REF: 46   OBJ: C2S5-2
   TOP: Israelites' relationship with God

9. ANS: A   DIF: A   REF: 53   OBJ: C3S1-2
   TOP: Indus Valley government

10. ANS: C   DIF: A   REF: 57   OBJ: C3S2-1
    TOP: Religion of the Aryan civilization

11. ANS: B   DIF: D   REF: 63-64   OBJ: C3S3-2
    TOP: Mandate of Heaven

UNIT 2—EMPIRES OF THE ANCIENT WORLD

Multiple Choice
Identify the letter of the choice that best completes the statement or answers the question.

_____ 1. Which statement BEST explains why Hinduism is one of the world's most complex religions?
   a. Hinduism is very similar to Buddhism and Christianity.
   b. Hinduism is no longer practiced in present-day India.
   c. Hinduism grew out of the overlapping beliefs of the diverse groups that settled in India.
   d. The religious texts of the Hindus are written in a language that no one understands.

_____ 2. Which statement applies to BOTH the Maurya and the Gupta empires?
   a. Both empires united diverse peoples within their empires.
   b. Both empires fought bitterly against Buddhism.
   c. Both empires had a loose government structure that gave power to individual villages.
   d. Both empires developed a type of decimal system.

_____ 3. How do Legalism and Daoism differ?
   a. Legalism emphasizes strict law and harsh punishment, and Daoism emphasizes that a government that governs least is best.
   b. Daoism emphasizes personal salvation, and Legalism emphasizes that a government that governs least is best.
   c. Legalism places one person in a position of supreme power, and Daoism creates a governing body of many.
   d. Legalism is an extension of the Daoist idea of government with additional laws and punishments.

_____ 4. In his attempts to unify China, emperor Shi Huangdi abolished feudalism, destroyed works of literature and philosophy, and also
   a. made Confucianism the official belief system of the state.
   b. lowered taxes.
   c. reorganized finances and imposed a government monopoly.
   d. constructed the Great Wall.

____ 5. How did the geography of Greece affect its trade and the spread of ideas?

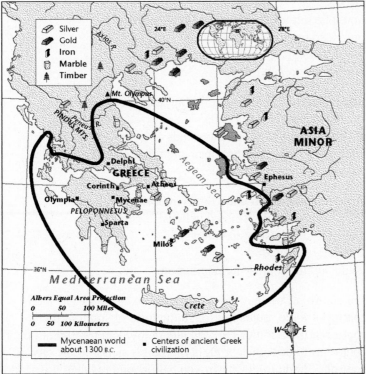

a. The Greeks were unskilled sailors, so it was difficult for them to travel across the rough waters of the Mediterranean.

b. Greece is located in mountainous terrain, so the Greeks could trade with other civilizations but only rarely.

c. Greece is located on the Mediterranean at a crossroads of different civilizations, so ideas and trade flourished.

d. The geography of Greece made the spread of ideas difficult because of the shallow water level of the Aegean Sea.

____ 6. Around 700 B.C., Athenians became unhappy with their form of government. What new type of government replaced it?

a. aristocracy   c. oligarchy

b. democracy   d. monarchy

____ 7. What was the cause of the Peloponnesian War?

a. Greeks sought revenge for the Persian Wars.

b. Sparta wanted control of the powerful Athenian army.

c. A Spartan murdered the Athenian ruler Pericles.

d. Many Greeks outside of Athens resented Athenian domination.

_____ 8. Plato rejected democracy because of the execution of Socrates. Why did Plato's student, Aristotle, reject democracy?
   a. He felt reason should be left to politicians, not the people.
   b. He thought it would lead to mob rule.
   c. He distrusted a single strong, all-powerful leader.
   d. He was suspicious of the "golden mean."

_____ 9. What is considered Alexander the Great's most lasting achievement?
   a. His vast empire included Greece and Persia.
   b. His victory at the Granicus River saved thousands of lives.
   c. He spread Greek culture to the Mediterranean and the Middle East.
   d. He successfully reunited Athens and Thebes.

_____ 10. Why did geography make Italy easier to unite than Greece?
   a. Italy was not broken up into small, isolated valleys.
   b. Italy was broken up into small, isolated valleys.
   c. The mountains were more rugged.
   d. The mountains could support a growing population.

_____ 11. How did conquests and control of trade routes benefit Rome by about 133 B.C.?
   a. Conquests and control of trade routes improved the lives of small farmers.
   b. Conquests and control of trade routes reduced unemployment throughout the region.
   c. Conquests and control of trade routes brought incredible riches to the city.
   d. Conquests and control of trade routes destroyed culture and reduced the need for slave labor.

_____ 12. How did the Romans view Greek culture, such as art, literature, and philosophy, during the Greco-Roman period of civilization?
   a. The Romans believed it was substandard.
   b. The Romans believed it would anger the gods and lead to mass destruction of their way of life.
   c. The Romans believed it lacked a sense of community pride.
   d. The Romans believed it represented the height of cultural achievement.

_____ 13. How was the work of Paul crucial to the spread of Christianity?
   a. He spread the teachings of Jesus beyond Jewish communities to gentiles.
   b. He developed the early structure of the Christian Church.
   c. He created the ritual of the Eucharist.
   d. Because he knew Jesus, his teachings converted large numbers of people.

_____ 14. How did the Mayas adapt to their environment?
   a. They worked at night when it was cooler and took siestas during the day.
   b. They cleared the rain forests and built raised fields that caught and held water.
   c. They built elaborate cave dwellings in the sides of cliffs.
   d. They built a complex system of irrigation channels.

_____ 15. How did Pachacuti, the Sapa Inca, dominate an immense empire from his small kingdom in Cuzco?
    a.   His army had better weapons and received intense training.
    b.   People in the region thought that he was the embodiment of the god Zeus.
    c.   After he had subdued neighboring peoples, he enlisted them into his armies.
    d.   He refused to be known as a divine ruler.

_____ 16. In the late 1100s, how did the Anasazi adapt to their environment in canyons of the southwest region of North America?
    a.   They created a complex irrigation system.
    b.   They built clusters of earthen mounds.
    c.   They built cliff dwellings.
    d.   They invented "floating gardens."

UNIT 2—EMPIRES OF THE ANCIENT WORLD
Answer Section

MULTIPLE CHOICE

1. ANS: C   DIF: A   REF: 76-78   OBJ: C4S1-1
     TOP: Hinduism as a complex religion
2. ANS: A   DIF: A   REF: 81-83   OBJ: C4S2-1, C4S2-3
     TOP: Maurya and Gupta empires
3. ANS: A   DIF: D   REF: 90-91   OBJ: C4S4-2
     TOP: Legalism and Daoism
4. ANS: D   DIF: A   REF: 93-94   OBJ: C4S5-1
     TOP: Shi Huangdi unites China
5. ANS: C   DIF: A   REF: 106   OBJ: C5S1-1
     TOP: Geography of ancient Greece
6. ANS: B   DIF: E   REF: 107   OBJ: C5S2-3
     TOP: Athenian government
7. ANS: D   DIF: A   REF: 114   OBJ: C5S3-3
     TOP: Peloponnesian War
8. ANS: B   DIF: A   REF: 116   OBJ: C5S4-1
     TOP: Ideas of Greek philosophers
9. ANS: C   DIF: E   REF: 121-122   OBJ: C5S5-2
     TOP: Alexander the Great
10. ANS: A   DIF: E   REF: 128   OBJ: C6S1-1
     TOP: Unification of Italy
11. ANS: C   DIF: A   REF: 133   OBJ: C6S2-1
     TOP: Economic effects of Roman conquests
12. ANS: D   DIF: A   REF: 137   OBJ: C6S3-2
     TOP: Romans' view of Greek culture
13. ANS: A   DIF: A   REF: 143-144   OBJ: C6S4-2
     TOP: The work of Paul
14. ANS: B   DIF: E   REF: 158   OBJ: C7S1-1
     TOP: Mayas adapt to environment
15. ANS: C   DIF: D   REF: 164   OBJ: C7S2-2
     TOP: Pachacuti's rule from Cuzco
16. ANS: C   DIF: E   REF: 168-169   OBJ: C7S3-1
     TOP: Adapting to desert environments/Anasazi

UNIT 3—REGIONAL CIVILIZATIONS

Multiple Choice
Identify the letter of the choice that best completes the statement or answers the question.

_____ 1. Which of the following was NOT a result of Pope Leo III crowning Charlemagne and proclaiming him Emperor of the Romans?
   a. The ideal of a united Christian community was revived.
   b. Islam advanced no farther into Africa.
   c. The emperor of the eastern Roman empire in Constantinople was furious.
   d. The split between eastern and western Christian worlds was widened.

_____ 2. What development led to the revival of trade throughout medieval Europe between 100 and 1300?
   a. Medieval engineers improved the Romans' road-building techniques, allowing traders to travel greater distances.
   b. The discovery of silver deposits in Scandinavia greatly increased the money supply.
   c. Overfarming of European land reduced agricultural production and forced leaders to open trade routes.
   d. Improvements in food production led to a dramatic increase in population.

_____ 3. Why did King John of England sign the Magna Carta in 1215?
   a. The Church forced him to sign it in order to set up the Estates General.
   b. His heirs insisted he sign it in order to establish a line of succession.
   c. The Crusades were bankrupting the country.
   d. His barons forced him to sign it because he was abusing his power.

_____ 4. What did Pope Urban II initiate at the Council of Clermont, and why?
   a. the Reconquista; to expel non-Christians from Spain
   b. the Crusades; to free the Holy Land from non-Christian control
   c. a schism; to excommunicate Henry II for violating Church law
   d. scholasticism; to support Christian beliefs using reason

_____ 5. For what reform is Justinian BEST remembered?
   a. He healed the schism between the Roman and Byzantine churches by conquering Constantinople during the Crusades.
   b. He pioneered the use of bank checks so that his subjects could have access to money wherever they were.
   c. He influenced the Roman Catholic Church and medieval monarchs, who modeled their laws on the principles of his code.
   d. He encouraged his subjects to improve their social class through scholastic and military achievements.

_____ 6. In describing a conquest between 1236 and 1241 led by Genghiz Khan's grandson, a Russian historian wrote, "No eye remained to weep for the dead." What was the historian writing about, and why did he describe it this way?

    a. The Golden Horses battle; Mongol warriors rode atop light-colored horses that wore protective eye shades.

    b. The Golden Horde; the conquest looted and burned Russian towns, killing most of the inhabitants.

    c. The Battle of Byzantine; hundreds of towns were burned by enormous fires set by Russian barbarians.

    d. The Russian Crusades; Crusaders plundered Mongol cities and forced their inhabitants to convert or die.

_____ 7. According to this table, within 50 years after Muhammad's death in 632, Islam had spread to present-day

SPREAD OF ISLAM		
Present-Day Country	Approximate Date of Introduction of Islam	Approximate Percentage of Muslims Today
Egypt	656	94%
India	1206	11%
Iran (Persia)	656	95%
Morocco	750	99%
Saudi Arabia	610	100%
Spain	750	less than 1%
Syria	656	90%
Turkey (Asia Minor)	1070	99.8%

    a. Egypt, Iran, Syria, and Saudi Arabia.

    b. Morocco and Spain.

    c. Saudi Arabia.

    d. Turkey.

_____ 8. What was one result of the cultural blending between Muslims and Hindus?

    a. the destruction of Buddhism   c. the Sikh religion

    b. the Mughal dynasty   d. the caste system

_____ 9. What feature was shared by the empires of Justinian, Ivan III, and Suleiman?

    a. absolute power of the ruler   c. feudal economies

    b. decentralized governments   d. religious intolerance

____ 10. Which ruler converted to Islam and made a *hajj* in 1324, forging new diplomatic and economic ties with other Muslim states while crossing Africa?
   a. Ezana   c. Sonni Ali
   b. Mansa Musa   d. Muhammad

____ 11. Under the Shilla dynasty, Korea became a tributary state of China. What is a tributary state?
   a. A tributary state consists of one or more villages and is located within a sovereign state.
   b. A tributary state owes its allegiance to another state and adopts its laws and customs.
   c. A tributary state acknowledges overlordship of another state but preserves its independence.
   d. A tributary state receives tribute from another state and uses these funds to fight wars.

____ 12. knight : chivalry :: samurai : ____
   a. shogun   c. bushido
   b. lord   d. daimyo

UNIT 3—REGIONAL CIVILIZATIONS
Answer Section

MULTIPLE CHOICE

1. ANS: B DIF: A REF: 183-184 OBJ: C8S1-2
   TOP: Charlemagne
2. ANS: D DIF: A REF: 198 OBJ: C8S4-1
   TOP: Agricultural revolution
3. ANS: D DIF: A REF: 208 OBJ: C9S1-2
   TOP: Magna Carta
4. ANS: B DIF: A REF: 216 OBJ: C9S3-2
   TOP: Crusades
5. ANS: C DIF: A REF: 236 OBJ: C10S1-4
   TOP: Justinian
6. ANS: B DIF: D REF: 241-242 OBJ: C10S2-2
   TOP: Mongol conquest/Golden Horde
7. ANS: B DIF: E REF: 256-258 OBJ: C11S2-2
   TOP: Islam
8. ANS: C DIF: A REF: 269 OBJ: C11S4-2
   TOP: Sikhism
9. ANS: A DIF: A REF: 273 OBJ: C11S5-2
   TOP: Absolute power
10. ANS: B DIF: D REF: 285-286 OBJ: C12S2-2
    TOP: Mansa Musa/Kingdom of Mali
11. ANS: C DIF: A REF: 314 OBJ: C13S3-2
    TOP: Korea
12. ANS: C DIF: A REF: 320 OBJ: C13S5-3
    TOP: Japan feudalism

UNIT 4—EARLY MODERN TIMES

Multiple Choice
Identify the letter of the choice that best completes the statement or answers the question.

_____ 1. Which statement correctly describes the Renaissance?
   a. It was a time in which European countries expanded their borders.
   b. It was a period in Europe's history associated with mass migration.
   c. It was a time of creativity and political, social, economic, and cultural change.
   d. It was an era synonymous with harsh rulers and economic hardship.

_____ 2. How did Johann Gutenberg's invention, the printing press, affect Europe in the late 1400s and 1500s?
   a. Books quickly became collectors' items and sold for very large sums of money.
   b. More people learned to read, and they gained access to a broad range of knowledge.
   c. The printing press provided hundreds of jobs for Chinese pressmen.
   d. Outraged rulers banned the use of the press, fearing it would be used for producing propaganda.

_____ 3. In the 1530s and 1540s, Pope Paul III became the leader of the Catholic Reformation. What was one of his main objectives during the reform movement?
   a. to revive the moral authority of the Church
   b. to bring a new leader to power in England
   c. to gain papal control over the Church of England
   d. to discredit Protestant religious leaders

_____ 4. How did the scientific method change science and research in the early 1600s?
   a. It created a process to train scientists for research fields.
   b. It defined a strict set of guidelines for using plants and animals for scientific research.
   c. It eliminated scientists' need to collect and accurately measure data.
   d. It created a step-by-step process used to confirm findings and prove or disprove a hypothesis.

_____ 5. Why did Europeans become interested in exploring a direct route to Asia that bypassed the Mediterranean?
   a. They sought a land free of religious persecution.
   b. They wanted direct access to the riches of Asia and desired a crusade against the Muslims.
   c. They hoped to develop trade relations with Muslim merchants.
   d. They thought a direct route would allow trader cartographers to make accurate maps of the region.

_____ 6. Study the map of Southeast Asia. How did geographic location affect sea trade between China and India?

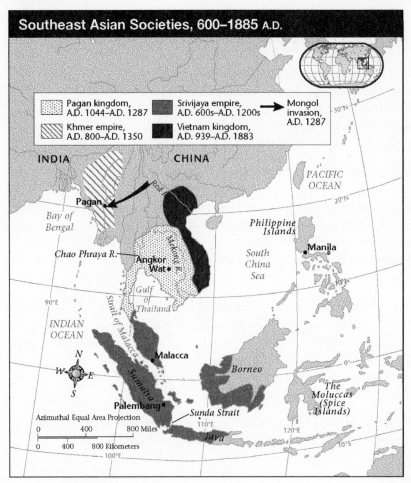

Southeast Asian Societies, 600–1885 A.D.

a. Sea trade between China and India had to navigate east around the Philippine Islands in the South China Sea.

b. Because of the winds and lack of a direct sea passage, trade goods could be shipped only over land.

c. All seaborne trade between China and India had to pass through either the Malacca or Sunda straits.

d. The lower plateaus that separate the mainland from the rest of Asia made trade faster.

_____ 7. In the 1500s, how did Spain conquer the Philippines so easily and expand its empire in the East?

a. Spanish troops were more familiar with the Philippine terrain than that of other island nations.

b. The Filipinos were already a Christian society and easily adapted to Spanish rule.

c. The Filipinos wanted to be ruled by a larger country in the hopes that their economy would flourish.

d. The Filipinos were not united and were easy for the Spanish to conquer.

_____ 8. How did the Tokugawa shoguns react toward foreign traders?
  a. The Tokugawas welcomed the foreign traders.
  b. The Tokugawas imposed strict trade laws on the foreign traders.
  c. The Tokugawas barred all foreign traders.
  d. The Tokugawas decided to allow limited trade with foreign traders.

_____ 9. What did the Europeans bring to the Taíno people that had a substantial impact on the population?
  a. They carried diseases, such as smallpox, measles, and influenza.
  b. They carried seeds, such as corn and wheat, that changed the diets of the Taínos.
  c. They brought guns and armor, which the Taínos used against each other.
  d. They introduced the Taínos to Christianity and the Aztec method of panning for gold.

_____ 10. How did other European countries, such as Portugal, England, and France, challenge Spain's power in the Spanish American colonies?
  a. The European countries continually invaded the Spanish colonies to weaken Spain's power and control.
  b. The European countries sent people from their lands to secretly settle in the colonies with the Spanish.
  c. The European countries traded illegally with Spanish colonists to get around Spain's strict control over colonial trade.
  d. The European countries blocked Spain's ports so that supplies could not reach the colonies.

_____ 11. Which word or words BEST complete the following paragraph?
  Britain and France were bitter rivals for power in the American colonies during the 1700s. Although France held more territory in America, the British colonies had more ____, which eventually ensured British dominance in North America.
  a. factories   c. equal rights
  b. wealth and fertile farmland   d. people

_____ 12. In the 1500s, why did the Atlantic slave trade begin?
  a. Smallpox had wiped out a large percentage of the male population in America.
  b. There was a need for labor in Spain's American empire.
  c. The American colonies needed workers on cotton and tobacco plantations.
  d. Portuguese rulers wanted access to prosperous East African coastal cities.

_____ 13. What was one of the main reasons Charles V lost control of his Hapsburg empire in the mid-1500s?
  a. Charles' strongest allies, the Ottomans, lost power in the Netherlands.
  b. A young King Philip sought to expand Spanish influence and won the support of Charles' subjects.
  c. The empire was scattered and too diverse for a single ruler.
  d. The people in these lands were devout Catholics and would not convert to Protestantism.

_____ 14. When Louis XIV became king, what measures did he take to strengthen the nation as a royal power?
  a. He expanded the bureaucracy, strengthened the French army, and followed mercantilist policies to bolster the economy.
  b. He withdrew from government affairs, did away with the government's bureaucracy, and gave more power to the people.
  c. He built a strong army and launched successful attacks on many surrounding countries to expand France's borders.
  d. He created a government composed entirely of French bourgeoisie and widened the gap between the wealthy and the poor.

_____ 15. Which of the following statements BEST characterizes Prussia following the Thirty Years' War?
  a. Prussia was a westernized society suffering from disease and famine.
  b. Prussia was a strong Catholic state, weakened by war but with important ties to Britain and Russia.
  c. Prussia was a new, unified Protestant power with strong military values.
  d. Prussia had a failing economy with a tax system that angered peasants, nobles, and clergy.

_____ 16. How did Peter the Great expand Russia's borders?
  a. He gained control of a warm-water port along the Black Sea and defeated the vast Ottoman empire, taking over their lands.
  b. He gained control of Poland and took over parts of Austria in a petition signed by Peter, Frederick the Great, and Emperor Joseph II.
  c. He defeated the Swedes to gain control of the land along the Baltic Sea, and he signed a treaty with China to gain rights to lands north of Manchuria.
  d. He successfully built the strongest army in Europe and blockaded each border of Russia to prevent mass migration to Russian lands.

UNIT 4—EARLY MODERN TIMES
Answer Section

MULTIPLE CHOICE

1. ANS: C   DIF: E   REF: 337   OBJ: C14S1-2
   TOP: The Renaissance period
2. ANS: B   DIF: A   REF: 345   OBJ: C14S2-3
   TOP: Invention of the printing press
3. ANS: A   DIF: A   REF: 353   OBJ: C14S4-3
   TOP: The Catholic Reformation
4. ANS: D   DIF: A   REF: 357   OBJ: C14S5-2
   TOP: The scientific method
5. ANS: B   DIF: A   REF: 364-365   OBJ: C15S1-1
   TOP: European motives for exploration
6. ANS: C   DIF: D   REF: 369   OBJ: C15S2-1
   TOP: Sea trade in Southeast Asia
7. ANS: D   DIF: A   REF: 374   OBJ: C15S3-2
   TOP: Spain and the Philippines
8. ANS: C   DIF: A   REF: 381   OBJ: C15S4-3
   TOP: The Tokugawas' attitude toward foreign traders
9. ANS: A   DIF: E   REF: 386   OBJ: C16S1-1
   TOP: Disease brought to Native Americans
10. ANS: C   DIF: A   REF: 393   OBJ: C16S2-3
    TOP: Challenging Spanish power
11. ANS: D   DIF: A   REF: 396   OBJ: C16S2-2
    TOP: France and Britain compete for power in colonies
12. ANS: B   DIF: E   REF: 399   OBJ: C16S4-1
    TOP: Destinations of enslaved Africans
13. ANS: C   DIF: A   REF: 412-413   OBJ: C17S1-3
    TOP: Hapsburg empire
14. ANS: A   DIF: D   REF: 418   OBJ: C14S2-3
    TOP: Strengthening France's royal power
15. ANS: C   DIF: A   REF: 429   OBJ: C17S4-2
    TOP: Prussia after Thirty Years' War
16. ANS: C   DIF: A   REF: 433   OBJ: C17S5-2
    TOP: Expansion under Peter the Great

UNIT 5—ENLIGHTENMENT AND REVOLUTION

Multiple Choice
Identify the letter of the choice that best completes the statement or answers the question.

_____ 1. What did the *philosophes* advocate using to better understand and improve society during the age of reason?
    a.   human nature   c.   critical argument
    b.   methods of science   d.   historical texts

_____ 2. How did Britain's geographic location contribute to its status as a global empire?
    a.   Because of its enormous landmass, Britain was able to nearly double its population in less than a century.
    b.   Britain became a global empire because its geographic location helped to spread its revolutionary ideals.
    c.   Geographic location placed Britain in a position to control trade.
    d.   Geographic location made it easy for Britain's population to work in other countries.

_____ 3. How did the Constitution of the United States reflect the ideas of the Enlightenment thinkers, such as Locke, Montesquieu, and Rousseau?
    a.   It focused on art and literature from the Renaissance as well as government policies that had served populations well in earlier days.
    b.   It reflected the thinkers' ideas that human beings were corrupted by the evils of society and that they should make efforts to reduce these evils.
    c.   The Enlightenment theory argued against placing too many limitations on people, so the framers of the Constitution established a government free of human restrictions.
    d.   It viewed government in terms of a social contract and created an elected government rather than a hereditary monarchy.

_____ 4. Study the circle graphs of population and land ownership in France. Which of the following statements explains why there was discontent with France's old regime?

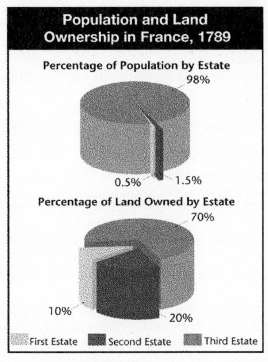

Population and Land Ownership in France, 1789

Percentage of Population by Estate
98%
0.5%   1.5%

Percentage of Land Owned by Estate
70%
10%   20%

First Estate   Second Estate   Third Estate

a. Although only 0.5 percent of the population belonged to the First Estate, they owned nearly all the land.

b. The First Estate ruled over the most land yet had the biggest population.

c. 98 percent of the population were members of the Third Estate, but they owned only 70 percent of the land.

d. 1.5 percent of the population were Second Estate members who worked on 20 percent of the land.

_____ 5. While drafting their constitutions, what did the National Assembly decide must be done to handle the huge government debt?

a. They voted to take over and sell Church lands.

b. They agreed to release the French Catholic Church from state control.

c. They immediately ended support of middle-class farmers and free trade.

d. They seized private property and reclaimed it as government land.

_____ 6. How did the Age of Napoleon affect Europe?

a. Europe was affected only slightly by cooperating with Napoleon and embracing the ideals of the French Revolution.

b. Europe eventually defended itself against Napoleon's advances, but his conquests spread many of the ideals of the French Revolution.

c. European nations saw Napoleon's armies as liberators and welcomed his advances.

d. Napoleon won support of the upper classes, but peasants' lands were taken away from them.

_____ 7. How did the Battle of Waterloo contribute to Napoleon's downfall?
   a. His troops suffered a massive defeat after holding the enemy for nearly 40 days, forcing Napoleon to surrender.
   b. After retreating for 1,000 miles from Moscow, Napoleon was killed by his own soldiers.
   c. After losing nearly 30,000 men, Napoleon's wife left him—a crushing blow from which he never recovered.
   d. His troops were crushed in a day-long battle, and Napoleon was forced to abdicate and to go into exile.

_____ 8. What two major developments in technology played an important role in triggering the Industrial Revolution?
   a. advances in military weapons and the invention of the automobile
   b. improved building materials and the discovery of coal
   c. the invention of the steam engine and improvements in producing iron
   d. the invention of the train and the improvement of roads across the nation

_____ 9. Why did the Industrial Revolution begin in Britain rather than in other European nations or the Americas?
   a. In addition to resources and technology, Britain had the right economic, political, and social conditions.
   b. Britain had the largest population and the greatest availability of working-age men.
   c. Other nations did not have ready access to a large number of ports and waterways.
   d. European nations provided Britain with funding for many of its technological advancements.

_____ 10. How did the introduction of the factory system affect workers' daily lives?
   a. Factories provided a relief from farm work because workers performed far fewer tasks per day than farmers did.
   b. Factory work, with long hours and poor conditions, proved to be even harsher than farm work.
   c. Factory workers received higher salaries for their work and enjoyed year-round work rather than seasonal farm work.
   d. The factories' machines required less maintenance and were much safer for children and women than the farm equipment.

_____ 11. What is the difference between utilitarianism and socialism?
   a. Socialism emphasizes individual freedom, and utilitarianism condemns industrial capitalism.
   b. Socialism states that government should regulate the means of production, and utilitarianism argues that there should be no government.
   c. Utilitarianism emphasizes individual freedom and the greatest happiness for the greatest number of people, and socialism condemns industrial capitalism.
   d. Utilitarianism sees class struggle between employers and employees as unavoidable, and socialism states that large social groups maintain peace and justice.

_____ 12. Each of the following was an aspect of the Old Order, which greatly appealed to conservatives in the early 1800s, EXCEPT
    a. the desire for royal families to be restored to the thrones they occupied when Napoleon swept across Europe.
    b. the support of an established church.
    c. the support of a social hierarchy in which lower classes respected and obeyed their superiors.
    d. the promotion of natural rights and constitutional government.

_____ 13. Why were the supporters of Louis XVIII, the ultraroyalists, unhappy with him?
    a. He restricted all the freedoms granted by the previous ruler.
    b. They despised constitutional government and wanted to restore the old regime.
    c. He revoked the rights of women and allowed poor factory conditions to continue.
    d. He created a two-house legislature, which they saw as dangerous.

_____ 14. What event sparked widespread rebellion in Latin America and provided Latin America with the opportunity to finally reject foreign domination and demand independence?
    a. Napoleon's invasion of Spain
    b. the arrival of European Christian missionaries
    c. an embargo on trade from Spain's main trading partners
    d. the French Revolution

UNIT 5—ENLIGHTENMENT AND REVOLUTION
Answer Section

MULTIPLE CHOICE

1. ANS: B   DIF: A   REF: 447   OBJ: C18S1-2
     TOP: Science in the age of reason

2. ANS: C   DIF: D   REF: 456   OBJ: C18S3-1
     TOP: Britain's location/Rise to global power

3. ANS: D   DIF: E   REF: 463   OBJ: C18S4-3
     TOP: The Constitution and the Enlightenment

4. ANS: C   DIF: E   REF: 469   OBJ: C19S1-1
     TOP: Estate population/Land ownership

5. ANS: A   DIF: A   REF: 475   OBJ: C19S2-2
     TOP: National Assembly reorganizes Church

6. ANS: B   DIF: D   REF: 490   OBJ: C19S4-1
     TOP: Napoleon's legacy

7. ANS: D   DIF: A   REF: 490   OBJ: C19S5-2
     TOP: The downfall of Napoleon

8. ANS: C   DIF: E   REF: 500   OBJ: C20S1-3
     TOP: New technology in Industrial Revolution

9. ANS: A   DIF: A   REF: 501   OBJ: C20S2-1
     TOP: Britain as the leader in technology

10. ANS: B   DIF: A   REF: 506   OBJ: C20S3-2
     TOP: Factory systems in industrial revolution

11. ANS: C   DIF: A   REF: 511   OBJ: C20S4-2
     TOP: Utilitarianism and socialism

12. ANS: D   DIF: D   REF: 518   OBJ: C21S1-1
     TOP: Conservatives and the Old Order

13. ANS: B   DIF: D   REF: 521   OBJ: C21S2-1
     TOP: Events leading to French Revolution

14. ANS: A   DIF: D   REF: 528   OBJ: C21S3-1
     TOP: Independence in Latin America

UNIT 6—INDUSTRIALISM AND A NEW GLOBAL AGE

Multiple Choice
Identify the letter of the choice that best completes the statement or answers the question.

_____ 1. In the late 1800s, supporters of monopolies believed that monopolies added to the general economic prosperity. What did the critics of monopolies say?
   a.   Monopoly cartels eliminated production quotas and controlled markets without considering quality.
   b.   In their pursuit of profit, ruthless business leaders destroyed competition and were free to set prices at any level.
   c.   Because ruthless business leaders refused to invest in railroad building, thousands were left unemployed.
   d.   Monopolies benefited the richest Americans, who sought to advance competition at the expense of progress.

_____ 2. All of the following were methods used by workers to improve the conditions of the workplace throughout the 1800s EXCEPT
   a.   workers held strikes and demonstrations to fight for improvements.
   b.   workers created unions to bargain on behalf of all workers.
   c.   workers used violence and destruction to prove how harsh conditions were for them.
   d.   workers created mutual-aid societies to aid the sick and injured.

_____ 3. How did Charles Darwin challenge existing scientific and religious beliefs?
   a.   Darwin argued that all forms of life had evolved into their present condition over millions of years.
   b.   Darwin showed how different kinds of atoms combine to make all chemical substances.
   c.   Darwin argued that the Earth was at least two billion years old and that life had not appeared until long after the Earth was formed.
   d.   Darwin uncovered the fossilized bones of prehistoric people in the Neander Valley.

_____ 4. How might the cannon pictured serve as a symbol of Bismarck's Germany?

   a.   The cannon symbolizes Germany's desire to defend its borders and maintain peace.
   b.   The cannon symbolizes Germany's interest in exhibitions.
   c.   The cannon symbolizes Germany's educated work force.
   d.   The cannon symbolizes Germany's industrialization and military power.

_____ 5. By 1815, Russia was considered a great world power, yet it remained economically undeveloped. Why?
   a. Russia did not have the availability of large amounts of capital as did other European countries.
   b. Russia concentrated its wealth in foreign affairs and national defense and neglected the country's economy.
   c. Russian leaders did not recognize the need to modernize their economy until it was too late.
   d. The Russian czars and nobles resisted reforms that might undermine their absolute rule.

_____ 6. If you were a Catholic or a non-Anglican Protestant in Britain during the 1820s, how would Parliamentary reforms have affected your life?
   a. You would have been given the right to vote.
   b. You would have been denied the right to own private property.
   c. You would have been required to register for the Royal Guard.
   d. You would have lost your seat in the Houses of Parliament.

_____ 7. As Britain became more democratic, why did free traders demand reforms that would put an end to protective tariffs?
   a. They believed that if defensive tariffs were restored to the marketplace, merchants everywhere would be able to sell their goods at higher prices.
   b. They believed that if protective tariffs were lifted, their sales taxes would be lowered and competition decreased.
   c. They believed that if the tariffs were abolished, merchants everywhere would have larger markets in which to sell their goods.
   d. They believed that if the tariffs were removed, people would benefit from an elimination of competition and a smaller marketplace.

_____ 8. What did the Dreyfus affair reveal about the social climate in Europe in the late 1800s?
   a. There was a rise in antisemitism.
   b. There was corruption in the lower classes.
   c. There was a growing tolerance for spying.
   d. There was a significant decline in religious oppression.

_____ 9. Economic growth and social reforms helped the United States become a world leader in what two areas?
   a. freedom and suffrage
   b. business and immigration
   c. industrial and agricultural production
   d. science and technology

_____ 10. In the 1800s, how did European countries begin to increase their contact with Africa?
   a. They sent explorers to push into the interior of Africa and missionaries to convert people to Christianity.
   b. They increased trade with Africa and imported more African slaves to their countries.
   c. They redirected trade routes so that they could become more familiar with African territory.
   d. They sent physicians and scientists to improve the standard of living for many African people.

____ 11. How do the graph and map explain why the Suez Canal in Egypt was so vital to London's economy?

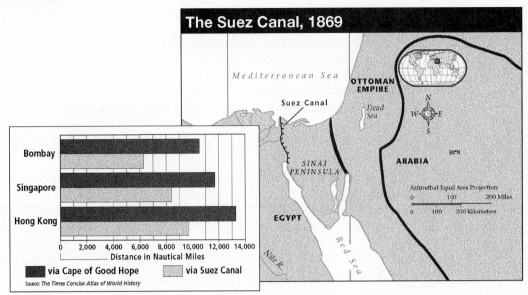

a. Owning the canal would save Britain from having to pay toll fees for the use of the canal.

b. The canal would hurt Britain's trade with Hong Kong.

c. The Suez Canal would increase the distance between Bombay and the Cape of Good Hope.

d. The canal greatly shortened trade routes, especially the one to India.

____ 12. Why were the British able to conquer India's vast territory?

a. Britain exploited the diversity of the nation, which was fragmented and unable to unite.

b. Most Indians did not speak or write English.

c. India was a vast territory with a small population.

d. The Indian people were attracted to the British way of life.

____ 13. The Taiping rebels of China, with Hong Xiuquan as their leader, fought for what social changes?

a. They fought for a voice in government decisions and for better conditions for workers.

b. They fought for the right to vote and the opportunity to adopt certain aspects of western culture.

c. They fought for land reform, community ownership of property, and equal rights for men and women.

d. They fought for religious freedom, the abolition of slavery, and traders' rights.

____ 14. How did European colonization in Southeast Asia impact the people and culture of the area?

a. The colonization brought disease and destruction to Southeast Asia, darkening the culture of the area for centuries.

b. The Europeans introduced modern technology and expanded commerce and industry in Southeast Asia.

c. The people of Southeast Asia rebelled against the European culture of wealth and promiscuity.

d. The Europeans stripped away Southeast Asian culture and replaced it with a westernized culture.

____ 15. Which statement BEST characterizes the relationship between Britain and the newly
independent countries of Australia and New Zealand?
   a.   Both countries severed ties to Britain.
   b.   Both countries remained colonies of Britain.
   c.   Both countries established penal colonies in Britain.
   d.   Both countries preserved close ties to Britain.

____ 16. How did western imperialism impact culture worldwide?
   a.   Western imperialism pressured people to conform to modern ways and believe in
        western superiority.
   b.   Western imperialism enabled missionaries to adopt local traditions and denounce
        Christianity.
   c.   Western imperialism kept developing countries from receiving modern medicine and
        education.
   d.   Western imperialism allowed ancient civilizations to retain their traditional ways of life.

UNIT 6—INDUSTRIALISM AND A NEW GLOBAL AGE
Answer Section

MULTIPLE CHOICE

1. ANS: B   DIF: D   REF: 550   OBJ: C22S1-3
    TOP: Monopolies
2. ANS: C   DIF: A   REF: 553-554   OBJ: C22S2-3
    TOP: Working-class fight for improvement
3. ANS: A   DIF: E   REF: 560   OBJ: C22S3-3
    TOP: Theories of Charles Darwin
4. ANS: D   DIF: A   REF: 574   OBJ: C23S2-2
    TOP: The Iron Chancellor
5. ANS: D   DIF: A   REF: 584   OBJ: C23S5-1
    TOP: Russian economic development
6. ANS: A   DIF: A   REF: 594   OBJ: C24S1-1
    TOP: Parliamentary reforms
7. ANS: C   DIF: D   REF: 597   OBJ: C24S2-1
    TOP: Protective tariffs
8. ANS: A   DIF: A   REF: 606   OBJ: C24S3-2
    TOP: Dreyfus affair
9. ANS: C   DIF: E   REF: 612   OBJ: C24S4-2
    TOP: U.S. leads world in industrial/Agricultural production
10. ANS: A   DIF: A   REF: 622   OBJ: C25S2-2
    TOP: European contact with Africa
11. ANS: D   DIF: A   REF: 629-630   OBJ: C25S3-3
    TOP: Suez Canal
12. ANS: A   DIF: A   REF: 631   OBJ: C25S4-1
    TOP: British exploit India's diversity
13. ANS: C   DIF: A   REF: 636   OBJ: C25S5-2
    TOP: Taiping Rebellion
14. ANS: B   DIF: A   REF: 651   OBJ: C26S2-1
    TOP: European impact on Southeast Asia
15. ANS: D   DIF: A   REF: 656-657   OBJ: C26S3-2, C26S3-3
    TOP: Relationship between Britain/ Australia/ and New Zealand
16. ANS: A   DIF: A   REF: 664-665   OBJ: C26S5-2
    TOP: Impact of imperialism on world culture

UNIT 7—WORLD WARS AND REVOLUTIONS

Multiple Choice
Identify the letter of the choice that best completes the statement or answers the question.

_____ 1. How did aggressive nationalism push France and Germany to the brink of war in the early 1900s?
    a. New weapons of mass destruction had placed Germany on the most-feared nations list.
    b. Germany sought retribution for its depressed economy, which it blamed on France.
    c. France yearned for revenge against Germany to regain its position as Europe's leading power.
    d. Germany longed to seek revenge against France for its lost provinces.

_____ 2. What ethnic tensions in Bosnia led to the assassination of Archduke Francis Ferdinand and launched World War I?
    a. A militant Serbian faction viewed Russia as a major political threat and vowed revenge for past injustices.
    b. The Serbians viewed the Austrians as foreign oppressors.
    c. When pleas for peace failed, the Serbian army nationalists began to mobilize with ally Russia.
    d. Germany saw the Archduke's planned visit as an outright declaration of war.

_____ 3. Look at the number of casualties of World War I in this chart. How did military technology impact the fighting during World War I?

Casualties of World War I		
	Deaths in Battle	**Wounded in Battle**
Allies		
France	1,357,800	4,266,000
British empire	908,371	2,090,212
Russia	1,700,000	4,950,000
Italy	462,391	953,886
United States	50,585	205,690
Others	502,421	342,585
Central Powers		
Germany	1,808,546	4,247,143
Austria-Hungary	922,500	3,620,000
Ottoman empire	325,000	400,000

Source R.E. Dupuy and T.N. Dupuy, *The Encyclopedia of Military History*

    a. Modern warfare created huge numbers of casualties.
    b. Airplanes were used to drop poison gas on German troops.
    c. English zeppelins were used to bomb German ground troops.
    d. British submarines were able to cut off vital German supply lines.

_____ 4. Which of the following was a major reason the United States exchanged neutrality for war in 1917?
   a.   Americans felt it was their duty to come to the aid of the Central Powers, who were being badly beaten.
   b.   The Germans had taken over a vital trade route between Britain and the United States.
   c.   The Germans massacred the entire population of a major British city, including civilians.
   d.   The Germans used their submarines to attack ships carrying American citizens and supplies to the Allies.

_____ 5. During Russia's March Revolution, the Czar was forced to abdicate, and a provisional government was formed. What happened during Russia's November Revolution?
   a.   Lenin formed a democratic government.
   b.   Bolsheviks took over the government.
   c.   The communist government was overthrown.
   d.   Stalin formalized a new government.

_____ 6. What economic reforms did Stalin introduce that led to the changes shown on this graph?

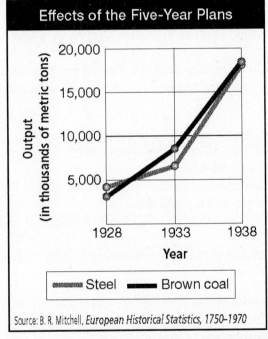

Source: B. R. Mitchell, *European Historical Statistics, 1750–1970*

   a.   His five-year plans all but destroyed the coal and steel industries in Russia, and living conditions for most people were substandard.
   b.   His five-year plans created a demand economy in which heavy industry thrived because of higher wages and a higher standard of living for most people.
   c.   His five-year plans resulted in strong increases in coal and steel output because he relied on foreign technology and central planning.
   d.   His five-year plans included a command economy and set high production goals for heavy industry, including steel and coal, which began to grow.

_____ 7. How did communism during the age of totalitarian control affect religion?
   a. Citizens were permitted free practice of any religion.
   b. Atheism became the official state policy.
   c. Protestant religious leaders were killed or imprisoned.
   d. Catholicism became the official national religion.

_____ 8. What world events led to the rising tide of economic nationalism that swept Latin America during the 1920s and 1930s?
   a. European trade fell following World War I, and the Great Depression reduced Latin American exports and increased the cost of imported goods.
   b. World War I dramatically increased trade with Latin American nations that provided supplies to the Allies, and the cost of imports fell.
   c. Trade with the United States dissolved during the Great Depression, but trade with Europe rose dramatically, causing an industrial rebirth in the cities.
   d. The price of Latin American exports to the United States rose during World War I and climbed even higher during the Great Depression.

_____ 9. What effect did Atatürk's radical reforms in Turkey have on nationalists in neighboring Iran?
   a. Iranian nationalists scaled back their efforts at modernization.
   b. Iran sought a middle ground that would improve the nation's economy without angering its allies.
   c. Iran resented Turkey's reforms, which initially made it a stronger military threat.
   d. Iran was inspired by Turkey's successes and rushed to modernize Iran and make it fully independent.

_____ 10. How did Gandhi's Salt March illustrate his philosophy of civil disobedience?
   a. The march began civilly with speeches by Gandhi and other leaders, who pledged to fast from eating products made with salt for 90 days.
   b. The march was against the civil laws enforced by the British government in the Salt colony of India, a holy land for Gandhi and his followers.
   c. Angered by the Indian government's monopoly on salt, Gandhi's followers set fire to the country's salt mines.
   d. The march, which began as a nonviolent protest, soon became a brutally violent rally in which thousands were arrested.

_____ 11. What foreign force caused the new republic of China to fall into chaos after 1912?
   a. The Silk Road was captured by Russian forces.
   b. Foreign powers increased their influence over Chinese affairs.
   c. The United States withdrew China's favored nation status.
   d. Yuan Shikai stepped down as president.

_____ 12. Why did steps taken by the major powers to promote peace following World War I have limited effects?
   a. Treaties created alliances that had an unfair advantage over enemy nations.
   b. The League of Nations was run by dishonest and disreputable men.
   c. There was no way to enforce bans on war.
   d. Germany refused to agree to any other nation's terms.

____ 13. Why was fascist, totalitarian rule in Italy under Mussolini popular?
   a. It gave most of the governing powers to the lower classes, who had been oppressed for centuries.
   b. It emphasized a state-controlled economy and eliminated a monopoly of the media and strict censorship.
   c. It promised a strong, confident government and instilled a sense of nationalism among Italians.
   d. Although it abhorred the democratic form of government, it gave citizens the right to free speech and freedom of assembly.

____ 14. How did Hitler's economic policies affect Germany before World War II?
   a. Economic conditions improved as businesses thrived, and unemployment was reduced.
   b. Unemployment rose significantly as Hitler pulled young men from jobs to join his Third Reich.
   c. They initially invigorated a struggling economy, but soon inflation spiraled out of control.
   d. They brought inflation under control, but unemployment and a slowdown in industry led to economic collapse.

____ 15. How did Londoners react to the London blitz?
   a. Londoners panicked, and thousands of refugees fled to neighboring France.
   b. Londoners launched a successful attack on German planes, destroying half of Hitler's fighter jets in less than 20 days.
   c. Londoners carried on their daily lives, seeking protection in shelters during the bombings, but British morale was not destroyed.
   d. Parliament ceased to meet for the 59 days of the bombardment, while much of the city was destroyed.

____ 16. Winston Churchill described Soviet control of Eastern Europe as an "iron curtain" dividing the continent. What did the iron curtain come to symbolize?
   a. the division of Europe into north and south blocs
   b. a growing fear of economic collapse that was quickly spreading across Western Europe
   c. the New Deal ideology that was feared and distrusted by Stalin's regime
   d. the growing fear of communism and the division of Europe into eastern and western blocs

UNIT 7—WORLD WARS AND REVOLUTIONS
Answer Section

MULTIPLE CHOICE

1. ANS: C   DIF: A   REF: 678   OBJ: C27S1-2
   TOP: Nationalism

2. ANS: B   DIF: A   REF: 682   OBJ: C27S2-1
   TOP: Ethnic tensions

3. ANS: A   DIF: E   REF: 687-688   OBJ: C27S3-2
   TOP: Chart reading

4. ANS: D   DIF: D   REF: 692   OBJ: C27S4-3
   TOP: U.S. entrance into WWI

5. ANS: B   DIF: A   REF: 704-705   OBJ: C28S1-1, C28S1-2
   TOP: Russian revolutions of 1917

6. ANS: D   DIF: D   REF: 710-711   OBJ: C28S2-2
   TOP: Stalin's economic plans

7. ANS: B   DIF: A   REF: 714   OBJ: C28S3-2
   TOP: Effect of communism on religion

8. ANS: A   DIF: D   REF: 724-725   OBJ: C29S1-3
   TOP: Nationalism in Latin America

9. ANS: D   DIF: D   REF: 729   OBJ: C29S2-3
   TOP: Turkey and Iran's modernization

10. ANS: A   DIF: A   REF: 732   OBJ: C29S3-2, C29S3-3
    TOP: Civil disobedience/Salt March

11. ANS: B   DIF: D   REF: 734   OBJ: C29S4-1
    TOP: Foreign imperialism in China

12. ANS: C   DIF: A   REF: 747   OBJ: C30S1-1
    TOP: Effects of peace efforts following WWI

13. ANS: C   DIF: A   REF: 760   OBJ: C30S3-3
    TOP: Popularity of totalitarian rule

14. ANS: A   DIF: A   REF: 763   OBJ: C30S4-3
    TOP: Economic policies of Third Reich

15. ANS: C   DIF: E   REF: 778   OBJ: C31S2-2
    TOP: London blitz

16. ANS: D   DIF: A   REF: 793   OBJ: C31S5-3
    TOP: Iron curtain

UNIT 8—THE WORLD TODAY

Multiple Choice
Identify the letter of the choice that best completes the statement or answers the question.

_____ 1. How did the two superpowers that emerged during the Cold War compete for influence over other nations?
   a. The Soviet Union and the United States competed by establishing colonies in Algeria, North Africa, and Asia.
   b. The United States and Germany competed through each country's military developments, leading to the arms race.
   c. The Soviet Union and the United States competed by offering economic and military aid to less-developed nations.
   d. The Soviet Union and the United States competed by supporting imperialism in the Middle East and Asia.

_____ 2. How did the oil crisis in the 1970s illustrate the problem of economic interdependence?
   a. All nations rely on oil, and when nations with oil resources underwent political crises, production was halted and prices soared, creating economic shock waves.
   b. The dependence of the United States on Middle Eastern oil was seriously damaged when Saudi Arabian oil fields were attacked by Afghanistan's rebel forces.
   c. Multinational corporations had brought new technologies to developing countries, which used this new technology to create alternative fuels at high costs.
   d. Less-developed nations, once dependent on the Middle East for oil, joined OPEC and were able to get substantial discounts on oil reserves.

_____ 3. What type of economy eventually led to the Soviet Union's collapse?
   a. a developing world economy   c. a command economy
   b. a nonsurplus economy   d. a demand economy

_____ 4. Which of the following led to the reunification of Germany in 1989?
   a. The European Union's euro currency brought economic success to France, a staunch ally of West Germany.
   b. Communism declined in the Soviet Union.
   c. The United States divided its military support between East and West Germany.
   d. Rebels in West Germany revolted against party leadership.

_____ 5. Following World War II, what factors led to Japan's economic success?
   a. the adoption of eastern economic philosophy that emphasized supply and demand economy
   b. the concentration on the production of high-quality agricultural products
   c. efficient, modern factories, adapted to the latest technology, and high-quality exports
   d. a trade agreement with China, the world's largest exporter of goods

_____ 6. Which statement BEST describes Vietnam in the years following the Vietnam War?
    a. Vietnam was a country divided by communism and dominated by capitalist investment.
    b. Vietnam was a country mired in poverty and unable to attract foreign capital.
    c. Vietnam was a country experiencing economic disaster caused by the elimination of trade embargoes.
    d. Vietnam was a country prospering in economic reforms and heavy industry.

_____ 7. How does the change in size of the European Union, shown in the map, reflect its changing role as an economic power?

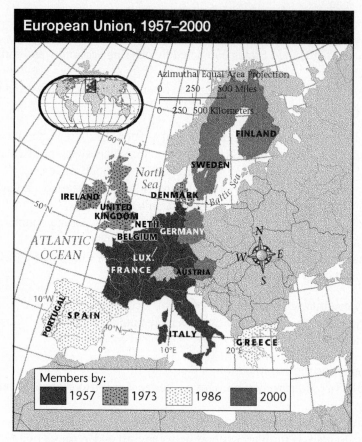

    a. The shrinking European Union reflects its weakening in the world marketplace caused by an inability of member nations to cooperate.
    b. The growth of the European Union demonstrates it is becoming a powerful economic force that can compete with the superpowers.
    c. The growth of the European Union shows that the superpowers have begun to weaken their stronghold on the world's trade.
    d. The shrinking of the European Union illustrates that it is weakening because of its new currency, the euro, and the Soviet republics' refusal to join the Union.

_____ 8. How did Deng Xiaoping improve China's economy?
    a. He created private ownership of property and businesses.
    b. He reopened schools.
    c. He created communes.
    d. He created the Red Guards.

_____ 9. Which phrase BEST completes this sentence? Since colonial days, a key cause of Latin American unrest has been the uneven _____.

a. distribution of government land   c. development of urban areas

b. support for democracy   d. distribution of wealth

_____ 10. What was the result of the partition of India in 1947?

a. The division further escalated the violence between Pakistani Hindus and Indian Muslims.

b. The division resulted in two economically diverse regions.

c. Clashes with British forces sharply divided the nation and led to widespread poverty.

d. Hindus in India migrated to the northern provinces, where thousands perished from starvation.

_____ 11. Look at this map of the Middle East. What conclusion can you draw from the number of desalinization plants located in this region?

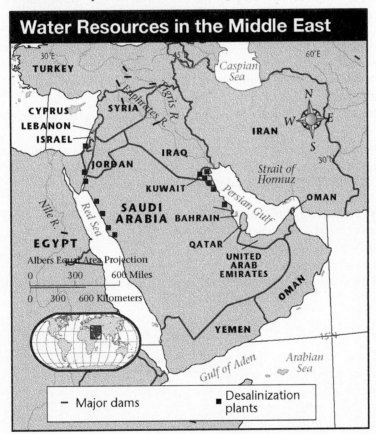

a. There are vast oil supplies in this region.

b. There are very few freshwater resources in this region.

c. Food production is the number one priority in this region.

d. Coal is the most valuable natural resource in this region.

____ 12. How did China influence the economic development of Taiwan?
  a. Chinese businessmen invested in Taiwanese companies.
  b. Taiwan grew economically because of China's acceptance of capitalism.
  c. China's cultural revolution allowed Taiwan to develop its high technology industry.
  d. China's reforms allowed Taiwan to invest in Chinese companies.

____ 13. Despite continued efforts for peace in the Arab-Israeli conflict, why was there a continuing struggle in the occupied territories?
  a. Israel refused to give up the territories until Arab nations recognized Israel's right to exist and Palestinian Arabs were displaced.
  b. Palestinian Arabs refused to give up their homes to Israeli refugees who secretly supported the PLO.
  c. Yasir Arafat returned the Sinai Peninsula to Egypt but not before dividing Jerusalem into territories.
  d. The Golan Heights was not recognized by the PLO, who feared Palestinian Jews' revenge for terrorist attacks.

____ 14. Which of the following is NOT a reason there was a growing spirit of nationalism in Africa following World War II?
  a. African soldiers who had fought in other parts of the world returned home disturbed by Africa's discrimination.
  b. Workers in wartime defense industries went on strike, demanding better pay and more freedoms.
  c. Missionary groups had spread Christianity to the African nations, and European powers established colonies in Africa.
  d. Following the war, the West no longer appeared an unbeatable force.

____ 15. In the 1930s, what did Brazil do to restore its failing economy?
  a. Brazil moved away from dependence on a single export.
  b. Brazil focused efforts on forestry.
  c. Brazil restored its silk trade with China.
  d. Brazil privatized the nation's businesses and restored personal business ownership.

UNIT 8—THE WORLD TODAY
Answer Section

MULTIPLE CHOICE

1. ANS: C   DIF: A   REF: 807   OBJ: C32S1-2
    TOP: Superpower influence on developing nations
2. ANS: A   DIF: A   REF: 813   OBJ: C32S1-1
    TOP: Oil crisis
3. ANS: C   DIF: E   REF: 844   OBJ: C33S4-2
    TOP: Economic collapse of the Soviet Union/Command economy
4. ANS: B   DIF: A   REF: 837   OBJ: C33S2-3
    TOP: German reunification
5. ANS: C   DIF: A   REF: 859   OBJ: C34S1-1
    TOP: Japan's economic success
6. ANS: B   DIF: A   REF: 874   OBJ: C34S4-1
    TOP: Vietnam after the war
7. ANS: B   DIF: D   REF: 832   OBJ: C33S1-3
    TOP: European Union
8. ANS: A   DIF: A   REF: 864-865   OBJ: C34S2-3
    TOP: Reforms in China
9. ANS: D   DIF: E   REF: 935   OBJ: C37S1-2
    TOP: Uneven distribution of wealth in Latin America
10. ANS: A   DIF: D   REF: 882   OBJ: C35S1-1
    TOP: India partition/Hindus & Muslims
11. ANS: B   DIF: E   REF: 890   OBJ: C35S2-2
    TOP: Map reading
12. ANS: D   DIF: A   REF: 868-869   OBJ: C34S3-1
    TOP: China's influence on Taiwan and Hong Kong
13. ANS: A   DIF: D   REF: 900   OBJ: C35S4-2
    TOP: Arab-Israeli conflict
14. ANS: C   DIF: D   REF: 909   OBJ: C36S1-1
    TOP: Nationalism in Africa
15. ANS: A   DIF: A   REF: 953   OBJ: C37S4-3
    TOP: Attempts to restore Brazilian economy